Bad Bob — The Randy Wonder Dog

THE HIGHLANDS village of Glenpeebles was in shock following the discovery of the body of Auld Dougal the shepherd up on the Moors. The poor man had been stabbed through the heart. It was Sgt Greenock's first ever murder case!

"DINNAE WORRY yersel'," said Dr McCulloch, the Forensics Officer. "Thanks tae modern science, we'll soon track the villain doon. Ye can be sure he'll hae left some fibres o' himsel', nae matter how wee." "I hope ye're richt," said Sgt Greenock.

"NOO, DINNAE let anyone near the body," said Dr McCulloch. "There's got to be nae contamination of the crime scene." Suddenly, Bad Bob the oversexed terrier made a lunge for his leg. "Och, get offa ma leg, ye filthy wee bas!" he exclaimed.

"GREENOCK! Control yir mutt!" the scientist shouted. "Bad Bob!" cried the sergeant. "Git aff the scientist's leg, ye mucky wee bugger!" But it took a smart truncheon swipe across the randy hound's haunches before he loosened his tenacious grip.

THE EMBARRASSED policeman helped the Forensics Officer to his feet. "Ye want tae get that mutt put doon!" McCulloch fumed. "Dinnae worry, sir," said Sgt Greenock. "I'll bray 'is nose wi' a rolled-up newspaper once I get the dirty fecker hame."

BUT BAD BOB was nearing the Billy Mill roundabout, and he made a bee-line for poor Auld Dougal's body lying on the ground. "Help m'boab!" cried Dr McCulloch distractedly. "The randy wee bas is wrecking the crime scene noo!"

"BAD BOB! Put awa' yir lipstick or there's nae supper fir ye!" shouted Greenock as he tried to pull the hound free of the body, but Bob was in the vinegar strokes. "Och! The wee bas is contaminatin' the crime scene wi' 'is doggy DNA!" cried McCulloch.

"A BUCKET o' cold water frae the burn'll tak the dirty wee bas's mind off 'is oats," said the constable. "No!" cried Greenock, but it was too late. Splash! "Och, ma feckin' crime scene!" cried Dr McCulloch. "Bad Bob! Bad Bob! Nae biscuit!"

'Ello! 'Ello! 'Ello! Wot's all this then? It's

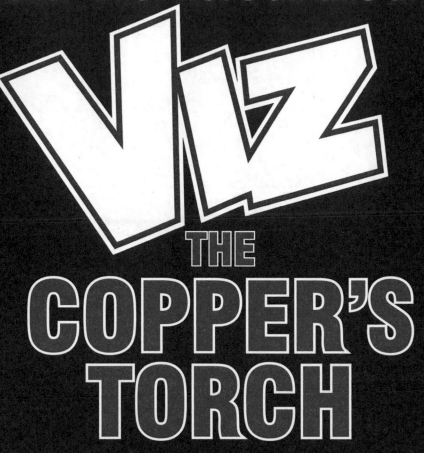

VIZ

THE COPPER'S TORCH

Suspicious Evidence of Foul Play from Issues 282~291

Chief Superintendents
Graham Dury and Simon Thorp

Detective Constables

Mark Bates, Alex Collier, Terry Corrigan, Simon Ecob, Tom Ellen, Barney Farmer, David Glasper, Mat Greaves, Lee Healey, Jacob Hutchinson, Davey Jones, Marc Jones, Shaun Madrid, Luke McGarry, Steve McGarry, Alex Morris, Paul Palmer, Tom Paterson, Aaron Rice, Tom Richmond, Paul Solomons, Kent Tayler, Nick Tolson and Stevie White.

Keystone Cops

Dharmesh Mistry, Kerin O'Connor and Stephen Catherall

Published by Dennis Publishing Ltd
31-32 Alfred Place, London WC1E 7DP

ISBN 978-1-78106-742-0
First Printing Summer 2021

Subscribe online at www.viz.co.uk
Find us at facebook.com/vizcomic and twitter.com/vizcomic

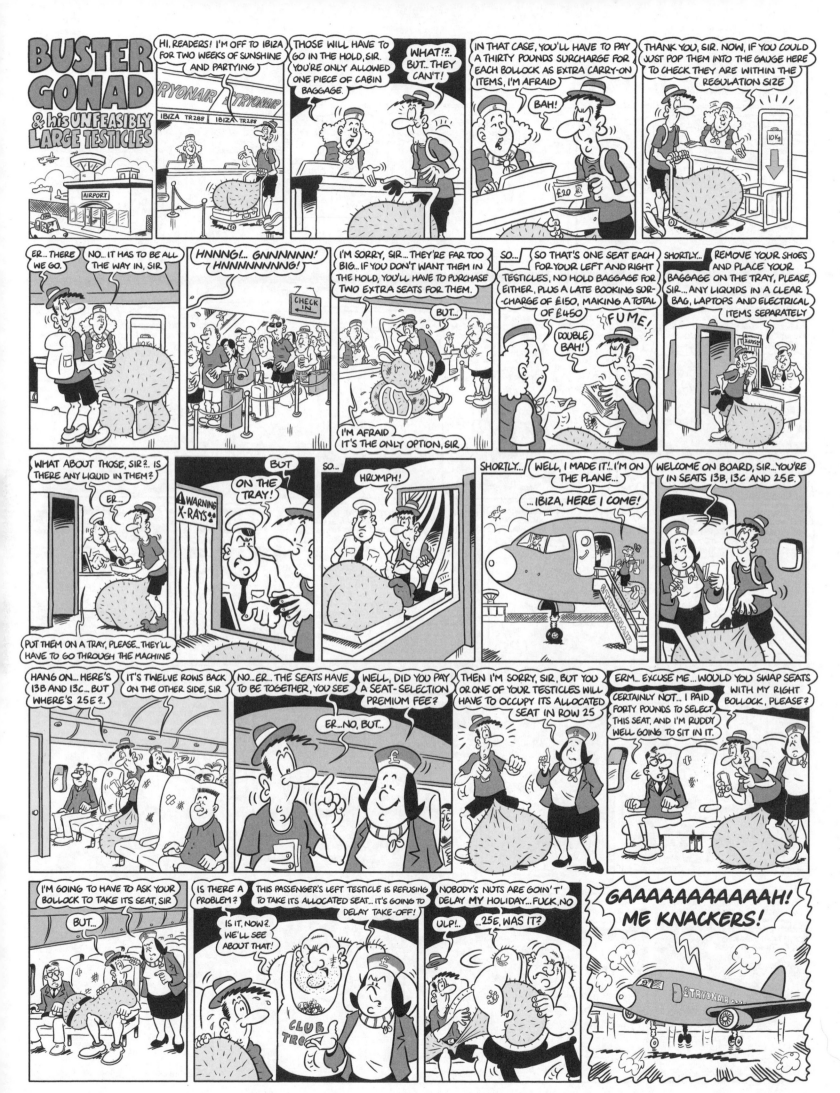

3

HULLO THERE RAFFLES, OLD CHAP! MAY I PROFFER YOU MY HEARTIEST SALUTATIONS ON THIS MOST LUMINESCENT NEW DIURNAL COURSE...!

MEH! BUNNY.

I COME BEARING THE MOST NEOTERIC EDITIONS OF THE PRINT PERIODICAL 'ALL THE YEAR ROUND'..!

HMM..?

I THOUGHT PERCHANCE WE MIGHT BINGE-READ THE LATEST CHAPTERS OF MR DICKENS'S ACCLAIMED SERIALISATION 'GREAT EXPECTATIONS'..!

TESTICLES TO THAT NOTION, BUNNY.

I READ A BOOTLEG.

MISS HAVISHAM SETS HER FROCK ABLAZE AND THUS PERISHES IN THE ENSUING CONFLAGRATION.

OH, SPOILER ALARUM, OLD BEAN.

...AND ANYWAY, I AM UNABLE TO MICTURATE AWAY THE EVENING WITH YOU, AS I'VE GOT A THERMOGENIC ASSIGNATION LINED UP TONIGHT!

OH YES..? WITH WHOM?

NONE OTHER, BUNNY, THAN PRINCESS FEODORA OF LEININGEN!

WHY RAFFLES.! SHE IS REPUTED TO BE QUITE THE BEAUTY!

INDEED. AND YOU KNOW WHAT THEY SAY ABOUT EUROPEAN BIRDS..? THEY EXCORTICATE THEIR STAYS AT THE DROP OF A FUCKING TOPPER, THEN IT'S MAMMARIES OUT FOR THE GENTLEMEN!

I'M ESCORTING HER TO THE THEATRE, THEN IT'S BACK TO MY ABODE FOR A SPOT OF HOW-IS-YOUR PATERFAMILIAS!

CAREFUL, RAFFLES. THE PRINCESS IS QUEEN VICTORIA'S MATERNAL HALF-SISTER, AND IS THEREFORE OF GREAT INTEREST TO THE NEWSPAPERMEN OF FLEET STREET!

I DARE VENTURE THAT YOU WILL PERFORCE HAVE TO NEGOTIATE SEVERAL WET COLLODION PHOTOGRAPHERS FROM THE ILLUSTRATED PRESS AS YOU RELINQUISH THE PLAYHOUSE.

PSHAW!

I THINK I CAN DEAL WITH A FEW OIKISH SMUDGERS OUT-SIDE A THEATRE WITHOUT CAUSING A COMMOTION, BUNNY!

LATER THAT NIGHT...

...WELL THAT WAS A LOAD OF ARCHAIC FECULANT. I DIDN'T LAUGH ONCE. WHAT DO YOU SAY, YOUR ROYAL HIGHNESS...SHALL WE ABSQUATULATE BACK TO MY PLACE FOR A QUICK GAME OF 'ENSCONCE THE BRATWURST'?

OH, LORD RAFFLES! DU BIST AWFUL! ≋ GIGGLE ≋

COME ON, THEN.

PRINCESS FEODORA! OVER 'ERE, PRINCESS! BIG SMILE FOR THE DAILY GRAPHIC!

SAY CHEESE FOR THE ILLUSTRATED LONDON NEWS, LORD RAFFLES...?!

THAT'S IT... JUST HOLD STILL, YOUR HIGHNESS!

THIRTY MINUTES LATER...

VERY WELL, YOU'VE HAD AN ELEGANT SUFFICIENCY OF OUR TIME NOW...

TAXI!

PHWOOAR! JUST HOLD IT THERE, PRINCESS... ABOUT A TWENTY MINUTE EXPOSURE SHOULD DO IT..!

...I SAY, YOU DIRTY LITTLE CONSPICATOR...ARE YOU ATTEMPTING TO UP-CRINOLINE MY BIRD?!

THAT PHOTOGRAPHIC APPARATUS IS GOING UP YOUR FUNDAMENT.

LEAVE IT, YOUR LORDSHIP. HE IS UNDESERVING OF THE VEXATION!

NO-ONE DOES THAT, YOU MALAPERT LITTLE MONOSYLLABLE!

PLEASE, YOUR GRACE, I'M NOT DESIROUS OF ANY ADVERSITY...

NOTWITHSTANDING, YOU HAVE AQUIRED A PLETHORA THEREOF, PAL..!

KINDLY FIND YOURSELF IN RECEIPT OF THE FOLLOWING...

SOCK!

STOMP! STOMP! STOMP!

DESIST, LORD RAFFLES! HE'S HAD A SUITABLE ABUNDANCE!

NEXT DAY... I SAY, RAFFLES...D'YOU FANCY BINGE-READING THE FINAL CHAPTERS OF MONSIEUR HUGO'S 'LES MISERABLES' TONIGHT?

ALREADY PERUSED THEM, BUNNY. JEAN VALJEAN CARKS IT.

"MY HUSGAND AND I..."

BUCKINGHAM Palace has announced that Her Majesty the Queen will have company while delivering her Christmas Day address this year… *in the shape of a puppet sidekick.*

Back in One's box: The Duke of Fluffington (back) and the Queen (in the box)

Palace reveal Christmas puppetry plan

The 91-year-old monarch is understood to have complained to courtiers that she fears the yearly royal broadcasts, which started in 1932, are becoming 'staid', and is said to have ordered that a goggle-eyed anthropomorphic puppet be constructed to join her on screen.

marionette

Sources in the Royal household said that the Queen presented the Master of the Rolls with a detailed design for the posh, buck-toothed marionette, which is to be called 'The Duke of Fluffington'.

The plans are thought to include a mechanism for Her Majesty to control the dummy's eyes, mouth and eyebrows, while the heir to the throne Prince Charles, hidden beneath the desk, controls its arm.

A draft of the 2019 Christmas Day speech leaked online last night includes scenes where The Duke of Fluffington throws the Queen's notes up in the air, sings the national anthem while she drinks a glass of water, and tries to steal her tiara. The slapstick havoc continues until the monarch threatens to put his Grace back in his box.

trouper

According to the draft, to end the broadcast, the puppet will rest its head on the Queen's shoulder and open and close its jaw while she sings Just The Two Of Us out of the corner of her mouth.

"This plan, while unusual, is nothing new," said royal commentator Dickie Arbiter. "We may not remember now, but the Queen's uncle Edward VIII, the Duke of Windsor, delivered his abdication address in the form of a fast-paced crosstalk routine with Archie off Educating Archie."

"And of course, there was also Princess Diana's bombshell 1996 interview with Orville the Duck," he added.

THE same thing happens every year. We British fellas traditionally spend Christmas Eve in the pub with our mates, making merry and celebrating the festive season. As the barman calls 'Last Orders' and we down our final drink and pull on our coats and scarves, we wish our friends the compliments of the season and set off home to our loved ones. Suddenly, as we step out into the cold of the car park, we feel an icy chill as we remember … *we haven't got a present for the wife or girlfriend.*

Our heart sinks. The only place in town still open is the 24-hour petrol station, and they don't sell fancy perfumes, fine lingerie or designer jewellery. There's nothing we can buy there that won't look like a thoughtless, last-minute, purchase.

Or so you might think.

Because eight-times-married relationship expert **FRANK SHITEHAWK** says that if you play your cards right, any old tat snatched from the all-night garage shelf can be successfully fobbed off as a loving gift only purchased after many hours of thought and consideration.

Here is Frank's exclusive guide to convincing your other half that – contrary to all available evidence – you're not a thoughtless twat who's just rolled half-cut out the boozer at quarter to midnight and come home via the services on the bypass.

ALL-NIGHT

Tired-looking Flowers

NOTHING says "I've left it too late to buy you a proper present" like a bunch of tired-looking flowers out of the bucket by the petrol station door. But once again, just a little thought before handing them over on Christmas morning can make all the difference. Look your wife in the eye, and explain that you were going to buy her a diamond necklace … only you decided that it could not have made her any more beautiful.

Tell her: "Then I saw these flowers, and they were so gorgeous I just had to get them for you." Deeply moved, she'll spend the next half hour fannying about with them in the kitchen, trimming the stalks off and arranging them in a vase, while you get your feet up in front of the Bond film, occasionally shouting through for another cup of tea.

with *VIZ* **Relationship Expert**
FRANK SHITEHAWK

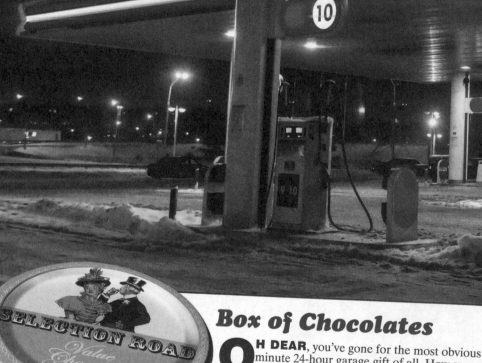

Five litres of Engine Oil

PRESENT the missus with a plastic can of 5W-30 Supalube on Christmas morning, and you're likely to get short shrift in return, even though you may have paid more than £20 for it at the all night garage till. But talk your gift up cleverly, and you could be oiling your way into her good books.

Explain that you've always admired her skin, and wanted to give her something that would enhance her glowing complexion. Tell her that whilst researching the subject exhaustively on the internet, you discovered that Castrol engine oil has been proved to be very good for the skin. Although there are cheaper brands of oil on the market – such as Briggs and Stratton lawnmower oil – only the best was good enough for the woman you love.

Offer to pour some of it on her and give her a nice sensual massage once she's got the kids off to bed. Just the prospect of such an intimate interlude will probably be enough to get you back in her good books, but in the unlikely event that she does decide to take you up on your offer, just empty a little bit of oil on her shoulders and smear it round gently and sensuously for a couple of minutes.

Afterwards, make sure you get it off your hands with some Swarfega, because it's probably quite nasty stuff. Warnings on the can say that frequent and prolonged contact with engine oil causes dermatitis, and can even be carcinogenic.

Box of Chocolates

OH DEAR, you've gone for the most obvious last minute 24-hour garage gift of all. How can you possibly dig yourself out of this hole? Believe it o not, it's a piece of piss. As you hand over the box, expl – in as heartfelt a manner as you can fake – that you kn how hard she works for you and the kids, and whilst it ma look like you take her for granted, you really don't.

If you take the opportunity to apply a little Vick's Vaporub under one of your eyes before handing the chocs over, with a little luck there'll be a tear glistening on your cheek, adding an extra layer of cod-sincerity to your thoughtful and heartfelt gesture.

Tell her not to share them. Say: "These chocs are just for you to indulge yourself." Don't worry, she'll invariably be so touched by your generous gesture that she'll offer you first choice, and you'll be able to snaffle a fistful of the best ones, leaving the gullible cow with the shit toffee ones and tooth-breaking butterscotch cracknels.

GARAGE GIFT GUIDE

Road Atlas of GB and N Ireland

EVERY garage has a pile of these dated books of roadmaps somewhere by the till, going cheap because no-one needs them any more in these modern sat-nav times. It might appear that presenting her indoors with one of these on December 25th would be a surefire way of guaranteeing you a festive season spent sleeping on the couch or in the Pharaoh's Tomb.

However, it's all a question of presentation. If, when you hand over the present to your missus, you suggest that you thoughtfully selected it as a guide to a myriad of wonderful days out that you fully intend to take her on, her reaction will be one of excitement. Encourage her to leaf through the atlas and fantasise about all the exciting places to which you fully intend to take her over the coming year … Ludlow, Devizes, Chapel St Leonards.

With her imagination fired up at the alluring prospect of all these romantic daytrips, she'll spend the rest of December 25th dreamily leafing through the maps in the book, while you sit with your feet up on the sofa, watching the telly and sipping from your 'World's Best Husband' mug.

£7.99

AA 2020

GREAT
BRITAIN
AND IRELAND

THE UK'S BIGGEST SELLING ROAD ATLASES

Scenic routes
Large 4 miles to 1 inch scale

Half a Dozen Ginster's Pies

EVERY petrol station has a selection of Ginster's Pies stacked in the fridge near the microwave oven, and if you don't consider buying your missus a selection of them as a Christmas gift, you're making a big mistake. As you hand her a carrier containing six Chicken and Bacon pasties, explain that to you, time is the most precious commodity of all, and any time spent away from her is time wasted. Use those exact words.

Tell her: "It's Christmas, and I don't want you slaving away in the kitchen cooking while I'm just napping in front of the telly." Again, use these exact words.

It's a double whammy win-win. You get brownie points for the perfect gift from a thoughtful spouse, plus you get Ginster's for your Christmas dinner. You don't have to try and force down her dried-up turkey, charred roasties and sprouts that have had their arses boiled off.

SOMETHING TO LEAF THROUGH DURING THE AD BREAKS IN JEREMY KYLE

Take a Shit 63p

Fab competition
6 weeks to live like a king!
WIN a VIP CANCER SCARE for two!

My boyfriend wanked off 1000 elephants...
And made me drink the spunk!

Hubby ran me over with steamroller...
then fed me into a paper shredder...
But I still love him!

**I BONKED the milkman...
and my cunt caught FIRE!**

My man's cock is two miles long... **and it's fucking my sister in the next town!**

Scan showed I was pregnant with a million baby crabs... but I'm going to keep them all!

A Magazine

A COPY of *Chat* or *Take a Break* may look like unimpressive sort of Christmas present, but here's the beauty of this idea: Tell her it's the gift that goes on giving, because you've just taken out a subscription to that magazine in her name! She'll be absolutely thrilled at such a thoughtful, personalised gift that will give her something bright and interesting to look forward to all through the forthcoming year.

A week later, when the next issue mysteriously "fails to arrive", explain that subscriptions can take some time to set up, especially over the busy Christmas period. When the following week's magazine likewise doesn't appear, suggest that it must have been lost in the post, and tell her you saw a news report where a sorting office got flooded. The next week, explain that you saw the postman sat in a layby, reading that magazine in his van, and suggest that he must be stealing your mail. After that, with any luck she'll have forgotten all about it anyway.

NEXT YEAR:
Frank Shitehawk runs down the Top Ten ways to put your missus's family off coming round on Christmas Day

LetterbOcks

Comic, P.O. Box 841 Whitley Bay, NE26 9EQ   letters@viz.co.uk

INSTEAD of just floating around the oceans moaning about getting tangled up in plastic, why don't turtles try a bit harder to evolve their way around the problem? You didn't see early primates complain when they had to develop three-dimensional sight to avoid snake attacks, they just got on with it. And who rules the Earth now?

D Attenborough, Ayia Napa

TEACHERS must stop children drawing happy faces in the sun when they are painting. The increase in global temperature is having a massive effect on the environment, melting polar ice caps, raising the sea level and fuelling severe weather patterns, not to mention the harm the solar radiation causes to human skin. The effects of global warming and skin cancers are no laughing matter. Drawing smiley faces in the sun simply belittles the truth of how serious these problems are.

Sonny Day, Skegness

WHAT a ruddy con this electricity is. They deliver it to you along a red wire, then they take it straight back off you in a black one. You never get to keep any of the electricity they have sold you.

Brian M, Sale

DO any of your readers know what delivery company the Acme corporation used to get their contraptions to Wile E. Coyote? Because 40 years ago they could deliver high-tech equipment straight to the customer in the middle of the desert in a matter of minutes. Nowadays you have to wait about 5 days for someone to throw your fragile electronic device over your neighbour's gate. Hardly progress, is it?

Humphrey Cushion, Hull

'SAVING You Money Every Day' my local Asda proclaims in big letters as you walk in. Well, the last time I went in there I came out £80 lighter. Saving me money my arse.

Eldon Furse, email

WHY hasn't George Orwell come up with a sequel to *1984*? He could easily have written *1985*, and maybe even *1986* to complete the trilogy. Or he could possibly have followed it up with a prequel called *1980* or something. There so much potential in the 198x franchise, it's a shame to see it go to waste like this.

Ben Nunn, Caterham

ST★R LETTER

I DON'T know why lepidopterists waste their time running around with those stupid nets. Surely it would be much simpler to collect the pupa in a jar, wait for it to hatch, and then Hey Presto, you have your precious butterfly without getting a hernia chasing after it.

Billy Wiffles, Cheam

THE cover of *Viz* issue 250 (Nov 2015) proudly proclaims to contain "All your favourite cartoons!" This is not the case. My favourite cartoon is the animated German porno version of *Snow White and the Seven Dwarfs*, as seen by tens of thousands of service personnel stationed in BAOR in the 70s and 80s. Please get your facts right on your covers in future.

Bob Pitt, Kendal

DOGS these days should be ashamed of themselves, whimpering over a firework. How do they think their dog forefathers felt during the Blitz, I wonder? Dogs today need to man up, the big fannies.

Mike Hunt, Bath

HAVE any of your readers noticed that impact craters on the moon look a bit like cats' bum holes? There. You don't get scientific insight like that on *The Sky At Night*.

Pandora Spox, email

THAT Dick Dastardly cartoon character and his sidekicks were a bit shit when you think about it. Me and my mate caught a pigeon with the works van the other morning and we weren't even trying.

Stephen Cochrane, Gateshead

SCIENTISTS say that a Mediterranean diet is the secret to a long life. Well I retired to Alicante a year ago and have had a hearty full English breakfast with chips all washed down by 10 pints of industrial grade lager every day while I've been here. Now I've just been diagnosed with chronic heart disease. I hope we aren't paying these "so-called" experts much.

Corky Crevice, Alicante

I'VE often heard the expression, "As fit as a butcher's dog." However, I've just found out that after a long, protracted illness, my butcher's dog is dead. So, I wonder what all the "so-called" experts out there have to say about that one.

R Apples, Dorking

I BOOKED a massage at our local Thai massage parlour in the hope that I would receive a 'happy ending'. Unfortunately, however, neither myself nor the masseuse had the courage to broach the subject and the massage ended without the finale I had hoped for, leaving me somewhat frustrated. All was not lost, however, as when the masseuse left the room, I finished myself off into my sock.

Jeffrie Jibs, East London

IN a letter of mine about a duck in a garden which I sent to you, but which you did not publish, I made reference to my 'uncle's brother.' I wish to clarify this obvious misattribution which your readers would not have had the opportunity to notice. I should have called Derek 'my uncle's brother-in-law.' I sincerely hope this letter is able to clear up any misunderstandings your readers would not have been able to have had.

Ben, Whitstable

52 Te Tellurium	53 I Iodine	54 Xe Xenon
84 Po Polonium	85 At Astatine	86 Rn Radon
116 UUh Ununhexium	117 UUs Ununseptium	118 UUo Ununoctium

I SOMETIMES feel a bit sorry for the element Astatine. From its name you would assume it is deadly poisonous, but it actually has a lot of beneficial uses. Probably. I mean, I'm not a chemist and I haven't looked it up or anything.

Agerton Crusty-Sock, email

YOU have to feel sorry for the royals, I reckon. All those free dinners and all that booze they never have to pay for must take its toll. I never gave this a second thought until I went on an all-inclusive to Benidorm last summer. After a week, I was like, "Enough already." So, God bless you Ma'am.

Tobamory Crumbs, Leeds

BACK in the 70s, you would always see footballers covered in mud on *Match of the Day*. These days they leave the pitch as clean as when they came out. Come on, footballers. Earn some of the millions you are paid and get covered in shit on *Match of the Day* again.

Terry Wilson, Lindfield

FUCKER DUCK

Panel 1: THERE IS NO SIGN OF BOWSER ANYWHERE, MUM! — WE'VE POSTED THESE "MISSING DOG" LEAFLETS THROUGH ALL THE DOORS IN THE NEIGHBOURHOOD!

Panel 2: WELL, LET'S CHECK OUR "HELP FIND BOWSER" APPEAL ON SOCIAL MEDIA. — YOU NEVER KNOW, MAYBE SOMEONE WILL HAVE SPOTTED HIM.

Panel 3: HUNH?! SOMEBODY HAS POSTED A REPLY SAYING THAT BOWSER IS PROBABLY DEAD! — AND THEY SAY THAT IT'S ALL OUR FAULT FOR LETTING HIM RUN AWAY IN THE FIRST PLACE!

Panel 4: WHAT... WHAT KIND OF A PERSON WOULD WANT TO WRITE SOMETHING LIKE THAT?

Panel 5: TAP TAP TAP TAP TAP TAP TAP TAP

TOP TIPS

PRETEND to be a professional footballer by looking up at an imaginary big TV screen each time you make a cock-up at work.
Swiss Tony, Tynemouth

HAVE an eye test when really drunk to get a pair of magic glasses that will make you see clearly when you're smashed.
Mark Stewart, Derby

FOOL the neighbours into thinking you are giving your wife an orgasm by flushing the downstairs toilet while she's in the shower.
Michael Thompson, Wales

DOCUMENTARY makers. Make places seem bigger by using Table Tennis tables as a dimensional comparison rather than football pitches.
Hampton Drabble, Goole

LADIES. Make your husband feel more important by wishing him 'Godspeed' rather than 'Goodbye' when he leaves for work in the morning.
Jamie Cuffe, Ashby de la Launde

A SHAVED cactus makes an ideal substitute for a courgette.
Eldon Furse, email

RECREATE that Wagamama dining experience at home by only serving half your family their meals. Then sporadically bring out dishes for the other half at 15 minute intervals.
Evesy, Hale Fen

A COURGETTE, after having fifty thousand tiny needles stuck into it, makes an ideal substitute for a cactus.
Eldon Furse, email

THE other night, my husband farted in the hallway and set off our smoke alarm. Have any other *Viz* readers done that?
Dr. Heather Jenkinson, Halesowen

* Well, readers. Have YOU ever farted and set off Dr Jenkinson's smoke alarm? Write in and let us know. Mark your envelope or email subject "I've farted and set off Dr Jenkinson's smoke alarm."

WHY does Roger Federer throw his sweaty sweatbands in to the crowd after a match, the dirty bugger? How would he like it if I threw my skid-marked undies at him after I'd been for a long run? Personally, I don't think he would.
Daniel, Bolton

I WOULD expect a prestigious publication such as *Viz* to include a few medical professionals amongst its readership. Could one of them please advise whether it is actually possible to wank yourself to death? I'm asking for a friend, of course. No, honestly, I am. His name is Mark Beresford.
Steve Crouch, Peterborough

IF you are doing a history exam this year and are struggling to remember the fate of Henry VIII's wives, I find that this little poem helps.
Died, died, died,
Died, died, died.
Kevin Osborne, Bury St Edmunds

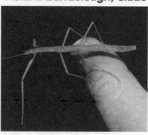

IT'S a shame that the Rear of the Year competition is for celebrities only, otherwise I think my wife would have a good chance of winning it. Hers is a lovely shape. Come on celebs, stop hugging the top awards for yourselves and let the real people have a go.
Hugo Beauregard, Leeds

I ORDERED a burger and fries in a rather snooty pub last week, and I was asked if I would like to pay an extra £1 to upgrade to 'skin-on fries'. How is leaving the skin on an upgrade? I'm not paying an extra quid to save them the hassle of peeling a few spuds.
Lynda Ruggles, Halstead

WHY is it that in popular literature, kids are always running away from home to join the circus? Surely with all that elephant shit, creepy clowns, dangerous lions and what-have-you, the reverse would be the case? I'd be off like a fucking shot.
Barrat Norman, Blackpool

IT'S all very well for people to say, "I'd lock them up and throw away the key." But I'd like to see them try collecting the slop bucket through the viewing hatch of the cell door. As a former prison screw, I've tried and it wasn't a pretty sight.
Roland Barraclough, Slade

DOES anyone else remember stick insects? You couldn't move for the fuckers in the 90s, and now I haven't seen one for so long that I'm not even sure they actually ever existed. The picture I've got of them in my head certainly doesn't fill me with much confidence.
Gustav Fox, Haggerston

* Do you remember stick insects from the 90s, or has Mr Fox simply imagined these strange bugs of the order Phasmatodea? Write in and let us know whether you think stick insects are real, or if they are merely a figment of Mr Fox's imagination.

DOES anyone know why J Geils was so ashamed that his angel was a centrefold in the song of the same name? I would have thought it was something to be proud about. Unless, of course, the magazine she was in was *Razzle*. Or *Aged Cunts*.
Joel, email

A 'SHORT back and sides' is all very well, but what about the top? This focus on the hair on the back and sides of the head is all well and good, but I reckon what happens on the top is most important. Come on barbers, think about the top!
Lyndon Larouche, London

IT'S all very well for Mr Larouche *(previous letter)* to criticise barbers for doing a short back and sides, but why does he not pour similar scorn on barbers who give their customers a flat top? Surely they are just as bad, concentrating as they do on the top, and leaving the back and sides alone. Where is your condemnation of them, Mr Larouche? What's sauce for the goose is sauce for the gander.
Torquil Ampleforth, Ely

I NOTICED this planter in our elderly neighbour's garden. It would seem that a pair of cherubs are spit-roasting a lamb, but not in the conventional manner.
Peter Flannery, Lazonby

ON PAGE 209 of last year's annual, *The Wizard's Sleeve*, Fat Al White asked if anyone could beat his anecdote about farting whilst standing next to Brian May. And your stories of breaking wind in the vicinity of the rich and famous came flooding in by the two. Here are the best two of the two that we received.

…I DROPPED my guts at a Van Morrison concert with rotund sports presenter Steve Rider sat in the seat behind me. He certainly had a "Grandstand" view of that beefy eggo, I can tell you.
Iain Devenney, Abingdon

…MY mate John, who drinks in the same club as me, once dropped his guts whilst standing next to late darts legend Eric Bristow at a bar as he was ordering drinks. The Crafty Cockney wasn't very happy and said to him "Was that you, you smelly cunt?" to which my mate John grinned and nodded. He then fucked off in a right huff.
Kevin Gould, Southampton

THE VIZ CROWN COURT

The criminal case you are about to read is fictional, but the proceedings are authentic. Consider the evidence set out before you carefully, because YOU are the jury, and your verdict will determine whether or not justice is done…

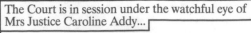

The Court is in session under the watchful eye of Mrs Justice Caroline Addy…

Will the defendant please rise..?

Edward Stanley Threadbare, you are charged that on March 3rd 2019, you did wilfully, and with malice aforethought, steal the saddle from a ladies' bicycle parked outside Fulchester Library, with the intent to sniff it for your own gratification.

How do you plead?

Not guilty.

Call the first witness.

The first witness for the prosecution, Chief Librarian Talulah Sultry, takes the stand…

Miss Sultry, please could you tell us what you saw when you looked out of your office window on the morning of March 3rd?

Yes… I saw a dishevelled man, bending down and sniffing the saddle of my bicycle, whilst performing a sex act upon himself through the pocket of his trousers.

And do you see that man in this courtroom today?

Yes. That is him in the dock. The beast!… the *FILTHY BEAST!*

OBJECTION!

This court is only concerned with the facts, Miss Sultry. Kindly keep your opinions regarding the defendant's character to yourself. Your witness, Mr Bartlett.

Thank you, your honour.

Miss Sultry, is it out of the question that the defendant - contrary to what you think you saw - was actually being a good Samaritan…?

Well, I hardly think…

I put it to you that my client, Mr Threadbare, an extremely short-sighted man, was closely checking your saddle, and indeed had spotted a sharp, metal spring sticking out of it…

What?…

…and, having decided to take that saddle home and mend it for you out of the goodness of his heart was, in fact, rummaging around in his pocket for the correct-sized spanner!

I know what I saw!

You indeed *saw*, Miss Sultry… but you do not *know*!

No further questions

But…

The next witness to take the stand is arresting officer PC John Scranage…

You arrested Mr Threadbare outside the library and accompanied him back to his flat above a wet fish shop in Scrap Road, did you not?

I did.

Could you tell the court what you saw when you entered Mr Threadbare's flat?

I saw a large number of bicycle saddles. I later found out there were 483 of them, to be precise… all from ladies' bicycles.

And what condition were these ladies' bicycle saddles in, PC Scranage?

They were prolifically stained with what the Police forensic laboratory later identified as human semen.

No further questions, Your Honour

The case for the defence begins its cross-examination…

Would you say, PC Scranage, that a person who has previously been convicted of a fraud necessarily makes a reliable witness in a criminal case?

Certainly not.

PC Scranage, before you became a policeman, did you or did you not make a living performing as a male stripper under the stage name of…

…Seymour Cock?

What!?! …I…er…

And before a show, did you or did you not stimulate your penis to a state of semi-tumescence before slipping an elastic band around the base in order to give the fraudulent impression that you were more well-endowed than was actually the case?

Erm...I...I...

Objection, your honour!

Objection sustained. This line of questioning has no relevance to the case being heard, Mr Bartlett. The jury will dismiss it.

I apologise, your honour. No further questions.

A hush descends on the court as the defence calls its only witness...

Calling Her Majesty Queen Elizabeth the Second!

You are...Her Majesty Queen Elizabeth II of Buckingham Palace, The Mall, London...?

One is.

Could you tell the jury where you were on the morning of March 3rd?

One was holding a garden party in the grounds of Buckingham Palace.

And what did you see?

One saw a man of the same average height and build as the defendant. He was wearing a top hat and a morning suit, and one only saw him from the back at a considerable distance...

I see. And could this man have been the man you now see in the dock, your majesty?

One couldn't rule it out, one supposes.

No further questions, your royal highness.

Your majesty, this man of average height you say you saw… how did you judge his height? Was he standing next to anyone?

He was standing next to a woman. One does not know who she was.

I see. So you cannot say with any degree of certainty whether she was extremely tall, like a professional basketball player, or extremely small, like her out of the Krankies...?

Well, one supposes, but one...

I put it to you, ma'am, that if you did not know who she was, you had no way of accurately assessing this woman's height, and therefore your statement that the man you saw was of average height is nothing more than conjecture.

B-but...

No further questions, your honour.

With the cases for the Prosecution and Defence now completed, Justice Addy begins her summing-up...

Members of the jury, you have heard the prosecution make an apparently strong case against Mr Threadbare. How did nearly 500 semen-stained ladies' bicycle saddles make their way into his flat? Had he stolen them with nefarious intent?

The prosecution offered no evidence that he had, and you must bear in mind that there is no law on the British Statute Books against anyone owning any number of bicycle seats and doing with them whatsoever he will in the privacy of his own home, however distasteful that may seem to you and me.

The defence, you may recall, offered us compelling evidence from Her Majesty the Queen, who told us that a man of the defendant's height and build was attending her garden party at the exact time that Mr Threadbare was supposedly quumfing Miss Sultry's bicycle seat over 200 miles away, in Fulchester.

On the other hand, you may decide that at the age of 92, her majesty's eyesight may not be everything it once was - and the fact that Mr Threadbare was arrested outside the library whilst in the act of trying to remove the seat from Miss Sultry's bicycle - casts some measure of doubt over the reliability of her testimony.

I ask you, the readers of *Viz*, to now retire and carefully consider your verdict.

VERDICT FORM

On the charge of Intent to Steal a Lady's Bicycle Seat for the Purposes of Auto-Erotic Sexual Gratification, I, a member of the Viz jury, hereby find the defendant, Edward Stanley Threadbare…

☐ Guilty

☐ Not Guilty

☐ Case Not Proven
(readers in Scotland only)

Cut out the form and return it to: *The Clerk of Fulchester Crown Court, PO Box 841, Whitley Bay NE26 9EQ,* to arrive no later than Boxing Day. The verdict and sentence, if any, will be announced in next year's annual. Enclose a self addressed envelope with a LARGE LETTER STAMP if you would like a free Viz pen.

SAVE ME FROM THES

Gardener's world turned upside down by bunny boilers

WHEN Preston-based freelance horticulturalist *Chorlton Wheelie* launched his landscape gardening business earlier this year, the jobs came flooding in and he thought he had found his niche. But the unmarried 58-year-old's dream of using his green fingers to earn an honest living soon turned into a nightmare, after all his female customers set about destroying his reputation with detailed accusations of theft and inappropriate behaviour.

And Chorlton says he knows exactly why his good name has been trashed so convincingly. He told us: "These nympho women are getting their revenge on me because I turned down their sexual advances."

According to Wheelie, who has lived in Preston all his life except for a 2-year sabbatical in London, an 18-month sabbatical in Durham and a 6-month suspended sabbatical, it's simply a case of sour grapes from his former customers. "They say Hell hath no fury like a woman spurned," he said. "And let me tell you, they're right."

"I spurned all them birds when they came on to me, and now they are getting their revenge by dragging my good character through the dirt."

Cold shower

Chorlton's problems began on his first job. After placing an advert in his local free-ads paper advertising his freelance landscape design, water features and exotic topiary start-up, he was contacted by a prospective customer who wanted a concrete shed base smashing up and taking away. Wheelie gave her a cash quote and the job was his.

Box clever: *A maze similar to the one that Chorlton was booked to design for the National Trust.*

EXCLUSIVE!

"She asked when I could come round and start work. I explained that I'd been booked to re-design a box hedge maze at a nearby National Trust property that week, but they'd had to cancel at the last minute, so I could go round and set-to straight away. Ten minutes later, I was stood in her back yard, braying the old concrete with a sledge hammer.

It was hot work, and after I'd been at it for an hour or so, the lady of the house came out with a cup of tea for me. As I necked my cuppa, I eyed her up and down. She was pretty good looking, in a blousy sort of way, with dyed blonde hair, big tits and long legs. I noticed that she never took her eyes off me, licking her lips and staring at my crotch through my trackie bottoms as I drank my tea.

Eventually she spoke. 'Braying at that concrete looks like hot work, Chorlton,' she said. 'Why don't you come in the house and have a nice cooling shower?'

'I'm feeling quite hot myself,' she continued, licking her lips seductively. 'I think I might join you in there.'

Now I've got nothing against being friendly with my customers, but what this bird was suggesting was strictly out of order, and I lost no time in telling her so. She seemed quite offended, like she wasn't used to having her sexual advances refused by tradesmen. 'You'd be well advised to reconsider,' she told me. 'Or you might regret it.'

rubble

I turned her down flat again and, with a face like thunder, she stormed back inside while I carried on knacking the concrete until the whole shed base was in bits.

Garden of iniquity: *58-year-old Chorlton's dream job became a nightmare.*

The price I'd quoted on the phone included removal of the rubble, so I chucked the lumps over the neighbours' wall and it was job done. I'd got the cash up front, so I got in my van and set off home, never giving my customer's earlier, unwanted sexual advances a second thought.

> ### 'I'm feeling quite hot myself,' she continued, licking her lips seductively. 'I think I might join you in there.'

But when I pulled into my street, I saw there was a police car parked outside my house. It didn't strike me as particularly unusual, as the filth often call round on a variety of misunderstandings of one sort or another. When I got out of my van, one of the pigs approached me and told me I'd been spotted stealing a load of women's underwear from a washing line at the property I had just left.

He asked me if he could take a look in the back of my van. I told him I had nothing to hide, but I had unfortunately lost the key moments earlier, so him and his colleague popped the back doors with a crow-bar.

What I saw when those van doors swung open made my blood run cold. The busty housewife whose unwanted sexual advances I had earlier spurned had clearly secreted several items of her sexy underwear in there while I was braying her shed base, then called the police to make a false accusation that she had seen me stealing them off the line. Which I hadn't.

pebbles

My blood ran even colder as that bird's words of warning came back to me: 'You'd be well advised to reconsider. Or you might regret it.'

At that moment, I suddenly remembered another job I had to go to, and ran off as fast as I could. The filth completely misunderstood the situation and immediately gave chase in their jam sandwich. They caught me a couple of hundred yards down the road when I stopped to get my breath back and have a spew.

I was arrested, taken back to the station and charged with knicker theft. On the advice of my brief, I admitted guilt and accepted a caution, even though I was completely innocent. As I left the station four hours later with my good reputation slightly tarnished, I ruefully reflected that the blonde piece had got her revenge on me, and vowed never to fall victim to sexual blackmail again. "

E SEX-MAD WOMEN!

Demolition man

A man with Chorlton's green fingers and eye for landscape design and garden creation is always in demand, and the very next day, Wheelie found himself in the back garden of a terraced house on the Callon estate, tasked with blowtorching a load of weeds and nettles.

The house had been empty for the thick end of a year and the yard was like a jungle. The new owners - a busty redhead and her boyfriend - wanted it cleared so they could pave it over to park their caravan up.

I quickly set to my task of clearing the weeds with my paraffin burner. It was hot work, and I was very grateful after half an hour or so when the bird came out with a refreshing can of lager for me. As I stood necking my drink, I looked her up and down. She was good looking, in an obvious sort of way, with big tits, long legs, and a smashing arse, but she wasn't really my type. I had took my shirt off, and I could feel her eyeing me up in my sweaty vest, like I was Bruce Willis.

'I like the way you handle that paraffin burner,' she said breathily, running her fingers up and down my bicep. 'You're clearly very good with your hands. Why don't you come in the house and show me what else you can do with them?'

barney

I know a chat-up line when I hear one, but I'm a professional. I just wanted to get the gardening job done and head off back home for my tea. She didn't look too happy when I knocked back her advance, and as I fired up the paraffin burner and set about the next patch of weeds, she slunk moodily back into the house.

To be frank, I didn't give that bird's clumsy pass a second thought until I got back home. Once again, there was a police car parked outside my house. 'Oh no, here we go again,' I thought to myself.

I was taken back to the station and charged with voyeurism. The woman had told the tit-heads that I'd climbed up a ladder outside the house to spy on her on the toilet. The coppers even had a photograph she'd given them, of me poking my head through the open toilet window.

She had clearly knocked it up with photoshop, because I would swear on my kids' lives, if I had any,

> *She was good looking, in an obvious sort of way, with big tits, long legs, and a smashing arse, but she wasn't really my type.*

that I never went up that ladder. To be fair, she'd made a good job of faking up the evidence on her computer. The lighting and perspective were very good, and she'd even got reflections in the glass and everything. My brief turned up at the station, and told me that expertly doctored photographic evidence is very hard to fight in court, and the easiest thing would just be to admit it.

Reluctantly, I took his advice. I also asked for fifteen other cases of voyeurism, which I also didn't do, to be taken into consideration.

The first two false allegations against Chorlton were just the start of his troubles. Over the next few weeks, he refused to give in to the sexual whims of even more of his attractive female clients, and found himself accused of

- Exposing his genitals, which were accurately described after his accuser somehow obtained his medical records

- Breaking into a garage and stealing a lawnmower, which coincidentally matched one he bought from a second-hand shop on his way home that very evening

- Taking a large number of "up-skirt" photographs, which his clients had taken themselves and somehow downloaded onto his mobile phone

Shed's up: The outhouse base wasn't all that Wheelie was expected to lay.

Oiling the deck

Not surprisingly, the heartless vendetta being conducted by all of Chorlton's attractive female customers was beginning to have an effect on his business. A booking to re-model Capability Brown's formal gardens at Chatsworth House and another to makeover the Blue Peter Italian sunken garden were both suddenly cancelled without explanation. However, a slightly smaller job to re-creosote an area of decking behind a council house on one of the estates in Ribbleton went ahead.

It was a terrible job, because the bird whose house it was had had a problem with rats. She'd put poison out, and there were now a load of dead ones under her decking, so I had to poke out as many as I could reach with a brush handle before I could start the job. It was a horrible job to do for twenty-five quid, but I needed the money to pay off a fine for something I hadn't done, and I quickly worked up quite a sweat.

It was a hot day, and when I'd cleared the rats from under about half the decking, the bird came out to do a spot of sunbathing. I took a moment while I was putting some rats in a bin-bag to look her up and down. I suppose a lot of blokes would have found her attractive, what with her blonde hair and fairly big knockers, but she didn't do a lot for me.

She climbed onto the sunlounger on a bit of the decking I'd already creosoted, laid down on her front and reached round to undo the straps on her bikini top. 'Excuse me Chorlton,' she purred seductively. 'Would you come over here and rub some sun cream into my back?'

She turned round and winked. 'And when you've done that, I'll turn over and you can do my tits and all.'

charlie

I suppose many men might have been tempted at the prospect of being paid twenty-five quid to spend the afternoon massaging oil into this woman's shapely knockers, but her invitation frankly left me cold. She simply wasn't my type. And anyway, I still had a load of decking left to creosote.

After I had passed up on her sexy invitation, despite it being a sunny afternoon, the atmosphere in the garden turned distinctly frosty. In fact, the sexy bird completely ignored me for the rest of the afternoon as I worked away at her decking, and didn't say a word to me as I picked up my tools and bin-bags of dead rats to leave.

Later that night, there was a knock at the door. It was the police, and they wanted to know if I could help them with their enquiries about a necklace and

Rat's not the way to do it! Chorlton smelled a rat when customer expected extermination with benefits.

some rings that had been reported stolen from the house where I'd been working. I told them I couldn't; despite my extensive criminal record for dishonesty, I'm as honest as the day is long.

But my protestations of innocence fell on deaf ears. They had a warrant, and quickly found the jewellery they were looking for. You could have knocked me down with a feather when the coppers pulled the stolen Tom out of my back pocket.

farnsbarns

I could only imagine that the bird with big tits at the house had set me up as revenge for me spurning her sexual advances. Clearly, she must have planted the jewellery in my trousers when I was bending over to rake rats from under the decking. Even worse, she'd clearly gone to a lot of trouble to frame me, even going so far as to leave big, creosote boot-marks up the stairs and across her bedroom carpet to the dressing table under the window.

She even denied having been sunbathing at all, saying that it was the middle of November, and she had been in town shopping when I broke into her house. Which, as I say, I didn't.

My brief told me to plead guilty again, as she had also somehow concocted overwhelming fingerprint evidence against me. The true tragedy of the situation is that, if I could only have forced myself to rub a bit of sun-oil into that bird's back and tits, I would have saved myself an awful lot of bother.

Chorlton's reputation has been so tarnished by his spurned nympho customers' vindictive accusations that he has decided to take a break from his gardening business. "I've had enough," he told us. "In fact, this has all been so upsetting for me that I've decided to leave the Preston area for eighteen months."

"Or I might be back in twelve months with good behaviour," he added.

EACH week, Romans clamoured to the Colosseum in droves to enjoy the magnificently gory spectacles put on by the authorities to keep their insatiable thirst for blood slaked. But where did they park? Outside the stadium was a vast area of hard-standing, with parking room for up to 5,000 chariots. Latecomers often found that competition for spaces was high, and fights to

the death often broke out between frustrated charioteers arguing over who got there first. Parking wardens - easily recognised by the dayglo feather plumes on their helmets - patrolled these parking areas, issuing a fixed 100 dinari penalty to anyone who failed to display a ticket, parked outside the designated lines, or whose horses had shat, although this fine was reduced to 50 dinari if the miscreant paid up within seven days.

PUTTING on a spectacular show of death each week wasn't cheap. Although the gladiators themselves weren't paid, and half of them were killed so didn't need feeding or transport home, the cost of shipping in fresh, hungry wild animals from the far-flung edges of the empire

was vast. Official merchandise was an important revenue stream for Colosseum management. Early versions of the foam hands that are popular souvenirs of modern sporting events have been found during excavations of ancient Roman sites. Instead of being made from open-celled polyurethane like their present day counterparts, these were fashioned from cork and calf leather, and came screen-printed with the crowd's favourite gladiator logos and catchphrases.

JUST like at a modern sporting event, overpriced, unpalatable refreshments were an important part of the experience for hungry crowd-members. Of course, modern hot dogs hadn't been invented two millennia ago, so instead Roman games fans chowed down on a 'Calidum Canis', a snack consisting of a cylindrical portion

of semi-cooked, pureed hog meat, oats and sawdust, served in a piece of leavened bread split along its length. This was offered with an optional spoonful of wet onions and a squirt of the cheapest *nullam consectetur condimentum* available from the Roman cash 'n' carry. And the games also existed two thousand years before the invention of ice cream. Instead, on hot days, citizens enjoyed a 'XCIX' - a primitive cold dessert made by cooling churned cream until it was semi-frozen, served in a cone with two chocolate flakes.

THE PEOPLE of ancient Rome had an insatiable thirst for blood and a ravenous hunger for death, and their giant theatre of destruction was the Colosseum. Here it was that the citizens of the world's greatest historical empire clamoured each week to witness men, women and wild beasts pitted against each other in spectacularly

Whom's Whom & Why is What...

AT THE COLO

IT WILL come as no surprise that illegal street vendors flogging cheaply produced knock-off merchandise to the crowds flocking to the colosseum were as prevalent at the games in Ancient Rome as they are today. On the surface, the foam hands they were selling may have looked indistinguishable from the official souvenirs available inside the stadium, but they were in fact of inferior quality, being made from tree bark and goat leather. While hawking their knock-off wares to the crowds, these Roman wideboys kept one eye out for customers and another for the Praetorian guards. If caught, they would face a stiff fine of 200 dinari and have their hands cut off.

violent battles, where the winners enjoyed glory and the losers paid the ultimate price. It must have been fucking great.

But how did it all work? It's time to step back two millennia to the year 22AD and take our grandstand seats in the stands above the action-packed, blood-soaked epicentre of the greatest empire the world has ever seen, to discover…

OSSEVM

GLADIATORS were true sporting heroes; they were the Christiano Ronaldos, Lewis Hamiltons and Serena Williamses of the ancient world. And just like at sports stadiums today, autograph hunters crowded round the Colosseum's dressing room doors in the hope of getting

a signed memento from their favourite stars. However, collecting gladiatorial autographs was a particularly unrewarding hobby to pursue in ancient Rome, as there was only a slim chance of fans actually meeting their heroes after the games, since half of them left the arena in bits, or inside the belly of a lion. And getting a signed memento from the gladiators who did survive the games was still unlikely, as only 5% of Romans were actually able to write their own name.

THE games were held primarily for the fun and relaxation of the spectators. But they were also places where business was done and deals were struck. And areas of the stadium, particularly those with good views of the sporting spectacle, were set aside for corporate hospi-

tality. Here, wealthy businessmen, such as those who owned chariot dealerships, slave auction rooms or wall-to-wall mosaic flooring warehouses, paid high prices for ringside seats and a 65-course meal with unlimited wine, in order to entertain important clients who paid scant attention to the thrilling life-and-death action taking place in front of them.

CROWD safety was an important issue every time thousands of excited Roman citizens crammed into the Colosseum to watch the spectacular displays of mass-slaughter taking place. Stewards were employed to show blood-thirsty fans to their seats in the stands, and were also on hand throughout the games to watch out for crowd trouble, keep the excitable audience members sitting in their seats, and identify anyone who had shouted something racist. And no matter how exciting the action taking place in the Colosseum - whether it was an enraged rhinoceros going head-to-head with two lions, or six blindfolded Christians chained to a hungry bear - the stewards had to keep their backs to the arena and their full attention focussed on the crowd.

NO MODERN sporting event is complete without a streaker - a young sports fan who, after a little bit too much to drink, decides to run onto the pitch in the altogether, much to the amusement of the crowd. And whilst nudity in ancient Rome wasn't quite the taboo it is these days, authorities took a decidedly dim view of anyone disrupting the games. Any high-spirited young citizen who 'did a streak' ran the risk of being caught up in the gory action, being hit by a flying arrow or savaged by a tiger. And if they did survive, they would pay for their thirty seconds of fame by being castrated, crucified to semi-consciousness, and then daubed in pitch and set on fire.

Next week:
Who's Who and What They Do in the
Miss World Beauty Pageant Bra-Fitting Room

NO, I MEAN IRIS... SHE'S PASSED OVER...

EEH! SHE 'AS! YA'VE GOT TO MAKE THE MOST OF EVERY DAY, 'AVEN'T YOU..?

YOU 'AVE, ADA...YOU'RE RIGHT..!

YOU NEVER KNOW WHEN THE GOOD LORD IS GOIN' T'SMILE DOWN UPON YOU AND GATHER YOU UP INTO 'IS BOSOM...

ANYWAY, 'AS 'ILDA GONE YET..?

NOT QUITE. BUT IT CAN'T BE LONG NOW, DOLLY. LOOK AT 'ER FACE.

PEACE 'AS DESCENDED.

YES... AND SOON SHE'LL DWELLETH IN THE HOUSE OF THE LORD...

THAT'S RIGHT, DOLLY...

ALL 'ER EARTHLY TROUBLES AND TRIBULATIONS WILL SOON BE OVER.

NO MORE TROUBLE WITH 'ER BUNIONS.

NO MORE GYP OFF 'ER BOWELS...

...OR THAT VARICOSE LABIUM SHE 'AD...

NOT THAT SHE EVER COMPLAINED... SHE WERE A MARTYR TO 'ER BOWELS AN' 'ER FANNY, SHE WERE, DOLLY.

...AND NO MORE BOTHER FROM THAT 'USBAND OF 'ERS, NEITHER.

DID 'E BOTHER 'ER A LOT, THEN, DID 'E..?

OOH YES. USED T'BOTHER 'ER SUMMAT TERRIBLE, 'E DID. THAT'S WHAT BRING 'ER LABIAL TROUBLES ON.

WELL SHE'LL BE GLAD T'BE FINALLY FREE OF THAT INDIGNITY, DOLLY.

DO YOU THINK THAT'S IT, ADA..? 'AS SHE GONE..?

I THINK IT MIGHT BE, DOLLY...

'ELLO MRS RABBITS! WAKEY WAKEY! TIME FOR YOUR TEA!

!?

OOH SMASHIN'! WHAT IS IT? GAMMON AN' MASHED POTATO.

CHAMPION!

EEH, THAT'S A NICE BIT OF GAMMON, THAT! BET Y'DIDN'T GET THAT AT SHELDONS... 'E DOESN'T DO GAMMON THAT NICE, SHELDON...!

YOU ENJOY THAT NOW, MRS RABBITS.

NYAM! NYAM! NYAM!

SCOFF!

CHOMP!

EEH. THAT'LL BE 'ER UNGER FOR THE GRAVE, ADA.

AYE. WON'T BE LONG NOW, DOLLY...

SCOFF! CHOMP!

BIGGER IS BETTER, or so the saying goes. And in many spheres of life - car engines, superyachts and men's genitals - it's hard to argue otherwise. But is it also the case when it comes to pets? Because like it it not, animals are getting *LARGER*, and it's a trend that's set to continue at an ever-increasing rate.

A few months ago, Knickers the gargantuan Australian cow made headlines around the world when he was saved from the slaughterhouse because he was simply too big to fit into the abattoir stall. The beefy steer stands a whopping 6'4" at the shoulder, towering over the other cows in his herd, thanks to his high octane diet of genetically modified oats and growth hormones.

And as powerful metabolic chemicals such as these leach into our own environment, it is inevitable that domestic animals will ingest them too. And once they do, they will start growing to previously unimaginable sizes. By the end of the decade, our pet shops could be filled with kittens the size of Shetland ponies, puppies the size of shire horses, and stick insects as big as trees. What will this mean to us on a day-to-day basis? How will our relationships with our pets change, and what are the practicalities of owning and caring for such titanic animals?

Let's take a peek into the very near future to consider how our everyday lives will be changed…

Down, boy: We'd better get used to it, but the days where we are bigger than our pets are numbered.

WHEN PETS GO ALL BIG!

CATS

When pets go all big, your king-sized ball of fluff and whiskers will not hesitate to launch a ferocious and almost certainly fatal attack on you, leaving your lifeless body torn limb from limb on the doormat, while he goes off to lick his giant arse in front of the fire.

And that's not the only threat cat owners will face in the future. Those who choose to keep their pets indoors will have to provide a suitably supersized litter tray. This could easily fill a whole room, and take hundreds of standard bags of kitty litter to fill.

The situation will be no more convenient for those who let their cats out to do their business. Today's six-inch square cat flap will be no use to an animal weighing upwards of three tons. Instead, a new cat-flap will have to be fitted that is actually larger than the existing door; meaning that cat-owners will have to make their way in and out of their house via a 'human-flap' set into it.

And whilst today's moggies' habit of scratching table legs and pulling threads on soft furnishings is a mild annoyance, the scythe-sized claws of the giant cat of the near future will be able to reduce everything in the room to matchwood and ribbons in mere minutes.

ALTHOUGH your innocent puss playing with a ball of wool on the mat looks harmless enough, in reality he has only one ambition in life… *to kill you*, after first tormenting you sadistically for half an hour. At his present size, little Mr Tiddles is unable to make his dearest wish a reality, but once he is boosted by hormones to the height and weight of a bull rhinoceros, it will be a whole different ballgame.

BUDGIES

"WHO'S a massive boy, then? Who's a massive boy?" will be the booming cry of the colossal budgie of the future. And you won't be able to perch him on the end of your finger, either. The height, girth and weight of seventies wrestler Giant Haystacks, he will simply sit on his reinforced steel perch all day, screeching for crackers in a deep Barry White-like baritone.

And you can forget about keeping Joey in a birdcage hanging up on a stand. The humungous budgie of tomorrow will require a giant coop half the size of the lounge, so you'll simply have to put a wall of bars across the room to stop him flying off out the window or the cat getting him.

To stop him from getting bored and pulling his own feathers out, you'll have to buy him a mirror six feet in diameter, a two-hundredweight church bell that he can hit with his beak, and a life-size plastic replica of himself with springs for legs. And you'd better open an account with your local DIY store, because you're going to need about 200 sheets of sandpaper *every day* to cover the bottom of his cage and catch his black and white droppings - each one the size of a ten-pin bowling ball.

DOGS

A DOG is man's best friend, and happily your bright-eyed, wet-nosed pal will be just as faithful and loveable once he has grown, literally, to mammoth proportions. But that doesn't mean that his new gargantuan size won't pose serious risks to you and your family. Stand in the wrong place when he's wagging his rolled-up-carpet-sized tail and you could be knocked off your feet, concussed, or even suffer serious internal injuries.

Ask Rover to roll over for a biscuit, and you'd better make sure you're standing in a safe place if you don't want to end up flattened into the floor like a pet-owning pancake.

What's more, whereas scooping Fido's poop in the park nowadays is a simple one-handed job, in the future each one of his stinking turds will be the side of a pillar box on its side. You're going to need a massive bag to pick it up if you're going to avoid a hefty fine. And then you'll need the help of several friends to lift it up and leave it dangling off a tree.

GOLDFISH

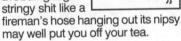

ASK anyone and they'll tell you that their happiest childhood memory is coming home from the funfair after winning a goldfish. But in the future, when pets go all big, that precious memory may be a thing of the past, as plastic bags capable of holding enough water to accommodate tomorrow's dolphin-sized goldfishes would rip off the nails holding them to the hook-a-duck man's prize board.

Furthermore, if you did manage to get such a massive fish home, where would you keep it? The bath would be far too small, and trying to balance a bowl the size of two Transit vans on top of the telly would be a recipe for disaster.

The only solution would be to commission an enormous, custom-made 10,000 gallon tank, and place it in the dining room. Over the coming years, watching your leviathan pet swimming backwards and forwards would provide you with countless hours of gentle relaxation; indeed, ownership of a goldfish is believed to reduce stress levels and lower blood pressure. Having said that, it is worth bearing in mind that the sight of your goldfish with a Brobdingnagian stringy shit like a fireman's hose hanging out its nipsy may well put you off your tea.

But anyone who's won a goldfish at the fair knows only too well the tragedy of waking up in the morning to find their new pet floating lifeless in its bowl. And picking him up by the tail and flushing him down the toilet will no longer be an option when Goldie weighs more than half a dozen bags of cement.

Bereaved owners will be faced with the unedifying prospect of having to chop their late pet up into single-flush-sized chunks before spending 24 hours repeatedly pulling the chain and waiting for the cistern to fill up, burying him in a big hole in the garden, or throwing him to the cat.

TORTOISE

GIANT tortoises already exist; they're a familiar sight in the Galapagos Islands as they slowly go about their daily business. But in the future, when pets go all big, tomorrow's enormous normal-sized tortoises will make the giant tortoises of today look like miniature-sized tortoises. That's because in the future, a normal pet tortoise will be as big as a VW Beetle, and weigh in at up to a ton or more.

Be prepared for a proportionately gargantuan food bill too. Your slowcoach reptile may not do anything of any interest, but he'll happily chomp his way through £60 worth of iceberg lettuces and cauliflower tops every single day.

Forget about using a small brush to paint your pet's name on its shell. You've got a lot of area to cover, so you'd better invest in a big roller and several gallons of lead-free paint. And don't forget to add your postcode in case your tortoise wanders off into a neighbour's garden.

Each Autumn, as its metabolism slows, you will have to place your tortoise in a cardboard box filled with torn-up newspaper and straw, and pop it into the garage to hibernate until Spring. And that means your car will have to be parked out on the street all winter.

Assuming he doesn't get eaten by rats while he's asleep in the garage, when your tortoise wakes up in Spring, you'll need a bathful of lukewarm water and a cotton wool ball the size of a spacehopper to wipe the gunk out of his eyes.

HAMSTERS

FOR many reasons, you would be well advised to avoid buying a household animal when pets go all big. But what if your child is sent home with the school hamster - the size of a fully grown polar bear - to look after over the summer holidays? You'd be perfectly safe from attack; hamsters are herbivores, and he should be quite happy nibbling on fruit, vegetables and sunflower seeds, although you'll need to source them in industrial quantities.

But it's worth remembering that hamsters also have notoriously bad eyesight. If he mistakes your finger for a carrot, you might accidentally get a nasty nip from his razor-sharp incisor teeth, each as big as a shovel, possibly losing a whole arm in the process, so it pays to be careful when poking tasty treats through the bars of his portacabin-sized cage.

As you will quickly learn, hamsters are nocturnal creatures; they sleep through the day, only becoming active after dark. It is likely you will quickly tire of being kept awake all night by the deafening sound of your furry lodger scurrying around his cage and scampering on his squeaky, twelve-foot diameter wire wheel.

It is not unusual for a hamster to die while someone else is looking after it, so don't be surprised if you go down one morning and find him rolled up dead in a huge ball of chewed-up toilet paper. If this happens, simply buy another one that looks the same from the pet shop, where they cost about £2.50.

NEXT WEEK:
With growth-inhibiting hormones leaching into the environment, it's a fact that domestic animals are getting smaller. We take a look into the future to see what will happen...

WHEN PETS GO ALL LITTLE!

SPOT THE CHRISTMAS CLUE

WITH DETECTIVE INSPECTOR BING "I'M DREAMING OF A WHITE CHRISTMAS" CROSBY

IN THE OFFICES OF SCOTLAND YARD'S CHRISTMAS CRIMES DIVISION

INSPECTOR CROSBY, WE'VE HAD A REPORT OF GUNSHOTS BEING FIRED — YOU'D BETTER GET ON TO IT!

BUT CHIEF, I'M IN CHARGE OF CHRISTMAS CRIMES!

A REPORT OF GUNFIRE DOESN'T SOUND PARTICULARLY FESTIVE!

THESE GUNSHOTS COULDN'T BE MORE CHRISTMASSY, CROSBY!

FOR THEY WERE HEARD IN A LOWLY STABLE IN THE LITTLE TOWN OF BETHLEHEM... OVER TWO THOUSAND YEARS AGO!

WE'LL USE THE POLICE TEMPORAL TRANSPORTER TO SEND YOU BACK IN TIME TO THE BIRTHPLACE OF JESUS, AND INVESTIGATE THESE GUNSHOTS!

RIGHTO, CHIEF!

SOON INSPECTOR BING CROSBY AND HIS SIDEKICK PC WHITE WERE BEING TRANSPORTED BACK IN TIME TO THE FIRST CHRISTMAS.

HUMMM!

AND, IN FIRST CENTURY PALESTINE...

HUMMM!

THANK GOODNESS YOU'VE COME, INSPECTOR. I AM THE VIRGIN MARY, MEEK AND MILD...

WE HEARD THREE GUNSHOTS COMING FROM INSIDE THE STABLE DRAWING ROOM...

BUT THE DOOR IS LOCKED FROM THE INSIDE, AND WE CAN'T GET IN!

PC WHITE KICKED IN THE DRAWING ROOM DOOR — GERTCHA!

GREAT SCOTT! IT'S THE THREE KINGS OF ORIENT ARE!

SOMEBODY HAS SHOT THEM AND STOLEN THEIR GOLD FRANKINCENSE AND MYRRH!

WHERE WAS EVERYBODY WHEN THE SHOTS WERE FIRED, MISS MARY?

I WAS HERE IN THE STABLE WITH MY HUSBAND JOSEPH AND THE BABY JESUS...

...AND OUR BUTLER CHIVES WAS OUTSIDE.

THAT IS CORRECT, INSPECTOR...

I WAS OUT COLLECTING FRESH HAY FOR THE BABY JESUS'S MANGER...

BANG! BANG! BANG!

SUDDENLY, THE STILL CALM OF THE SILENT NIGHT WAS SHATTERED BY THE SOUND OF GUNFIRE!

HMM, AND THE DRAWING ROOM DOOR WAS LOCKED FROM THE INSIDE, MEANING NOBODY COULD ENTER OR LEAVE...

WELL... NOT QUITE, INSPECTOR...

YOU SEE, THE DRAWING ROOM DOOR HAS A CAT FLAP IN IT ~ BIG ENOUGH FOR A SMALL PERSON TO CRAWL INSIDE WITH A GUN...

...A TINY INFANT, FOR EXAMPLE!

INSPECTOR CROSBY, LOOK! I'VE FOUND THE STOLEN GOLD FRANKINCENSE AND MYRRH!

IT'S HIDDEN RIGHT HERE IN THE BABY JESUS'S MANGER!

LOOKS LIKE AN OPEN AND SHOT CASE, INSPECTOR...

THE INFANT CHRIST MURDERED THE THREE KINGS OF ORIENT ARE IN ORDER TO STEAL THEIR VALUABLES!

I'M NOT SO SURE!

DID YOU SPOT THE CLUE?

THE MURDERER WAS IN FACT... CHIVES, THE BUTLER!

OR PERHAPS I SHOULD USE HIS REAL NAME...

...THE HOLY GHOST!

GASP! A GHOST IN A BUTLER DISGUISE!

BEING A SPOOK, IT WAS EASY FOR THE HOLY GHOST TO FLOAT THROUGH THE LOCKED DRAWING ROOM DOOR AND SHOOT THE THREE KINGS OF ORIENT ARE..

THEN HE TOOK THEIR GOLD, FRANKINCENSE AND MYRRH AND PLANTED IT IN BABY JESUS'S MANGER!

ALL RIGHT, I ADMIT IT! I DID IT BECAUSE I WAS JEALOUS OF ALL THE ATTENTION THE BABY JESUS WAS GETTING!

SO I DECIDED TO FRAME HIM FOR A MURDER, IN ORDER TO TEACH HIM A 'LESSON'!

GOOD WORK, INSPECTOR CROSBY! BUT WHAT MADE YOU SUSPECT THE BUTLER?

SIMPLE! HIS STORY ABOUT OVERHEARING THE GUNSHOTS JUST DIDN'T ADD UP...

DID YOU SPOT THE CLUE?

"CHIVES" CLAIMED THAT HE WAS OUTSIDE COLLECTING HAY WHEN THE STILL CALM OF THE SILENT NIGHT WAS SHATTERED BY THE SOUND OF GUNFIRE...

BUT WE ALL KNOW THAT CHRISTMAS NIGHT IS FAR FROM SILENT, AND THE AIR IS FILLED WITH THE SOUND OF SLEIGH BELLS JINGLING, RING TINGLE TINGLING TOO (RING-A-LING A-DING-DONG-DING).

BANG! BANG! BANG!

XX7

The Secret Agent with the XX Permit to Assassinate (a bit like James Bond, but hopefully sufficiently different to avoid legal action for copyright infringement from Eon Productions and the estates of the late Cubby Broccoli and Ian Fleming).

...So that's your mission, XX7... Kill the head of S.K.I.R.M.I.S.H. in his Pacific volcano hideaway before he signs off his Plutonium deal with the Kremlin.

I see.

Good luck... Oh, and XX7... Make it look like the Chinese are behind it.

Leave it to me, M.

Here you go, XX7...Your tickets to Singapore, your fake Visa, and your false passport.

I'll pick them up in a minute, Pennyfarthing. I've just got to pop down and see Q first, to sort out a bit of a problem with one of my gadgets.

Shortly...

Ah, XX7. What do you think of these RPG-launching brogues?

Very impressive Q. But I'm actually here to get this changed.

Your grappling hook Rolex? What seems to be the problem? It's still ticking.

Yes, but it's stopped firing the carbon fibre escape line out when you twist the bezel...it's supposed to fire over 500 yards...

...I've only used it once, when I got chased off the top of the Eiffel Tower by a giant with metal teeth. It worked fine that time, but now it only fires the line out a couple of foot, tops.

Hmm, I see what you mean, XX7.

Have you got the receipt?

Yes, it's here.

Hmm. It's out of warranty, I'm afraid.

No, no... I took out the extended warranty... Three years parts and labour, see?

Yes, but that only covers you for defects in manufacture, you see, not misuse or reasonable wear and tear.

Wear and tear?! I've only used the bloody thing once!

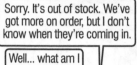

The Friendliest People in the Land!

A NEW survey has confirmed that residents of Yorkshire are twice as likely to tell you they are the friendliest people in the country than are people from anywhere else in the country.

Tyke my word for it: Yorkshireman Martin

God's Own County tops cordiality-claiming pops

An academic study found that almost 90% of conversations with someone from Yorkshire include a claim that people from Yorkshire are friendlier than anyone else. "I don't think that anyone who has spoken with anyone from Yorkshire will be surprised by the results," said Professor Honey-Boy Zimba, of Halifax Baths University, who conducted the survey.

fundamental

"A conversation can begin on almost any topic, for example the weather, the fundamental duality at the heart of man's soul, or whether that dress was blue or gold, and within a few short minutes the claim that Yorkshire people are the friendliest in the country will be made," said Zimba.

The news that the county had topped the list was welcomed by Yorkshire chef James Martin. "I always say that Yorkshire people are the friendliest people in the country. Having said that, we speak as we find and we don't suffer fools gladly," he told us from his home in Hampshire.

human

In a separate survey, people from Yorkshire were found to be the 34th actual friendliest people in the country, just below scaffolders, doctors' receptionists and people who work in amusement arcade change booths.

27

THE WAR OF EN

RELATIONS between Meghan Markle and Kate Middleton – famously fractious at the best of times – are at an all time low, following a series of foul-mouthed and acrimonious confrontations between the rival royal sisters-in-law. And now palace insiders fear that their infamous rivalry, which has even boiled over into doorstep catfights on the Sandringham estate, could be doing irreparable harm to the reputation of the monarchy.

"Everyone knows that the Duchesses of Sussex and Cambridge don't really get on, but in the past they've always managed to keep things civil," said Ingrid Ffartsucker, editor of *Majestic* magazine. "But now the hostility between them is out in the open and plain for everyone to see."

"They can't bear to be in the same room as each other," Ffartsucker added. "It's like the Queen Mother and Wallis Simpson all over again."

palace

A palace insider revealed that the pair's relationship hit the rocks on Christmas day, when Meghan opened her present from Kate. He told us: "It was three pairs of Sloggi knickers, but not the briefs; they were the really big type. And they were extra large size."

"Meghan went absolutely ballistic, poking Kate in the chest and screaming in her face. 'Don't you say I've got a fat arse,' she ranted. 'If you want to see a fat arse, you want to take a look in the mirror. And anyway, I'd rather have a fat arse than flat tits.' To which Kate replied that she might have flat tits, but at least her tits were real," he continued.

"Well, Meghan wasn't having that, and she went for Kate. Wills and Harry had to intervene to hold the two duchesses apart. It was all very unpleasant, and to say there was an awkward atmosphere throughout Christmas dinner would be the understatement of the century," said the insider. "The Queen and Prince Philip just didn't know which way to look. They clearly didn't want to get involved in case they were accused of taking sides."

It is understood that the Sussexes were supposed to be going round to the Cambridges for tea on Boxing Day, but the invitation was cancelled at the last minute, with Kate saying she had a headache. "Everybody knew that wasn't true," said the insider. "She was clearly

Put up your Duchesses: Sussex (above) and Cambridge (opposite) went for each other.

The silk gloves are off as Meghan and Kate square up for Battle Royal

still seething over Meghan's flat-chest jibe from the previous day."

maze

The glamorous rival sisters-in-law managed to call a temporary truce in front of the press pack when the entire royal family attended a New Year's Day service in Balmoral. The insider told us: "The Queen gave the pair of them a proper bollocking in the car, telling them in no uncertain terms that they had to patch it up and keep it friendly for the cameras."

But although relations between the two appeared cordial as they smiled for photographers on the church steps, resentment and anger was still bubbling just below the surface. And that unpleasantness boiled over a couple of weeks later, following an incident involving Kate and William's eldest son Prince George.

The insider told us: "George had got a goal for Christmas, and he was having a kickabout on the lawn when he booted his football over the fence into Harry and Meghan's back garden."

"Meghan came out the French windows with a vegetable knife, burst the ball, and threw it back over the fence," he continued. "The toddler ran back in the house in floods of tears. Seconds later, Kate came out to remonstrate with her sister-in-law, who by this point was hanging out her washing."

"'Hey, what kind of woman busts a little kid's ball?' she shouted. Meghan put down her washing and came up to the fence. 'It's the hundredth time he's kicked the fucking thing over,' she shouted. 'I told him if he did it again, I'd bust the fucking thing. He's had it coming.'"

"The Duchess of Cambridge wasn't having that. 'Hey, don't swear in front of my kids,' she said, jabbing her finger

This Crown Ain't Big E

Kate or Meghan... One of them's got to go, and we're giving YOU the chance to decide which!

FOLLOWING the success of Brexit, it is clear that the best way to decide any important national question is by Referendum. So we're holding a UK-wide plebiscite to decide once and for all by a simple majority which Duchess – Sussex or Cambridge – has to go. We've got together with Buckingham Palace, and they have have agreed that the Viz readers' mandate will be legally binding.

This is YOUR chance to make your voice heard and settle this issue before it becomes a full-blown constitutional crisis.

HOW TO TAKE PART

Next Thursday, cut out the Referendum Voting Paper *(right)* and take it to a corner of the room where nobody can see what you are doing. Tie a short, blunt pencil to something nearby, such as a drawer handle, window catch or tap, and use it to make a cross in one of the two boxes. Remember, you are voting for which one you wish to EXCLUDE from LEAVING, not the one you do NOT wish to exclude from REMAINING.

When you have cast your vote, fold it in half and post it to: *The Duly Appointed Returning Officer, Viz Royal Referendum, c/o Viz Comic, PO Box 841, Whitley Bay NE26 9EQ.* At some indeterminate point in the future, the losing Duchess will be told to leave, at which point she will have two years in which to pack her bags and fuck off, unless an extension to the fucking-off period is mutually agreed between her and the royal family at the very last minute. Or not.

GLAND'S ROSES

Balmoral outrage: Queen gave Duchesses right royal bollocking.

in Meghan's face. 'Swear in front of your own kids if you want to, but not in front of mine, you foul-mouthed get.' 'Hey, don't you fucking tell me how to bring my own kids up,' replied Meghan. 'I'll swear in my own fucking garden if I want to.'"

"Kate took George back in the house with her hands over his ears," said the insider. "Later, she reported the incident to the Queen."

It is understood that Her Majesty sympathised, but refused to take sides in the dispute. "She told Kate the two of them would have to sort it out between themselves, and if they couldn't they'd just have to stay out of each other's way," the source said.

But a few days later, the warring duchesses were scheduled to appear together for a royal walkabout in Windsor town centre. Instead of mingling, Kate and Meghan pointedly chose to greet the crowds on opposite sides of the street. "They smiled for the cameras, but the tensions were evident," said the insider. It was clear to anyone watching that they couldn't stand the sight of one another."

tips & alistair

Things came to a head last week, when Kate was having her hair done at a Sandringham boutique in preparation for a night at the Royal Opera House. "Kate was being very indiscreet while she was having her hair washed, telling her hairdresser that she didn't think Meghan ought to be in line to the throne," said the insider. "She told him, 'You have to be a virgin on your wedding night to

be the Queen, and she's definitely not that, because she was married to someone else before she met Harry.'"

"The hairdresser seemed very uncomfortable, and kept trying to change the subject, or shut the conversation down," said the insider. "And with very good reason."

"Because what Kate didn't know was that her sister-in-law was under one of the dryers, and she had heard every word."

"Meghan went ballistic, and leapt up out of her chair to have it out with Kate. 'You're just jealous,' she screamed. 'Just because you've only ever had one cock up you.' The Duchess of Cambridge wasn't having that. 'At least my fanny hasn't been spoiled for my husband by someone else. Not like your welly top,' she spat back."

"'That's rich, calling mine a welly top,' shouted Meghan. 'You've pushed three fucking kids out yours. Your fanny must be like a drayhorse's collar. I bet William has to tie a fucking broom across his arse so he doesn't fall in.'"

mungo & midge

According to shocked onlookers, the two duchesses then went for each other and started a full-on catfight in the salon. "They were rolling round the floor, pulling at each other's hair and trying to scratch each other's faces," said Mrs Edna Lukewarm, 73, who was visiting the salon for her weekly pink rinse. "It was most undignified. I've lived in Sandringham for forty years and I've never seen the Queen behaving like that."

Royal protection officers, who were waiting outside the salon, saw what was happening and rushed in to pull the battling pair apart. BBC royal correspondent Nicholas Witchell told us: "You may think that was an end to the matter, but believe me this thing isn't over by a long chalk. Kate and Meghan still have beef."

The bad blood between the two duchesses is thought to be the bitterest royal feud since 1937. In that case, the newly crowned King George VI ostracised his brother the Duke of Windsor after he borrowed some garden shears and brought them back with a nick in the blade which, according to the His Majesty "...wasn't there when he lent the bastards off me."

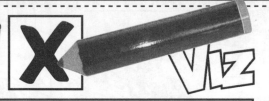
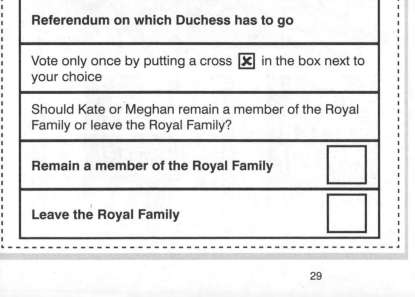

THE BROON WINDSORS

Y'COULDNAE GIE US A LIFT TAE THE POST AFFICE TAE PICK UP MA CIVIL LIST, COULD YE, MAW? AWNLY I HAEN'T GOT MA DRIVIN' LICENCE NAE MORE, HEN.

SORRY PAW. A'M CATCHIN' UP WI' MA PAPERWORK...

...THIS BLUIDY COMMONWEALTH DISNAE RUN ITSEL' Y'KEN.

...AN' A'M DAEIN' THE STATE OPENIN' O' PARLIAMENT THIS AFTAE. ASK ONE O' THE BAIRNS TAE TAK YE INSTEAD.

MUMBLE! GRUMBLE!

SO...

OCH SON, TAK YIR AULD MAN TAE PICK UP HIS BAWBEES, WILL YE...?

NAE CHANCE, PAW.

WEE MOTOR TRIPS LIKE THAT ARE PROPER DAMAGIN' TAE THE ENVIRONMENT.

PAH.

AN' ANYWAY, AH'M AFF TAE FLY AWA' ONE O' MA CASTLES IN MA PRIVATE HELICOPTER TAE TAK A LOOK AT MA NEW SOLAR PANELS.

MUMBLE! GRUMBLE!

SHORTLY...

AH, KATE, HEN. YE'LL GIE ME A LIFT TAE TH' POST AFFICE, WAUN'T YE...?

SORRY GRANPAW.

MA CAR'S STOWED OOT WI' SEATS FUR A' THE WEE HEIRS TAE THE THRONE!

OCH, FUD! HOW AM AH SUPPOSED TAE PICK UP MA CIVIL LIST?

COME ON OOR GEORGE. AH'LL TAK YE FUR A HAPPY MEAL AT THE RITZ!

BRAW!

HMM! AH WONDER...!

SHORTLY...

AH'LL JUST GET MA BEST CROON JEWELS ON FUR THE STATE OPENIN' O' PARLIAMENT...

WHIT THE...?! WHIT'S HAPPENED TAE MA JEWEL CHEST?!

AN' MA SCEPTRE O' STATE... IT'S GOAN AN' A'!

GRAN'MAW! SOME BAHOOKIE'S NICKED THE WHEELS AFF OOR LOUIS'S PRAM!

WAH! WAH!

EH?!

HELP MA BOAB!

WHIT IS IT, STEP-MAW?

MA GREAT BRAW STRING O' PEARLS... THEY'RE GAWN!

WE MUST HAE BEEN BURGLED!

AYE, WE HAE!... AN' AH KEN WHO BY, AN A'!

PHILIP! WHIT D'YE THINK YE'RE DAEIN'? CUM 'ERE AN' AH'LL GIE YE TWENTY RAPID, YE THEIVIN' AULD BAS!

AH CANNAE STOP, MAW!...

...THAE POST OFFICE SHUTS AT TWA!

FASTER, YE LAZY WEE BAS! FASTER!

SEE YE LATER, MAW! HEHE!

WHEEEE!

HONK! SCREECH! SMASH!

WIBBLE! WOBBLE!

Speech bubbles in comic: "ARE YE ALRICHT, YER HIGHNESS?" / "AYE, NO BAD, PAL. THE SUN WIS LOW IN MA EYES, YE KEN." / "YE COULDNAE GIE ME A LIFT TAE THE POST AFFICE, COULD YE...? AN' PUT THE BLUE LICHTS AN' NEE-NARS ON, AINLY THEY SHUT IN FUFTEEN MINUTES."

LUCKY CAROL

You do the maths!: TV 'brainbox' Vorderman admits she was clueless.

Brainbox star reveals she can't do maths

EX-COUNTDOWN diva *CAROL VORDERMAN* revealed this week that she has no idea how she got any of the solutions right during her tenure as the arithmetic co-host on the long-running Channel 4 show. And she told reporters that she had simply *guessed* the correct answer every single time.

The buxom brainiac revealed how she had always struggled with mathematics at school. "I've never been able to do sums," she told reporters at a press conference. "Numbers just don't make sense to me at all."

"Honestly, I could never do my times tables in class. I just used to guess at the answers, but I always seemed to get them right."

jammiest

"I imagine I must be the jammiest person in the world," she added.

The broadcaster explained that she went to try out for the job on *Countdown* for a bit of a laugh, never thinking she would be successful. "When I went to the audition, I was just expecting to wear a tight dress and flip over a few numbers. But when a particularly complicated equation popped up and stumped the contestants, the crew turned to me to solve it," she said.

"Well, I didn't have a clue, but I wrote down some gibberish on the

EXCLUSIVE!

board. You could have knocked me down with a feather when it turned out I'd got it right!"

Vorderman was given the presenting role on the show, but feared it was only a matter of time before she was rumbled. "I thought my luck wouldn't last, but at the time I just really needed the money," she said.

artfulest

Curvy Carol made her first *Countdown* appearance in November 1982, in what was to be the first ever programme broadcast on Channel 4. She said: "I only had to guess one maths problem on the first episode and unbelievably managed to get it right again."

"I couldn't believe I'd get away with it for a second time. I was a bag of nerves, because I was sure that humiliation was just around the corner."

But as weeks turned into months, and months to years, her luck with the mathematical connundrums kept going.

"I used to be standing there praying that the contestants would

get it right. But every time they didn't, I just seemed to be able to pull it out of the bag by scribbling random numbers on the board," she joked.

saladest

"None of my friends believed me when I told them that I was guessing all the solutions and writing down any old numbers and plus and minus signs. But when they tested me down the pub, they quickly discovered that I clearly didn't have a clue how to solve even the simplest maths problem."

The busty *Loose Women* presenter joked that her bizarre luck with the *Countdown* maths problems didn't extend to other areas of her life. "I started to think that if I could do it on Countdown, maybe I'd be as lucky when it came to the National Lottery," she said. "But to this day I've never even won a tenner for three numbers."

taxest

Chesty Carol worked on the show for 26 years, correctly guessing the solutions to over 15,000 number-based head-scratchers, the chances of which, according to proper mathematicians, was one in 180 trillion trillion trillion trillion trillion.

Professor Brian Cox took to Twitter to put these odds into context. "You'd have to take a '1' followed by as many zeros as there are grains of sand on Planet Earth," the epaulette-jacketed egghead tweeted.

coffinest

However, others say that the infinitessimally small odds of chance being responsible for Carol's quarter century of arithmetical success point to there being another cause.

"I am convinced that Carol is the reincarnation of Horus, the Egyptian god of mathematics," said roly poly TV astrologer Russell Grant. "In my opinion, the ancient deity, who was really, really good at sums, was doing the calculations through Carol and controlling her voice and the hand she held her marker pen in on the show."

"And since she got a bit long in the tooth and got replaced, he's been doing the same for Rachel Riley too," he added.

LETTERBOCKS

Viz Comic, P.O. Box 841 Whitley Bay, NE26 9EQ : letters@viz.co.uk

IF I was a contestant on *The Apprentice* and I took the early morning phone call, I wouldn't tell any of the other fuckers that they were being picked up by the car in 20 minutes. Then when Sir Sugar saw that I was the only one who could be arsed showing up, I would win. And if it ever came out what I did, he'd give me an extra million quid for showing initiative. Probably.

Fat Alan, Little Lever

HOW come left-handed people moan like fuck about scissors, but they're quite happy to drive cars with the gearsticks the right way round? They want to get their stories straight.

Andy, Inverness

WHEN my wife jumps into a cold pool her nipples grow enormous. Yet when I jump into the same pool, my knob shrinks to a walnut. Once again, it seems one rule for ladies and another for men. Will there ever be equality in the world?

Perry Winkle, email

MARTIN Lewis is a jammy sod. He's become a multi-millionaire by effectively saying "shop around for the best deal" on primetime TV for half an hour every week since 2012. If the bosses at ITV are reading this, I'm prepared to do that for half of whatever he is being paid.

T.O'Neill, Glasgow

WE'VE all used the taunt "Liar, liar, pants on fire!" But does anyone know why? I've known plenty of bullshitters in my time, but disappointingly I've never seen their underwear spontaneously combust. Maybe it was one of those barbaric medieval punishments, where if someone told a fib their breeches were set on fire. Perhaps Dr. Suzannah Lipscomb or some other prominent historian could write in provide the answer to this "burning" question.

Tarquin Bulldogs, Derby

YESTERDAY I found one of my old Matchbox cars that I hadn't seen for years. It's a 1977 Lamborghini and they go for about 25 quid on eBay. That colonic irrigation has nearly paid for itself.

Inego Pipkin, Chorley

THE other day my wife called me a 'misogynist.' I cleverly replied "No, I think you mean a 'MISTERogynist', you daft old mare." I was very pleased with my comeback, but then she threw a plate at me and broke my spectacles.

Mr. Willy Balls, Banbury

I CAN'T believe what a bunch of bastards the chasers on *The Chase* are. I've just watched a Celebrity Special in which two celebs were about to win £63,000 for a children's charity. Then the woman chaser with black hair beat them at the last minute and they lost the lot except for a consolation £1000. So there you go. "Fuck you poorly kids. I'm the chaser and I've just stopped you from getting £62,000. Yours sincerely, A.Cunt, ITV Studios."

David Wardle, email

ST★R LETTER

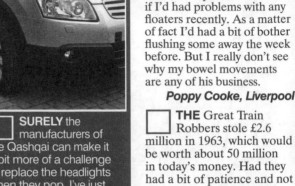

SURELY the manufacturers of the Qashqai can make it a bit more of a challenge to replace the headlights when they pop. I've just gone in under the bonnet to put a new driver's side bulb in, and I've still got the skin left on two of my knuckles. Come on, Nissan, is that all you've got?

Hampton Dirts, Epping

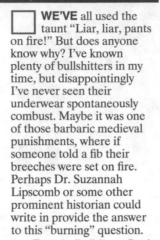

I WAS stuffing a defrosted chicken recently and I noticed that it didn't seem to have a fanny, just a big arsehole. I was puzzled about this and have spent the last week in the local park, looking at the reproductive organs of ducks and geese. There hasn't been a fanny in sight on any of them. Come on, Bill Oddie, what's going on?

T Steel, Hornchurch

WHENEVER twins are depicted in films, one of them is always the "evil twin." Well, I'm a twin myself, but even though our kid can be a bit of a twat sometimes, I wouldn't go as far as to say that he was evil.

Don Chandelier, Leic.

THE audiences at the opera and ballet really get on my tits. They think they look hard, done up like bouncers in their DJs and Dickie bows, but they don't scare me one bit, and I reckon I could have any one of them any day of the fucking week. Puccini was a prick and Nijinsky was a wanker. There. Come and have a go if you think you're hard enough.

Newton Isaacs, Goole

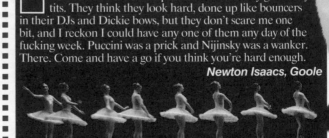

WHY don't you see cats on fences having shoes thrown at them when they make a racket in the middle of the night any more?

Big Dave, Redditch

WHILE I was having my eyes tested last week, the optician asked me if I'd had problems with any floaters recently. As a matter of fact I'd had a bit of bother flushing some away the week before. But I really don't see why my bowel movements are any of his business.

Poppy Cooke, Liverpool

THE Great Train Robbers stole £2.6 million in 1963, which would be worth about 50 million in today's money. Had they had a bit of patience and not jumped the gun, it would have been a much more successful heist, I reckon. So much for being master criminals.

Gritley Mews, Carlton

I WISH female porn stars would stop gazing lovingly into the eyes of the man ramming his cock up their arse. He's paid to be there. I'm the one doing all the wanking. Sometimes it's like they don't care about me at all.

Laurel Hardy, Billingham

THERE seems to have been a spate of learned articles on the internet and in the quality press recently about the effect of pornography on the brain. Now I'm no scientist and naturally I never look at the stuff, but I'd have thought the main effect would be on the knob.

Peter Hall, Dorking

I OWN a beautiful little cat who simply does not fart, ever. Do any other readers have a small pet who displays such outstanding control over its sphincter?

Bluey, Australia

CAN anybody explain to me how the moon actually works? It seems that it is quite often a different shape from one week to the next. I'm no Isaac Einstein or Alfred Newton, and I was wondering if there might be as many as four moons, each of a different shape, ranging from a quarter one to the big round one.

Terry Farricker, Blackpool

WITH reference to that picture of that bloke kissing that bird's arse. If we define the arse as the *Gluteus maximus* and *Gluteus minimus* muscles together, then he is not kissing her arse at all, rather the lateral border of her quadriceps muscle, in other words, her leg. Perhaps the noted anatomist, Professor Alice Roberts could clarify this, possibly using her own arse to demonstrate?

Nick Lyon, Truro

AFTER studying closely, I think that picture of that bloke kissing that bird's arse is fake, just like the moon landings. If you look closely, there's a shadow around his lips, suggesting they didn't land on the surface of the buttocks. What's more, the shadow cast by his nose is from a different direction from that cast by her arse. And the background looks like a Hollywood backdrop, where it was probably shot.

Desulph Daz, M' brough

HOW come we don't follow America's lead and start writing spectacular musicals about our cities and towns? They have done New York, Chicago, Oklahoma and probably more. So come on, Andrew Lloyd Webber and Tim Rice, get penning some toe-tappers about places like Oldham, West Houghton and Rawtenstall, you pair of idle bastards.

Joseph Dreamcoat, Derby

I WAS giving my wife a special treat the other night, which I won't go into detail about, because it's a private matter between man and wife. But it got me wondering why it's called a rim job. Do any of your more perverted readers know the origin of this term?

Berkley Cuboid, Tooting

BY the expression on his face, I think Professor Brian Cox is always just about to tell a joke. The other night he was on about a big bang or something and said, "After its initial expansion, the universe cooled sufficiently to allow the formation of subatomic particles, and later simple atoms. Giant clouds of these primordial elements..." blah blah blah. After five minutes, I gave up waiting for the punchline. I'd probably heard it before anyway.

Helmet Brim, Torquay

I CAN'T for the life of me think why Guy Fawkes waited until the 5th November to carry out his gunpowder plot. He should have done it on 31st October, so that if he was stopped by the police, he could have simply said that he was out in fancy dress for Halloween. He could have claimed that any gunpowder found on him was going to be used to 'trick' any unsuspecting monarch who failed to give him a treat.

Matt Varnish, Staines

WHY don't we have Boy Scouts knocking on our doors offering 'Bob a job' any more? I know five pence isn't a lot for washing both my cars or digging over my front and back gardens. But when I joined up with them as a youngster, I took an oath to God and the Queen to keep my promise, and as I recall there was fuck all mention of inflation.

Stan Bagheera, Nottingham

THEY say that people are nicer and friendlier up North. Well I live down in Surrey and I'm a right cunt, so there may be some truth in it.

Ben Nunn, Caterham

I RECENTLY heard the Greek national anthem and it was absolute shite. Why don't they just use *Grease* from the film of the same name? And I'm sure the Bee Gees wouldn't mind because they'd be getting a shit-load of royalties, especially after international football matches.

Crompton Scuttlebut, Bristol

THINGS CAN ONLY GET FETA

YOUR scientific questions about Greek sheep's cheese, answered by mop-top feta-lovin' Britpop boffin Professor BRIAN COX

Dear Professor Cox,

According to the Multiverse Theory, there must be at least one universe out there in which feta cheese does not exist. What happens if you order a Greek salad in that universe? Do you simply get a bowl of cucumber, tomatoes, olives and onions, and if so, will it be cheaper?

Mrs Ada Pustule, Athens

Brian says: *"I've just had a quick squizz at my big Multiverse Theory Excel spreadsheet, and I can confirm that in the Feta-less Universe, a Greek salad will set a diner back around £2.80. Which sounds like a decent deal until I tell you that, in the Feta-less Universe... cucumbers, tomatoes and olives don't exist either! So, you're essentially paying the thick end of three quid for a bowl of chopped onion."*

Dear Professor Cox,

Has anyone ever sent some feta into space? If they haven't, why not, and are there any plans to send some feta into space in the near future?

Mrs Edna Fistula, Sparta

Brian says: *"At time of writing, Mrs Fistula, no Greek sheep's cheese has ever left the Earth's orbit. This is because feta is a famously weak and crumbly foodstuff, and the absence of gravitational pull upon leaving our planet's terrestrial atmosphere would cause a block of it to break apart and potentially jam a spaceship's intricate machinery. For this reason, astronauts on every manned lunar mission in history have had to make do with hard, northern European cheeses, such as Cheddar (Apollo 8), Gouda (Apollo 10) and Emmental (Shenzhou 9)."*

Dear Professor Cox,

What would happen if you filled the Large Hadron Collider with feta?

Dennis Cartilage, Ashford

Brian says: *"Well, I wouldn't recommend it, Dennis. I once left half a Peparami and a can of Lilt in there by accident, and their particles collided within the machine to create a grapefruit-flavoured sentient sausage measuring 26 miles in length. It took three months to destroy the hideous abomination, and you wouldn't believe the bollocking I got off the CERN president afterwards. So I imagine that if you filled the LHC with feta, you'd probably generate a super-conscious block of sheep's cheese roughly the size of Wales."*

● **Have YOU got a query about feta cheese that also relates in some way to the intellectual and practical activity encompassing the systematic study of the structure and behaviour of the physical and natural world through observation and experiment? Then why not write in to: 'Things Can Only Get Feta!' c/o Professor Brian Cox, Viz Comic, PO Box 841, Whitley Bay, NE26 9EQ.**

THE REAL ALE TWAT

ONCE MORE UNTO THE BREACH CASKETEERS!

STIFFEN THE SINEWS AND SUMMON UP THE BLOOD FOR OUR FRIDAY NIGHT SESH!

LET US ELBOW OUR WAY THROUGH THE MERRY THRONG AT THE BAR, AND SAMPLE TONIGHT'S GUEST ALE SELECTION...

WHAT TH-?!

OH NO, NO, NO, NO, NO! THIS IS ALL WRONG! THIS ISN'T HOW ONE QUEUES IN A PUB!

YOU'RE NOT SUPPOSED TO STAND IN A LINE LIKE YOU'RE WAITING TO USE A CASHPOINT MACHINE!

WHERE IS THE GLORIOUS FREE-FOR-ALL SCRUMMAGE AT THE BAR? THE TACTICAL JOSTLING FOR POSITION?

THE WELL-HONED SKILL AT CATCHING THE BARPERSON'S EYE?

I'M NOT STANDING FOR THIS, CASKETEERS!

FORWARD TO THE BAR! WE'LL SHOW THESE PEOPLE HOW IT'S DONE...

HOY! THERE'S A QUEUE HERE, YOU KNOW!

YOU WAIT YOUR TURN!

THIS IS INTOLERABLE! AND TO ACCUSE ME OF QUEUE-JUMPING! OUTRAGEOUS!

JUST BECAUSE THESE AMATEURS ARE IGNORANT OF TRADITIONAL PUB ETIQUETTE!

WE SEASONED DRINKERS ARE EVER MINDFUL OF DECENCY AND FAIR PLAY AT THE BAR.

I BELIEVE THAT THIS YOUNG LADY WAS BEFORE ME.

I ALWAYS SHOW THE UTMOST CHIVALRY WHEN WAITING TO BE SERVED!

COME ALONG, MY DEAR, SQUEEZE IN!

NEXT PLEASE!

THAT'S US, COMPADRES!

QUICKLY, NOW — COMMANDEER THOSE BARSTOOLS!

THREE FOAMING TANKARDS OF FULCHESTER VALLEY IPA PLEASE BARLORD!

EXCUSE ME...

IF YOU'VE FINISHED GETTING SERVED, COULD YOU MAKE SOME ROOM AT THE BAR...?

THIS IS NOT A FAST FOOD OUTLET — IT'S A PUB!

AND I'M GOING TO SIT HERE WITH MY FRIENDS AND ENJOY A FEW PINTS OF ALE, IF YOU DON'T MIND!

ER...A PINT OF BITTER, THREE PINTS OF STELLA AND A WINE AND SODA PLEASE.

COMING UP.

YOU PEOPLE THINK YOU CAN WALTZ INTO OUR PUBS AND TRAMPLE OVER CENTURIES OF CUSTOM AND TRADITION!

QUEUING UP IN A LINE AT THE BAR INDEED! IT'S SO SOULLESS!

IT REDUCES THE TIME-HONOURED SOCIAL RITUAL OF ORDERING A PINT TO NOTHING MORE THAN A STERILE FINANCIAL TRANSACTION!

I'LL JUST PASS THE TRAY OVER... >GRUNT<

GOT IT, THANKS...

WELL I WILL NOT SIT BY AND WATCH OUR PRECIOUS HERITAGE BE SWEPT ASIDE...

CLANG!

I WILL STAND UP FOR THE TRADITIONS OF THE GREAT BRITISH PUB!

CRASH!

WHAT THE FUCK?!

AND, IN THE CAR PARK

EXCUSE ME, IS THIS THE QUEUE FOR THE KICKING?

YES, IT IS. OOF! OW! OOYAH!

34

BIG VERN

I'VE BEEN LOOKING FORWARD TO OUR SUNDAY AFTERNOON TRIP TO THE MUSEUM ALL WEEK, VERN!

ME TOO, ERNIE.

Welcome to Fulchester Museum

SHORTLY... ...THE NEXT PART OF OUR GUIDED TOUR TAKES US BACK TO THE FOGGY COBBLED STREETS OF OLD FULCHESTER, BACK IN THE MID-TO-LATE 1700s.

RESPECTABLE MEMBERS OF THE PUBLIC RARELY STEPPED OUT AFTER DARK IN THOSE DAYS AS THE TOWN TEEMED WITH THIEVES, CUTPURSES AND MURDEROUS VAGABONDS.

LAW ENFORCEMENT WAS LEFT TO A HANDFUL OF "THIEF TAKERS"...

...WHO COULD BE RECOGNISED BY THEIR DISTINCTIVE UNIFORMS...

RAN, ERNIE! IT'S THE FACKIN' PEELERS!

SCARPER!

FWIT! FWIT! FWIT!

CLICK!

RAM! WALLOP!

FWIT!

CLICK!

YOU'LL NEVAH TAKE ME ALIVE, COZZA!

CLICK!

FIZZLE! P-PHWOT!

...THE BOW STREET RUNNERS WERE FOUNDED IN 1744 BY JUDGE HENRY FIELDING, AND WERE THE PRECURSORS TO THE METROPOLITAN POLICE, ESTABLISHED IN 1829...

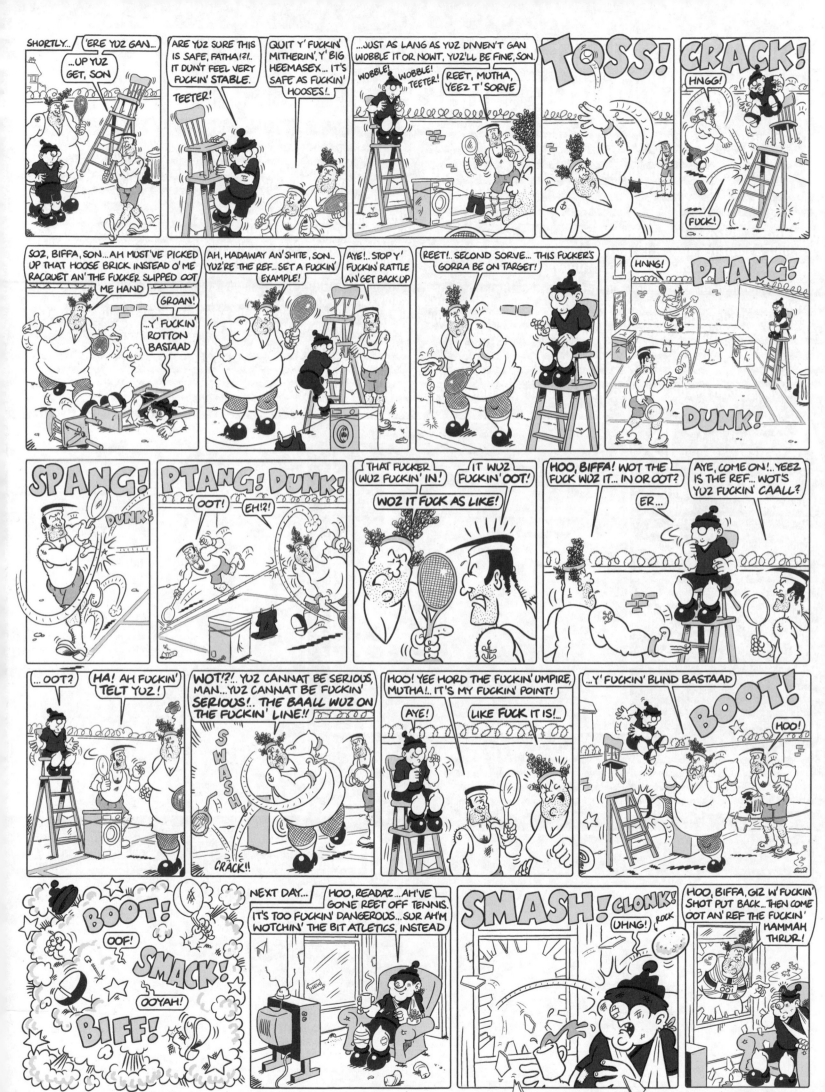

Countdown to our funny future in Outer Space... COME

IT IS NOW exactly fifty years since Neil Armstrong became the first man to set foot on the moon, and his "one small step" on the lunar surface back on July 20th 1969 has gone down as one of the most momentous events in human history. But whilst no-one decries the brilliant feats of science, engineering and sheer bravery that took those astronauts on their million-mile space adventure half a century ago, it is perhaps now time to admit that the Apollo 11 mission wasn't very funny.

Over the course of the entire eight-day voyage through space to visit our nearest planetary neighbour, not a single memorable gag was cracked by the three Apollo 11 astronauts or any of the 200-strong Mission Control team back in Houston. Even the crew's splash landing 900 miles southwest of Hawaii wasn't played for laughs, with the straight-faced spacemen missing every single opportunity to deliver side-splitting one-liners while being winched out of the rolling North Pacific and onto the deck of the SS Hornet.

What a wasted chance. You can bet your moonboots that if any of today's top TV comedians, such as Sarah Millican, Phill Jupitus or Michael McIntyre, had been crewing the iconic mission back in 1969, not only would Apollo 11 have been a voyage of inter-galactic discovery, it would also have been a laugh a minute.

Just think of the hilarious gags that big-boned comic Jo Brand could have woven out of a weightless walk across the lunar surface. Or the slapstick mayhem that knockabout funnyman Lee Evans could have wrought whilst capering about in the Sea of Tranquility, sweating like a pig in a spacesuit that was two sizes too small for him. And late madcap Hitler-impressions comedian Freddie Starr would certainly have had the Mission Control scientists splitting their sides at their computer consoles as he cavorted about the lunar surface with swastikas drawn on the legs of his spacesuit.

With plans now well advanced for NASA astronauts to re-visit the moon within the next decade, let's take a look at what preparations are underway to make 21st century lunar missions much more of a laugh-fest than their dismal, po-faced 1960s predecessors.

ANYONE who's been to see a Whitehall farce in a West End theatre will tell you that a man's trousers falling down is one of the funniest things on earth. But would it also be one of the funniest things on the moon? Scientists warn that the force of gravity on the lunar surface is just one sixth of that on our home planet, meaning that once an astronaut's braces snapped, it would take his spacesuit strides up to five seconds to slowly drift to the ground, revealing his bare legs and the suspenders holding his socks up. The joke would be telegraphed a light year in advance, and not even a fellow crewmember playing a descending note on a helmet-bound swannee whistle could make such a gag even slightly amusing.

For this reason, NASA boffins are hard at work developing a pair of vertically elasticated spacesuit trousers with a spring-loaded strap running down from the waistband to the astronaut's socks. As soon as the spaceman's braces give, his trick strides will be briskly yanked down with six times the force of lunar gravity, mirroring the descent of their earth-bound counterparts and thus guaranteeing a proper slapstick guffaw from the millions watching on TV.

EVERYBODY remembers Basil Fawlty's gourmet night roadside meltdown, when he hilariously attacked his conked-out Austin 1100 with a branch. But the arid atmosphere of the moon supports no vegetation of any kind, meaning than an astronaut would have nothing to hand with which to launch a similar attack should his Lunar Rover unexpectedly break down during an exploratory mission across its desolate, crater-pocked surface.

Of course, the astronauts could take a suitable branch with them when they blast off from earth, but then the audience would see it and the gag would be ruined. Just like in *Fawlty Towers* back in the seventies, the joke relies on the spaceman frustratedly running off camera and returning, branch in hand, seconds later.

NASA intend to get round the problem by blasting a selection of suitable branches up to various locations around the moon well in advance. When their Lunar Rover conks out, future astronauts can be confident that, lying in a lunar crater nearby, they will immediately be able to lay their hands on just the piece of leafy, bonnet-bashing foliage they need to get a proper belly laugh from their frustrated antics.

OY on the MOON

◁**A**SK any stand-up what the essence of comedy is, and they'll tell you… "Timing." Even the best joke can be killed stone dead if the punchline is delivered slightly too quickly or slowly. And with a future moon-based double-act's radio signals taking the thick end of eight seconds to criss-cross the void between the lunar surface and their earth-bound audience, timing gags could become a real problem for comedians.

Fast-paced crosstalk routines of the sort made famous by the Two Ronnies, Peter Cook and Dudley Moore, and Mike and Bernie Winters, would be almost impossible to perform on the lunar surface. Punchlines would have to be delivered before the set-up, and then the gagsters would have to leave a sixteen second silence before the next line, so they weren't talking over the audience laughter.

▽**W**HEN asked to name their favourite TV comedy moment, absolutely everybody in the UK willl answer without hesitation: that bit in *Only Fools and Horses* where Delboy fell through the bar that they're always going on about on the telly. But woe betide any comic who attempted a similar rib-tickler on the moon's surface. Exiting backwards from the lunar lander without realising that his astronaut colleague had removed the ladder, for instance, would be fraught with problems.

On earth, the resultant pratfall would have the audience splitting their sides with laughter. But up on the moon, it would be the joke - not the astronaut - that would fall flat. The moment he nonchalantly stepped into the gravity-free vacuum of space, he would simply float about like a balloon, leaving the audience stony faced and una-mused.

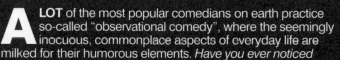

◁**A** LOT of the most popular comedians on earth practice so-called "observational comedy", where the seemingly inocuous, commonplace aspects of everyday life are milked for their humorous elements. *Have you ever noticed how all footballers wear tight shirts? Why do women always go to the toilet in large groups? Grown men who go trainspotting…. what's all that about?* Down here on earth, there is a literally limitless amount of "gear" from which a stand-up can draw his inspiration, and which his audience will immediately recognise.

But only 12 people have ever been on the moon, and of them, only 4 are still alive. Any witty observations that a lunarbound Michael McIntyre might make about craters, moondust and spacesuit coathangers would have a vanishingly small audience chuckling along. For this reason, NASA intend to ditch any observational routines and concentrate on recruiting fast-talking, wise-cracking double acts in the style of Hale and Pace, Cannon and Ball or Little and Large, to crew future moon missions.

Happily, NASA boffins have come up with a solution: tiny, upward-facing thrusters mounted on each side of the spaceman's helmet will blast him downwards to land arse-first on the lunar surface. It will be one small step for man, one giant leap for comedy.

◁**E**VER since the custard pie was invented, it has been a staple of the slapstick comic's toolbox. Seeing one of these sloppy, paper plate-borne desserts getting pushed squarely into the face of an officious victim provides any comic with a guaranteed laugh at the climax of their comedy routine. And the aftermath, as the victim slowly wipes custard from his eyes before giving the audience an exasperated look, gets even bigger guffaws from the audience.

But up in the airless vacuum of space, such tried and tested knockabout routines would barely raise a titter. A pie pushed onto the mirrored front of a spacesuit helmet would have just a tiny fraction of the comedy value of its timeworn terrestrial counterpart, leaving the millions watching history being made stony faced and unamused.

Sadly, the challenge of updating this comedy staple to the space age has proved too much even for the boffins at NASA. Although high-tech experiments involving in-helmet custard sprayers and remote servo-driven devices to wipe the astronauts' eyes were successful, Mission Control eggheads concluded that they simply lacked the comic appeal of their traditional, tried and tested earth-bound slapstick counterparts.

***Next Week** - We look at the future of improv comedy in the Marianas Oceanic Trench, 20,000 leagues beneath the sea.*

OO-ER! WE'RE HAVING OUR SCHOOL VACCINATIONS TODAY — I HOPE YOU DON'T FAINT AT THE SIGHT OF YOUR OWN OIL, TINRIBS!

HI. I'M BARBIE. I LOVE YOU VERY MUCH.

HEH HEH! I DO ENJOY SEEING THESE BRATS BEING CAUSED DISCOMFORT!

GIVE THIS ONE A GOOD HARD JAB, MATRON!

MR SNODWORTHY! STOP THE VACCINATIONS AT ONCE!

I'VE JUST DISCOVERED THAT THEY ARE DANGEROUS!

ACCORDING TO THIS THING I SAW ON FACEBOOK, VACCINES CONTAIN A TOP SECRET MIND-CONTROL DRUG!

THE BIG PHARMACEUTICAL COMPANIES USE VACCINES TO TURN US INTO ZOMBIE SHEEPLE LIBTARDS!

THE SAME IS TRUE OF ALL SO-CALLED "MAINSTREAM MEDICINES".

LEMSIPS, CALPOL, JUNIOR DISPRIN — ALL THESE ARE USED BY THE GOVERNMENT TO ENSLAVE OUR MINDS!

WE'LL HAVE NO MORE "BIG PHARMA" IN THIS SCHOOL!

MATRON, I WANT YOU TO THROW THE CONTENTS OF THIS MEDICINE CABINET INTO THE BIN!

WELL I WOULD, HEADMASTER BUT WE'VE RUN OUT OF BIN BAGS.

THE GOVERNMENT MUST HAVE STOLEN OUR BIN BAGS TO PREVENT US FROM THROWING AWAY THEIR MIND-CONTROL VACCINES!

MY FANTASTIC ROBOT CHUM CAN PROVIDE YOU WITH A BIN BAG HEADMASTER!

HI. I'M BARBIE. I LOVE YOU VERY MUCH.

FIRST WE USE ONE OF TINRIBS'S SOUP CANS TO MAKE A SMALL INCISION IN MR SNODWORTHY'S SCALP...

SNIK!

OUCH!

NEXT WE CAREFULLY POUR A BOTTLE OF SULPHURIC ACID FROM THE SCIENCE LAB IN THROUGH THE INCISION...

SULPHURIC ACID

HISSSSS

AIEEEEEEEE! IT BURNS!

AND HEY PRESTO! MR SNODWORTHY'S INNARDS HAVE COMPLETELY DISSOLVED, LEAVING AN EMPTY SKIN BAG!

HISSSSSS

g'urk!

WELL DONE, YOUNG TAYLOR!

SWEEP!

SNODWORTHY'S SKIN MAKES AN IDEAL BIN BAG FOR THE DISPOSAL OF THESE EVIL MIND-CONTROL PHARMACEUTICALS!

FROM NOW ON THIS SCHOOL WILL ONLY PRACTISE ALTERNATIVE MEDICINE!

I HAVE INVITED DOCTOR GRIFTER QUACKPOT FROM THE INSTITUTE OF HOMEOPATHY AND MAGIC PIXIE DUST TO BE THE NEW SCHOOL HEALTH ADVISOR.

SHORTLY

SO GOOD OF YOU TO COME, DOCTOR QUACKPOT!

THE PUPILS ARE ALL GATHERED IN THE SICK BAY WAITING FOR YOU TO GIVE THEM YOUR ALTERNATIVE MEDICAL CHECK-UP.

EXCELLENT! I WILL GIVE EACH CHILD A DOSE OF THIS HOMEOPATHIC INFUSION OF HERBS AND PIXIE DUST.

THIS WILL PROTECT THEM AGAINST THE MIND-CONTROL CHEMICALS WHICH THE GOVERNMENT PUTS IN THE WATER SUPPLY.

HOMEOPATHIC INFUSIONS MY ARSE! THOSE BRATS NEED PROPER DRUGS!

I'LL NIP AHEAD TO THE SICK BAY AND INJECT THE KIDS WITH POWERFUL ELEPHANT STEROIDS!

TRIP!

WAH!

WHO LEFT THAT DRATTED ROBOT LYING THERE?

EE-YOW!

I'VE LANDED ON THE SYRINGE AND INJECTED ELEPHANT STEROIDS INTO MY SCROTUM!

HELP!

BLOAT!

MY TESTICLES ARE EXPANDING TO A GARGANTUAN SIZE!

I SHOULD SAY, HEADMASTER, THAT I HAVE NOT YET DECIDED WHETHER TO ACCEPT THE POSITION OF YOUR SCHOOL'S HEALTH ADVISOR...

FIRST I MUST BE SURE THAT YOU ARE FULLY COMMITTED TO THE PRINCIPLES OF HOMEOPATHY AND ALTERNATIVE MEDICINE...

WHAT'S THIS? THE ONLY THING YOU APPEAR TO HAVE IN YOUR MEDICINE CABINET IS A MASSIVE LOAD OF BOLLOCKS!

HELP!

SPLENDID! IN THAT CASE, I ACCEPT THE JOB! HOORAY!

CELEBRITY GHOST ENCOUNTERS

ACCORDING to a recent poll, a terrifying 39% of the British electorate believe that a house can be haunted. Meanwhile, a chilling 35% of the UK - who are all legally allowed to vote in UK elections - believe in ghosts, whilst a frightening 9% of people - who are trusted to have their say in a referendum - even go as far as to claim that they've communicated with the dead.

We asked 5 celebrities about their paranormal encounters with the hope of finding out, once and for all, whether ghosts are real or not, which they're obviously not.

ANDY FORDHAM *Darts Player*

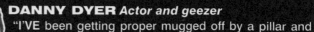

"I'M convinced that ghosts exist because I've personally been followed by some sort of malevolent poltergeist since I was about 30 stone. Wherever I go in my house, I hear the eerie sound of squeaking floorboards and often, after dinner, my wife will tell me that she can smell an acrid aroma reminiscent of sulphur, as though our house were built upon some kind of hell-mouth to the underworld. Weirdly, wherever I live the bulbs inside my fridge burn out in no time at all, leaving electricians baffled and giving me no other option than to assume that my kitchen is possessed by Zuul, The Gatekeeper of Gozer, who made his most famous appearance in the original *Ghostbusters* film. Me and the missus have tried moving house but the same thing happens wherever we go. Very spooky."

DANNY DYER *Actor and geezer*

"I'VE been getting proper mugged off by a pillar and post ever since I found out that I'm related to that slag Edward III. And now that the spooky fucking melt has figured out that me and the Mrs have got a bit of bunce, he's been doing my swede in every night, floating around the place and giving it the Big I Am. Everyone says I've gone completely radio rental, but I've seen the creepy little mug with my own mince pies. I wish I'd never gone on *Who Do You Think You Are?* because now I'm wasting my time bowling into the local church and trying to get the local rev to come over and stripe up the creepy little plum with holy water until he does one."

John Suchet *Newsreader*

"I BELIEVE in ghosts because when I was a little boy me and my friend Kevin cycled up the road to an old, abandoned house in our village so that we could break in and scare ourselves. Whilst we were in there, we saw the ghost of Brian Belo, star of *Big Brother 8*. It was terrifying but the whole thing was made even more spooky when you consider that Belo wasn't even born until 35 years later and didn't even appear on British Television until 2007, so how did I even know who he was? It's even more spooky because he's not even dead. The entire thing sends a shiver down my spine."

RACHEL RILEY *Presenter*

"EVERYONE who works on *Countdown* knows that ghosts exist because the studio has been haunted by the ghost of Richard Whiteley for the last 10 years. Quite often during filming, he'll put up sinister messages using the magnetic letters, or scrawl satanic runes onto the whiteboard during the numbers round which makes editing the show very difficult. And nobody likes to be the last one to leave the studio because there's always things flying around and bursting into flames. On more than one occasion production staff and contestants have ended up getting killed. I never knew Richard when he was alive but if this is how he behaves when he's dead, I can't say I'm a fan."

DAVID ATTENBOROUGH *Naturist*

"I'VE always wondered whether albino animals are actually ghosts. I'm told by zoologists and biologists that they categorically aren't and it's simply something to do with skin pigmentation but I'm still not sure. They certainly look a bit spooky to me."

Drunken bakers

That morning

There's no rush. Always a lull after Christmas.

Even so...

We'll sort it tomorrow.

Forecast gives snow.

BAKERY

No...

BAKERY

Is fuckin' pissin' in.

Blocking the hole might be an idea.

Nah, laughing in the back. Snow always melts.

Soon

We've fucked up here.

I know what we should do –

– mull wine.

It's ready.

We'd no brandy so I used Messer Schmitt.

Wh-what f-fuckin' w-wine is th-this?

We was out of wine too. It's Frosty Jock.

Wh-what the fuck is F-Frosty Jock?

Frosty Jock

8.5% VOL

WHISKY WHITE CIDER COCKTAIL DRINK

Two quid.

Don't taste very *mulled*.

None of that shite neither.

Found an orange, dropped that in.

Let's get that fuckin' bin out...

Don't help or nothing.

Where've I seen this bloody bin?

You fuckin' –

50P PIES

Some pissheads ain't their fault!

Ten Bob Pasty –

– Bastards!

DAME OF THRONES

Biggins joins cast of HBO blockbuster

FLAMBOYANT panto star CHRISTOPHER BIGGINS is set to surprise *Game of Thrones* viewers when he joins the show's cast for the HBO blockbuster's eighth and final series. The veteran entertainer, 70, will dress up to play The Widow Clegane, mother of Sando and Gregor Clegane, better known as the Hound and the Mountain.

Series producer David Benioff told us: "Game of Thrones is known as a dark, gritty, and violent drama, and we thought it would be nice to introduce an element of family-friendly pantomime fun to the show for this final series."

"Biggins's brand of over-the-top, camp slapstick has had kiddies and grown-ups alike rolling in the aisles at provincial theatres up and down the country for years," said Benioff. "And when George RR Martin saw him as Mother Goose at the Pavilion Theatre, Rhyl last Christmas, he immediately went home and wrote a big part for him into his scripts for the new season."

empty

"Luckily, the *On Safari* star had an empty diary between January and December, and he was able to fly to Ireland to shoot his scenes with his on-screen sons, played by Rory McCann and Hafbor Julius Bjornsson," he continued. "He fitted in on set straight away."

EXCLUSIVE!

According to show insiders, season 8 viewers will be glued to their screens watching scenes including…

● *In episode 2, in the wake of a massacre at King's Landing, the Widow Clegane tries unsuccessfully to hang out her sons' blood-soaked washing on the line while her giant pink and yellow spotty bloomers keep falling down*

● *In episode 3, she decides to bake a cake as a peace offering to the Lannisters, following a recipe on a radio cookery programme. But when her back is turned, her sons, the Hound and the Mountain, keep changing the channel backwards and forwards between a sports commentary and a gardening programme, with disastrous results*

● *In episode 4, one of the Faceless Men breaks into the her cottage in the dead of night to murder her. By a series of unlikely coincidences, the*

Our story Biggins! How larger-than-life star may appear in hit show

assassin ends up wearing one of her voluminous nightdresses, and the pair come face to face through a window. The Widow Clegane takes this to be a mirror and tries repeatedly to 'catch out' her reflection

● *In episode 5, dressed as Carmen Miranda – complete with a three-foot high fruit hat and outsize maracas – the Widow Clegane leads the whole cast in the 'Gangnam Style' dance routine through the streets of King's Landing*

But it won't all be light-hearted fun and games for Biggins, who shot to fame in the 1970s as camp convict

Luke Warm in hit BBC sitcom *Porridge*. True to the *Game of Thrones* tradition, his character is set to meet a terrible end. An insider told us: "In a shocking plot twist, all three of the Cleganes, including Biggins, are taken prisoner by the Army of the Iron Islands."

dempty

"At the climax to the final episode, the Widow Clegane's eyelids are cut off and she is forced to watch her sons' brutal executions before the skin is peeled from the top half of her body and she is pegged out for the ravens," he added.

PRINTER IS COMING!

Thrones fans up in arms over inkjet product placement

Kicking up an ink: Epson printer makes appearance in HBO blockbuster.

THERE was a storm brewing in the Twittersphere last night, after HBO announced a multi-million dollar product placement deal for *Game of Thrones*, which fans say is inconsistent with the show's feel and tone.

A spokesman for the series yesterday revealed that the much anticipated final season will be sponsored by EPSON Printers, and is set to feature "at least one scene" in which *GoT* characters use – and then briefly discuss the merits of – a wireless inkjet printer.

HBO's Embedded Marketing Executive, Neville Largethumb, told reporters: "We are thrilled to unveil our new product placement deal with Epson. We feel that *Game of Thrones* and Epson are a match made in product placement heaven, and we believe it will feel perfectly natural to see everyone's favourite *GoT* protagonists operating an Epson as part of their daily routine."

wraps

The scripts for the new season are being kept firmly under wraps, but sources indicate that the scene in question will feature none other than Warden of the North, Jon Snow, who will be seen scanning some pamphlets on an Epson WorkForce WF-77 All-In-One Wireless Inkjet, before turning to Daenerys Targaryen and saying, *"Whether I'm in the office or at home, I always use an Epson. Text and images have NEVER looked sharper."*

"The exchange will last all of ten seconds", Largethumb claimed. "It will be so subtle that fans will barely notice it."

pittas

However, a quick glance at social media this morning would appear to suggest otherwise.

Twitter user @GrahamOfThrones78 fumed: "There is NO INDICATION in any of George RR Martin's source material that wireless inkjet printing technology even exists in the *GoT* universe. Seeing the Bastard of Winterfell scan, Xerox, photocopy or print – even for a short period – will be extremely jarring and will ruin my enjoyment of the show #Despicable #BoycottSeasonEight."

Fellow *GoT* fan @FellowGoTfan chimed in with: "Never seen a plug socket ANYWHERE in Westeros, Essos or Sothyros #HowsJonGonnaPlugItIn? #ThisIsBullshit #FuckHBO."

News of the controversial deal follows a similar product placement tie-in arranged by Netflix for season three of its regal drama *The Crown*. The series, which follows the Royal Family throughout the 1970s, will be sponsored by Rockstar Video Games and is set to feature "at least one scene" in which the Queen plays – and then briefly discusses the merits of – *Red Dead Redemption 2*.

ALL ABOARD FOR THE WESTEROS MIDLANDS!

A BLACK Country town is celebrating its links to HBO blockbuster *Game of Thrones* with the launch of a bus tour around local sites linked to the hit show. And Tipton, near Dudley, is now bracing itself for an influx of millions of fans from all over the world, keen to sample all the *Game of Thrones* landmarks and points of interest around the town.

Tipton tourist chief launches Game of Thrones bus trip initiative

"Tipton probably isn't the first place that springs to mind when you think about *Game of Thrones*," said the council's Head of Tourism Hugo Guthrie. "But you'd be amazed by how many incredible links this town has with the world's most popular television programme."

"And our 5-hour executive coach tour takes in all those sights and places of interest, giving visitors the chance to breathe in the atmosphere and see everything and more that Tipton has to offer."

commentary

And according to Guthrie, many of the show's biggest stars will be travelling on the bus, giving passengers a running commentary as they make our way around the town's streets. "They will be explaining how Tipton has shaped *Game of Thrones*, and offering a unique insight into what it's like to appear in a world famous show with so many fascinating local links," he guaranteed.

Pressed by reporters to explain which stars he was referring to, Guthrie confirmed that **Charles Dance**, **Emilia Clarke**, **Peter Dinklage** and **Kit Harrington** had all been approached. "We wrote to them six weeks ago, and they haven't got back to definitely say no yet, so that's a very good sign," he said.

in the family

Guthrie said that 65-seater tourist coaches will leave Tipton Bus Depot on Leasowe Road every half hour, more frequently during school holidays. "We've managed to keep the price down by negotiating a great deal with my brother-in-law who runs one of Tipton's leading coach hire companies," he told reporters.

Anyone taking the *Game of Thrones* tour will pay £30 (£15 for

Capping it off: George RR Martin's actual cap will not feature in the coach tour.

children under 3 or pensioners over 85) for the 5-hour excursion, which will include the chance to…

∗ *Visit a pillar box used by one of the series's biggest stars*

∗ *See an authentic replica of George RR Martin's cap*

∗ *Meet one-to-one with Tipton's leading Game of Thrones expert*

Mr Guthrie told us: "For the diehard *Game of Thrones* fan, this trip will be the experience of a lifetime."

"West Midlands Game of Thrones coach tours don't get better than this," he added.

Throne together: Tipton tourist chief Hugo Guthrie (inset) says 5-hour Game of Thrones coach trip will be "experience of a lifetime".

TIPTON GAME OF THRONES TOUR ITINERARY

0.00 Leave Tipton Bus Depot on Leasowe Rd

0.15 Ash Road. 25-minute stop to disembark and look at the home of Mr John Pavey, who owns and has read nearly all of George RR Martin's *A Song of Fire and Ice* novels, which are the inspiration for *Game of Thrones*. Passengers will have the chance to chat to Mr Pavey about his experiences reading the books, pose for 'selfies', and get their tour programmes signed by him.

0.45 15 minutes stop at the pillar box on the corner of Silvertrees Road and Birch Street, where Jerome Flynn – who plays mercenary Bron in the show – is thought to have posted a letter to his mum in 1995 whilst in the area filming an episode of *Soldier Soldier*. Passengers can get down, stretch their legs, take photos and even post their own letters in the very same box.

1.05 A short comfort break back at the Bus Depot on Leasowe Rd to use the toilets and get refreshments from the vending machines in the waiting room. Then it's back on the bus.

1.25 Arrive at Ace Video on Union Street, where passengers can go in and see a boxed set of the first seven series of *Game of Thrones* for sale on a shelf. (Due to limited space inside the shop, only five visitors can enter at any one time, so you will need to be patient. But don't worry, everybody will get a chance to see the boxed set.)

2.00 Back to Mr Pavey's house on Ash Road, in case he wasn't in earlier or there was something someone forgot to ask him.

2.30 New Cross Street. A one-hour stop to visit a stall on the covered market which sells caps very similar to the sort of caps that George RR Martin wears. Passengers can take pictures of the caps on the stall, chat to the stallholder about his *Game of Thrones* hats, and try on or even buy a cap of their own to show the folks back home. Then it's back to the Ash Rd Bus Depot again for another well-earned toilet break and go on the venders! Then it's back on board the bus for a ten-minute drive West along Sedgeley Rd.

4.00 Arrive at Bean Drive disused railway track, and disembark to spend 15 minutes looking at a horse (similar to those ridden by the Dothraki in their quest for the Iron Throne of the Seven Kingdoms), which is tethered to a metal spike on the grass verge next to the lay-by. Passengers can take pictures of the horse, but are warned not to get too close, as this horse – unlike the Dothraki's steeds – has been known to nip children.

4.30 The highlight of the trip – a half-hour stop on Brick Kiln Road for a 20-minute photocall with a genuine star of *Game of Thrones*'s brother. Tipton panel beater Malcolm Cavendish's brother Stewart (also a panel beater) appeared in the Season 5 finale as a crowd extra in the iconic 'Walk of Shame' scene and here is a chance to meet and greet him in person (Malcolm not Stewart). Passengers can ask Mr Cavendish to ask his brother what it was like filming that scene, whether it was really a body double, and whether he got to see her fanny.

4:45 Back to Ash Road for a final chance to pick Mr Pavey's brain before the tour's end.

5.00 Tour finishes and passengers disembark back at Leasowe Rd Bus Depot, for final use of toilet facilities and venders.

GAME OF THRONES SEX SECRETS OF YOUR FAVE BICCIE

THE only thing better than sitting down to watch *Game of Thrones* is sitting down to watch *Game of Thrones*… with a nice plate of biscuits on your lap! Rich Teas, Hobnobs, Custard Creams or Nices… the choice is yours. But did you realise that the type of biscuit you prefer says a lot about which character out of *Game of Thrones* you are in bed?

That's according to leading TV psychiatrist **DR RAJ PERSAUD**, who has now put his 2008 3-month suspension from the General Medical Council for dishonesty firmly behind him. He told us: "There is overwhelming scientific evidence to suggest that our favourite biscuits are an accurate indicator of which *GoT* star we most closely resemble between the sheets. And anyway, 2008 was a long time ago, so let's draw a line under the past and move on."

"The D and A in our cells causes everyone to be a particular *Game of Thrones* character sexually. It's a scientific fact that the same strand of D and A is also responsible for releasing pleasure-giving endorphins in our brains that make us prefer one sort of biscuit over another when we are eating biscuits. Something like that anyway."

"Eleven fucking years. Come on. Get over it," he added.

And now, Dr Persaud has crunched through the biscuit data to offer us these crumbs of scientific wisdom to reveal how…

Which Biscuit you prefer from your Teatime biscuit assortment says a lot about which Game of Thrones character you are in bed.

CUSTARD CREAM

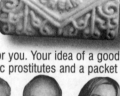

A small biscuit, but one with an extremely sweet centre, just like the rightful heir to Casterly Rock, Tyrion Lannister. And if this biscuit is your favourite, you share Tyrion's extreme carnal penchant for sex with multiple partners. Gang bangs with four, five or even six participants are nothing out of the ordinary for you. Your idea of a good night in is a Bacchanalian orgy with a dozen gymnastic prostitutes and a packet of custard creams all to yourself.

Celebrity Custard Cream lovers:
Tommy Walsh, Clive Anderson, Amber Rudd

RICH TEA

This is the blandest of biscuits, and it goes completely floppy with the quickest of dunks in your cuppa, much like the Master of Whisperers, Lord Varys. As a eunuch, emasculated in childhood by an evil sorcerer, this upstanding Member of the Kings Small Council is consistently unable to gain an erection. And sadly, those of you who rate rich tea as your number one biccie are similarly unable to achieve tumescence no matter what erotic enticements are laid before you.

Celebrity Rich Tea lovers:
Piers Morgan, Jeremy Clarkson, Pele

BOURBON

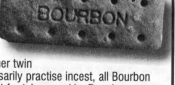

The sugary sweet exterior masks a dark secret – a sinister fondant filling, much like the Queen of the Seven Kingdoms, Cersei Lannister, who engages in sex with her twin brother Jaime. And whilst they won't necessarily practise incest, all Bourbon lovers also hide a shadowy side; a penchant for taboo nookie. Dogging, pegging, golden showers and Boston pancakes are all grist to these biscuit lovers' illicit bedroom mill.

Celebrity Bourbon lovers:
Una Stubbs, Len McCluskey, Little Jimmy Krankie

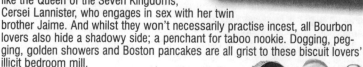

JAMMIE DODGER

Look down on the top of a Jammie Dodger and you will see red, just like the hot tempered Lord of Dragonstone, Stannis Baratheon. Unable to control his passions, it is likely that when Baratheon is getting down and dirty with Mellisandra, the Red Woman, he regularly spends his money before getting to the shops. Ask any man who loves Jammie Dodgers to name the bane of his life, and he'll tell you without hesitation: Premature ejaculation.

Celebrity Jammie Dodger lovers:
Chris Packham, Alfie Boe, Gary Lineker

PARTY RING

Brightly coloured with its shiny iced coating, the Party Ring immediately catches the eye, just like the Red Woman, Mellisandra when she strips off in *Game of Thrones* as she does at the drop of a hat. And just like this scarlet necromancer, anyone who picks the party ring as their biscuit of choice is an incorrigible exhibitionist, who can only get their kicks by having sex in a public place. If you see two people having it off on a beach, in the park, or in a Wetherspoons smoking shelter, chances are they'll be tucking in to a packet of post-coital Party Rings the moment he's shot his bolt.

Celebrity Party Ring lovers:
Katie Hopkins, Eddie Large, Hans Blix

HOBNOB

The Hobnob is surely the hardest, most brutal biscuit in the Teatime Assortment. Ruthless, unyielding and with a cruel streak running through it, it is the cookie equivalent of *Game of Thrones* sadist Ramsay Bolton. And if you like tucking into these more-ish treats, then it's certain that you share the Bastard Lord of the Dreadfort's sadistic sexual proclivities. Bondage, BDSM, spanking, ball-gag-play and auto erotic asphyxiation are just a few of the vile practices you get up to in your bedroom-cum-dungeon.

Celebrity Hobnob lovers:
Eamonn Holmes, Paul Hollywood, Princess Michael of Kent

NEXT WEEK: Dr Raj reveals what your favourite flavour of Revels says about which *Game of Thrones* character you would be in bed if you were a *Coronation Street* star.

IGUANA SUE!

Pet shop man takes GoT to court

A BELFAST pet shop owner has launched legal action against HBO, the producers of *Game of Thrones*, after the show's production staff allegedly damaged three of his lizards. FINTAN MCBEAMISH, manager of Stranmillis Exotic Pets, claims that the show's special effects team borrowed three valuable iguanas to use during filming of the latest series, before returning them in a damaged state.

He told us: "They came in the shop and asked if I had any lizards that looked a bit like dragons. I showed him my iguanas, and they asked if they could borrow them."

"They said they were going to film them and then blow the film up to make them look a hundred times bigger than what they were. I said they could rent them for fifty pounds a week, as long as they brought them back in good nick. They promised they would look after them and I would have them back by Friday."

"... even threw in a free bag of dead baby rats to feed them on," added Mr McBeamish.

lizards

However, on Friday there was no sign of the lizards being returned. And it was only after another fortnight and repeated phone-calls to Titanic Studios that they were finally dropped off at the shop by a runner. "He apologised for them being late, but said that they'd fallen behind on the shooting schedule," said Mr McBeamish.

"When I asked him for the hundred quid to cover the extra two weeks' rental, he told me it was nothing to do with him and I'd have to bill George RR Martin direct."

McBeamish was glad to have his lizards back, but when he looked in the box, he got a shock. "My iguanas had been absolutely trashed," he said. "They were all covered in glue and bits of rubber where they'd had wings and spikes stuck to them. And one of them had even been painted blue."

Mr McBeamish immediately set about trying to clean up his damaged animals, but he found that washing up liquid and a nailbrush had no effect on them. "In the end I had to use turps and a Brillo pad," he told us. "I got most of the mess off, but there was still loads of glue and stuff stuck under their scales that I couldn't reach with the bristles."

scotsmen

And McBeamish, who has run the shop for more than twenty years, was horrified at what he found next. "One of them had had a disposable cigarette lighter stuck in its mouth, presumably to make it breathe fire," he told us. "The cruel special effects people had Araldited it onto the roof of its mouth."

"In the end, I had to prise it out with a lolly stick, and even then I had to leave some bits of broken plastic stuck to the poor thing's palate."

A company spokesman confirmed that HBO had borrowed the lizards, but he insisted that they had been properly looked after and had been returned in the same condition they were when they were borrowed. "Game of Thrones production staff always take great pains to ensure that no animals are harmed during the making of the show," he told us. "If Mr McBeamish's lizards were returned to him covered in paint, glue and bits of plastic, or with cigarette lighters stuck inside them, they must have been like that when we got them."

pickets

But the exotic pet shop owner flatly refutes HBO's version of events. "Bullshit," he told us. "Those lizards were in top A1 condition when they left this shop, and they were trashed when I got them back."

Indeed, he now fears he won't be able to sell the iguanas in his shop. "They are in a right old state. I'll have to sell them at a knock down price, and that's going to leave me well out of pocket," he fumed.

"Ordinarily, iguanas go for about two hundred pound a pop, but I'll lucky if I get thirty quid for these as a job lot," said Mr McBeamish.

"I might even have to bin them."

Forage your way to cosplay glory, with...

Ray Mears' Cut-Out-n-Keep Game of Thrones Costume Survival Guide

W HETHER we're attending a costume party, or attempting to re-inject some spark into our sex life, we all love dressing up as *Game of Thrones* characters. However, a store-bought *GoT* outfit can be pricey – often setting a buyer back hundreds of hard-earned pounds. If only there was a way to get that authentic Westeros look WITHOUT doing a 'Red Wedding' on your wallet...

Well, now there is!

We've teamed up with big-boned TV naturalist **RAY MEARS** to bring you this fantastic 'cut-out-n-keep' guide to making your very own *Game of Thrones* costume from the natural detritus in Britain's woodlands. *"That's right,"* says Ray. *"Believe it or not, everything you need for a great GoT cosplay outfit can be found FOR FREE on the forest floor."*

Here, the salad-shunning survivalist talks us through three iconic *Game of Thrones* looks, and how they can be achieved quite simply using Mother Nature's bounty.

KHAL DROGO

T HIS burly Dothraki warlord has an instantly recognisable style, which can be easily replicated in any verdant area. First things first, crush some ripe blackberries in your hand, before dragging your fingers carefully down each shoulder to recreate Drogo's dark purple tribal markings. For his moody black-rimmed eyes, simply locate some fresh badger dung and smear it generously onto your eyelids – taking care not to get any faecal matter into your retinas or iris. For the Dothraki battle armour, rip several long strips of bark from a nearby tree, and then wrap them tightly around your wrists, torso and waist, accessorising with a few snazzy field mushroom 'belt buckles'. Drogo's trademark ponytail can be achieved by simply trapping and killing a squirrel, then affixing it to the back of your head with tree sap. Finally, for the warlord's bushy beard, stick clumps of brown lichen moss to your face with mud, before hanging a couple of conkers off the end of your chin. *Hey presto* – you're ready to saddle up and reclaim the Seven Kingdoms!

JOFFREY BARATHEON

A MORAL sadist Joffrey is the *GoT* character fans love to hate, and dressing up as this boyish bellend is sure to cause a stir at any *Thrones*-themed knees-up. Joffrey's iconic golden crown is the most important element of his costume – and luckily it's the exact same size and shape as the average bird's nest! Once you've tracked down your nest and shooed away its inhabitants, crack any eggs you find inside and use their yolk to paint your 'crown' yellow, employing a frayed twig as a paintbrush. For Joffrey's multi-coloured regal frock, simply stitch together a rudimentary bodysuit from various different kinds of leaves, using goose grass for cotton and a porcupine quill as a needle. Now there's only one thing missing: the boy King's trademark crossbow. For this prop, attach a sturdy tree branch to the curved rib bone of a dead sheep, before threading some bindweed through as string. *Bob's your uncle* – you're the spitting image of everyone's favourite incest-born bastard!

DAENERYS TARGARYEN

F OR female *GoT* fans, there's only one cosplay costume worth considering: the Mother of Dragons herself, Daenerys Targaryen! Use thick clumps of pampas grass or white weeping willow for her distinctive platinum hair – or, if you happen to be near a farm, simply chop off a horse's tail and plonk it on your head. A frog with two large oak leaves stuck to its back makes an ideal miniature shoulder-dragon, whilst a simple pine cone is a superb stand-in for one of Daenerys' precious dragon eggs. Kill and skin a passing deer to fashion your dress and cape, and for the Queen's iconic diagonal silver chain, simply dig down into the earth until you strike iron, manganese, lead, zinc or tungsten. Any of these semi-precious metals can then be moulded into a chain-shape and heated over a birch bark fire until they solidify. And that's your Stormborn costume – *Khal-eesi* as one, two, three!

What's for GoT, mam?

STARTING THIS WEEK – GAME OF THRONES RECIPE CARDS!

BUILDS WEEK-BY-WEEK INTO A COMPREHENSIVE 1000 RECIPE GAME OF THRONES INDEX SYSTEM.

YOUR FIRST 4 CARDS **FREE** WITH THIS ISSUE

WE'VE ALL BEEN THERE. We've spent so much time binge-watching the latest box set of *Game of Thrones* that we haven't had time to cook a proper evening meal for the family. What wouldn't we give to be able to cook tasty and nutritious food while getting a fix of our favourite Swords 'n' Dragons fantasy? Well now you can!

We've teamed up with the *Game of Thrones* stars to bring you their favourite recipes. Every five weeks for the next 250 issues, we'll be printing four recipe cards to cut out and keep, eventually building into your own comprehensive 1000 recipe cookery compendium. The *Game of Thrones* recipe collection will cover everything from starters to main courses and desserts. Recipes such as *Ramsay Bolton's Carrot and Coriander Soup with Home-made Sourdough Croutons*, *Lord Baelish's Braised Liver and Onion Goulash with Swede Mash* and *Khal Drogo's Coconut-frosted Pineapple Upside Down Cake* are sure to get your family's taste-buds tingling.

To claim your *FREE* recipe card index box, fill in the form which will be printed in *Viz* issue 533 (on sale Thursday February 11th 2044) and send it with a cheque for 3.5 space credits to cover post and packing.

---

1 Cersei Lannister's Scrummy Cheese Scones

"*After I've been fucked by my brother and walked bollock naked through the streets of King's Landing, I like nothing more than a hot cheese scone with plenty of butter. Yum-yum!*"

INGREDIENTS:
Cheese (grated)
Self-raising flour
Butter
Salt
Milk

METHOD:
Preheat the oven to 220°C / Gas 7. Lightly grease a baking sheet.

Mix the flour and salt and rub in the butter.

Stir in the grated cheese, then add the milk to get a soft dough.

Turn onto a floured work surface and knead lightly. Roll out to 2cm thick. Cut into 6 – 8 pieces using a circular cutter

Brush the tops of the scones with a little milk.

Bake until well risen and golden, 12 to 15 minutes. Cool on a wire rack.

---

2 Tyrion Lannister's Beef Hotpot

"*Spending the night with a load of whores at Littlefinger's Brothel can really take it out of you. But a plate of my nourishing beef cobbler soon puts the lead back in my pencil!*"

INGREDIENTS:
Beef (cubed)
Onions
Carrots
Peas
Sweetcorn
Beef stock

METHOD:
Preheat the oven to 160°C / Gas 3.

Brown the beef cubes in oil in small batches on the hob over a high heat in a large oven-proof casserole.

Remove the beef with a slotted spoon, lower the heat then add the onions and carrots to the dish. Cook over a low to medium heat until softened (10 minutes or so).

Return the beef to the pot, add the stock, peas and sweetcorn and transfer to the oven for a couple of hours.

---

3 Theon Greyjoy's "No Cock" au Vin

"*I had my charlie chopped off by Ramsay Bolton, but that doesn't stop me enjoying this delicious meat-free French favourite, made with a tofu-based chicken substitute.*"

INGREDIENTS:
Tofu
Flour
Red wine
Onions
Salad onions (to garnish)

METHOD:
In a large skillet heat the oil and then sear the sides of the tofu cubes in the oil in a single layer for 2-3 minutes until slightly brown.

Remove the tofu and add the onions to the pan. Cook gently for ten minutes until golden and softened.

Add a spoonful of flour to the onions and stir for a minute to cook out the flouriness.

Gradually add the red wine to the onion and flour mix until you end up with a rich sauce.

Return the tofu and cook for another twenty minutes.

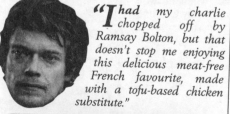

---

4 Hodor's Chocolate Chip Sherry Trifle with Tangerine Segments

"*Hodor! Hodor!*"

INGREDIENTS:
Hodor (Hodor)
Hodor
Hodor
Hodor Hodor
Hodor
Hodor Hodor

METHOD:
Hodor! Hodor! Hodor! Hodor! Hodor! Hodor! Hodor!

Hodor! Hodor! Hodor! Hodor! Hodor! Hodor!

Hodor! Hodor! Hodor! Hodor!

Hodor! Hodor! Hodor! Hodor! Hodor! Hodor! Hodor! Hodor! Hodor! (Hodor! Hodor!)

Hodor! Hodor! Hodor!

Hodor.

LOVE 'EM or hate 'em, you just can't ignore 'em, especially if you're stood by the bird enclosure at the zoo or walking past a nesting colony, for example the one at Uppalapadu, India. They're PELICANS, and with their flat feet, long beaks and trademark flappy throats, they are instantly recognisable. But how much do you really know about these pouched, inland or coastal water birds? Here are...

22 THINGS YOU NEVER KNEW... *ABOUT* PELICANS

01 THE Peruvian Pelican *(Pelicanus thagus)* is very badly named. That's because, unknown to the bonkers scientist who named it, in addition to Peru the large-beaked bird can also be found in Chile and as also an occasional visitor in southern Equador. In 2008, one was even recorded near São Paulo... *in south eastern Brazil!*

02 THE huge beak of a pelican can hold 3 gallons of water. That's enough to fill 0.000004544 Olympic-size swimming pools!

03 THE word pelican comes from the South American word 'pelicano', which is Spanish for pelican.

04 IF you wanted to buy a pelican, you'd probably have to save up for quite a while. Because although they're not actually for sale anywhere, if they were you'd probably have to shell out hundreds of pounds for a basic pink-backed or spot-billed species, and perhaps up to a thousand pounds or more for a top-of-the-range great white.

05 HOLLYWOOD director Steven Spielberg got the idea for *Jurassic Park* after seeing a pelican that had had its feathers shaved off for charity. "It was very prehistoric-looking, like some sort of raptor," he told LBC's Eddie Mair. "I was with my friends Jeff Goldblum and Laura Dern at the time, and the bald pelican started chasing them round a catering kitchen, stopping every now and then to breathe on some glass. I went home and wrote the script that very night."

06 THE collective noun for a group of pelicans is variously a 'brief', a 'pod', a 'pouch', a 'scoop' or a 'squadron', so it's all bollocks.

07 THE only anagram of the word pelican is 'panicle' - a botanical term for a small, loose cluster of flowers.

08 THE only other one is 'capelin' - a North Atlantic fish resembling a smelt.

09 IT is well known that grapes and chocolate are very bad for dogs, but it is not known which foodstuffs are poisonous for pelicans. "Tragically, the research just hasn't been done," says TV's Supervet Dr Noel Fitzpatrick. "It's a horrible thought that pelicans could be dying needlessly all over the world after being fed treats that are harmless to us but deadly poison for them."

10 AFTER being scooped up by a pelican whilst paddling in the lake in St James's Park, Calvin Phillips, the world's smallest man, spent almost three days passing through the large bird's digestive tract. After Phillips was shat out onto the riverbank, a little the worse for wear but thankfully unharmed after his ordeal, he told reporters that the worst part of his experience was the six hours he spent in the bird's crop, being ground down by small pebbles which seemed to him the size of boulders.

11 A WILD pelican can live for up to sixteen years. That's the same age as Boris Becker when he won Wimbledon, Donny Osmond when he topped the charts with *Puppy Love*, or Idris Elba when he sat his GCSEs, gaining 2 As, 3 Bs and a C.

12 AND a D in history and a U in physics.

13 AT a recent Sotheby's auction of showbiz memorabilia, a stuffed pelican originally belonging to legendary rock wild man Keith Moon sold for £38.50 plus a 15% buyer's premium and VAT, making a total of £53.13. The buyer was pelican-mad former US rapper MC Hammer, real name Stan Burrell.

14 AT the height of his pop fame, it was estimated that Burrell's trademark 'hammer pants' trousers could hold 18 gallons of piss.

15 A FULLY grown Dalmatian pelican can have a mass of up to 12kg, meaning it is attracted towards the centre of the earth with a gravitational force of 117.7 Newtons. But what few people realise is that the earth is also attracted to the centre of the pelican with an equal and opposite force.

16 PELICANS live on every continent except one - Antarctica - and bird scientists are baffled as to why. "It's a complete mystery," says Cambridge University Ornithologist Dr Dalibar Singh. "Our best guess is it's because it's fucking freezing."

17 THE egg of a Great White Pelican is larger than a hen's egg, which means it would take longer to boil - and even longer than that if you wanted it hard-boiled for sandwiches!

THE BACONS

18 AS well as being birds, pelicans are also a type of zebra crossing, a kind of fountain pen, a baseball team from Michigan, and a brand of 70s supermarket own-brand chocolate biscuit that was trying to cash in on the success of the Penguin.

19 ACCORDING to Charles Darwin's book *On the Origin of Species by Means of Natural Selection*, pelicans evolved over millions of years from earlier, more primitive pelican-like birds with different size beaks and feet. However, theologians disagree, claiming that God created the pelican some 6,000 years ago with the same size beak and feet it has now, along with the owl, and the bat, and the ossifrage and all of their kind that do dwell in the trees and do flyeth in the firmament.

20 RECENT advances in Artificial Intelligence mean that many skilled human professions are under threat, but it is unlikely that pelicans will ever be replaced by robots. "As far as I know, no-one is currently developing a computerised machine that spends the day floating around on a pond, scooping fish up into its beak and occasionally going up to the bank for a shit," says Coventry University cybernetics expert Dr Kevin Warwick. "Until they do, pelicans' jobs are safe."

21 UNLIKE mammals, pelicans don't suckle their young and therefore don't have tits.

22 THE largest tits ever seen in a film belonged to adult actress Chesty Morgan. Her cult film, *Deadly Weapons*, is most notable for the fact that it features no pelicans at all, except a few in the background of a couple of shots.

Next Week: 20 Things You never Knew About Spoonbills

THE Male Online

Is that you Beryl?

BERYL!?

It's cats and dogs out there!

Ha! Don't tell the bloody *greentards*.

Those *clowns* are still banging on about how July was the hottest on record!

It was.

Snowflakes are melting in July

Well? Was June the hottest on record? May? April maybe?

It's not quite so simple...

In fact, why isn't *today* the hottest on record? But *only* until tomorrow?

That isn't how it works.

Oh I *seeee*.

This *unstoppable* process switches on and off to suit.

I don't know *exactly* how it works, but I trust the scientists.

We've had enough of experts, Beryl...

Weather is more *extreme* now, not just hotter. Brian Cox said the –

I'll stop you there, shall I?

Thankfully, a few of us manage *not* to go cow-eyed over that simpering middle-aged *Beatle*.

Contrary thinkers like Littlejohn might never be menopausal heartthrobs –

– but at least *they* understand the motorist.

What the heck does Richard Littlejohn know about science?

What do *scientists?* Hm? Eh?

More than bloody Littlejohn!

Richard is entitled to his opinion, as are we all...

You can't have an *opinion* about scientific facts!

Ahh, here we go – *burn the heretics.*

And *who* is this haunted eskimo girl they keep wheeling out?

MailOnline

She's a green campaigner.

Not that *green* though – ker-ching!

It isn't as if she needs it either, I read her mother was in ABBA.

I don't think she was...

The creepy so-and-so pops up daily with some world leader or other. It's like The Omen!

This rain is getting ridiculous.

Ooh, don't tell me, let me guess – global *wettening?*

This is Britain. It rains. It always rained. Rain is *literally nothing*.

Later

This rain isn't even *slightly* warm, Beryl.

BUY Viz

51

LORD OF THE STINGS

ASK anyone from Land's End to John O'Groats to name the most exciting job they can think of and the answer will always be the same: *undercover cop.*

Every single human being on Earth is mesmerised by the thrilling lives of these secretive tough guys – hard-boiled police officers who assume new identities to gain the trust of the very criminals they are attempting to bring down. And from *Donnie Brasco* and *The Departed* to *Reservoir Dogs* and *Kindergarten Cop*, we can't get enough of seeing these covert coppers on the big screen.

But as always, the glitz and glamour of Hollywood is a far cry from the truth. In reality, the dangerous, exhausting and fully immersive nature of the job can play havoc with an undercover cop's personal life and mental stability.

Just ask **JEDWIN CHAPSTICK**.

Nice not to see you! Chapstick, identity hidden for his own safety.

Thrice-divorced dad-of-eight Jed has long been the most effective, feared and ruthless 'deep cover' agent in the Daventry Police Department. Over the past twelve months, the intrepid 66-year-old has single-handedly infiltrated and exposed literally tens of high-level crime syndicates, using an ingenious litany of false names, invented backstories and cunning facial disguises.

In fact, so skilled is Jed at his job... *that he often fools his fellow officers!*

"I've lost count of the times my shit-witted colleagues in the Daventry PD have mistook me for a genuine criminal," chuckles 20-stone Jed. "Honestly, if I had a quid for every time they'd got the wrong end of the stick during a sting operation and misguidedly chucked me in clink, I'd have enough to post bail for my current stint."

Speaking to us from the Nuneaton prison cell where he is presently serving six months after being wrongfully arrested whilst infiltrating a prostitution racket, Jed revealed all about the most eventful stings of his colourful career – and laid bare the true cost of being a top-level undercover cop.

On the Fiddle

Chapstick's scarcely believable story began back in July 2018, following a lengthy period of unemployment.

State of address: Jed used numerous adandoned house addresses to sign-on with DSS.

EXCLUSIVE!

❝ I was down the newsagent one morning, stocking up on cider and cigs, when I noticed a sign Blu-Tacked up in the window. It said: 'Daventry Police Department seeks new recruit for dangerous yet rewarding work... Only the best need apply.' Now, I'd been jobless for a good three decades due to a long-standing fatigue-based illness that doctors have yet to diagnose, but which I definitely suffer from. At the time, though, my third wife was up the duff with my eighth sprog, and I was sorely in need of cash. So I took the card, thinking: 'Why not?'

I called the number later that day and was shocked to find it was a direct line to the DPD's chief of police – Commissioner Hank McMurphy. He spoke in a gruff, Irish-American accent straight out of the 70s cop shows that I very occasionally watch on the Dave channel while the wife's out at work. He informed me that taking this job would mean rubbing shoulders with the lowest criminal scum imaginable. I'd be sinking deep into society's most sordid cesspools and getting my hands dirty in order to keep the streets clean. He added that the job was so dangerous I was forbidden from telling anyone about it, even my darling missus, Carol, for fear of jeopardising her safety. To protect my identity, not one single DPD officer would even know I existed.

I would become a ghost. A shadow. A faceless man.

benefit

Thinking only of my desire to put food on the table for my beloved wife, and keep up with child support payments for my less beloved two previous wives, I accepted without hesitation.

McMurphy explained that my first job would be to infiltrate and expose a gang of local low-lifes who were defrauding the benefits system. 'I got the DA crawlin' up my ass over this horseshit, Chapstick,' the chief growled. 'I want you to track down these scumbags – become one of 'em, see what makes 'em tick. And when you've got enough evidence, I want you

"I've pulled more undercover operations than you've had hot dinners", says top cop Jed

to bust those bozos so fast it'll make their goddam heads spin. Capeesh?'

As luck would have it, the fraudsters in question drank regularly in my local pub, and I'd often overheard them boasting about how easy it was to cheat the system. Disguising myself as one of them, in stained tracksuit bottoms and a hooded sweatshirt to hide the wire taped to my chest, I approached them one evening and asked for tips on how to fiddle the dole. Suspecting nothing, the gang began spilling their deceitful secrets, and just like that, I was on the inside.

In order to gain their trust and maintain my cover, I began signing on at the Daventry nash under twenty-six different names. For the addresses, I used various abandoned or derelict houses in the area. I kept this undercover operation up for months, meeting with my new 'friends' most evenings to secretly record our discussions about defrauding the hard-working British taxpayer. With every unearned cheque I cashed, I felt sick to my stomach. But I reminded myself I was doing this dirty work for a good reason: to bring these scumbags to justice.

After six months, I decided I had all the evidence I needed to bust the gang wide

> *In order to gain their trust and maintain my cover, I began signing on at the Daventry nash under twenty-six different names.*

open. But as fate would have it, the very evening I was planning to pull the sting was also the evening that my cover was blown.

I was in the pub, having a few drinks with my 'associates' before whipping out the handcuffs and bringing them in, when two Daventry PD officers entered. They told me someone at the nash had uncovered a false claimant named 'Jedwinda Chapstickio,' one of my many aliases, and that I was under arrest on suspicion of benefit fraud.

burn

I didn't know whether to laugh or cry. These morons were blowing a sting operation I had spent literally months setting up. Seething, I whispered, 'Don't worry lads, I'm filth too, I'm just undercover,' but the fuckwitted duo slammed me to the ground and frogmarched me outside to their van. I tried to tell them I had stacks of evidence back at my house that would bring down the entire East Midlands benefit fraud network, but they simply wouldn't listen. I was fined ten grand, and sentenced to 140 hours community service.

It was the first time my criminal infiltration skills had worked a little too well. Sadly, it wouldn't be the last... ❞

The Beat Goes On

His first assignment may not have gone entirely to plan, but Officer Chapstick had well and truly caught the undercover bug.

❝ All my nash cash had gone on that wrongful ten grand fine, and my missus and ex-missuses were still firmly on my case for sprog support. So, I got straight back on the phone to Commissioner McMurphy and asked for my next assignment.

'You're a loose frickin' cannon, Chapstick,' the chief roared. 'But goddam it, you get results. Listen up and listen good,' he continued. 'I want you to play this next one by the book, see, or the DA will run my fat ass up the goddam flagpole.'

The commissioner went on to explain that my next job would be to infiltrate and take down an illegal dog-fighting ring. Apparently, a group of heartless reprobates were forcing innocent pooches to scrap to the death in the car park behind a pub just so they could place bets on the winner.

The very idea made me sick to my stomach. I couldn't wait to sling these sleezeballs into the cells where they belonged.

need

As luck would have it again, the boozer where it went on was my local, so it wasn't difficult to find out when the next fight was taking place. And as luck would also have it, I owned a Bull Terrier at the time that I had to get rid of sharpish following a minor face-biting incident. So, one evening, I told the missus I was heading out to dump the dog in the canal, when in fact I was setting off on my latest undercover sting.

I arrived at the pub wearing my trusty wire under my vest, ready to collect all the evidence I needed to put these scuzzbuckets away for a long time. A large crowd had already gathered out the back, so to maintain my cover, I entered fifty quid into the pot and signed my dog, Tyson, up for the first fight. He was drawn against a big fuck-off Mastiff, also called Tyson. For the case to stand up in court, I had to let the action properly commence before I made the bust, so I flicked my Tyson's bollocks until he was foaming at the mouth, and then let go of his chain. He tore across the concrete towards his

Dogged pursuit: Jed attempted to bust illegal dog-fighting ring at his local, using his beloved pet, Tyson (right).

THE KING HELL

rival, but before he could make contact, the sound of sirens filled the air, and there were blue lights flashing all around us.

I couldn't believe it. Another meticulously planned sting was ruined by my cock-witted Daventry PD colleagues.

Mistaking me for a genuine dog-fight participant, two officers slammed me to the ground and placed me in handcuffs. I was screaming 'I'm Jed Chapstick! I'm a deep cover agent!' But, of course, my identity was hidden from all but the top brass. These entry-level dolts wouldn't even know of my existence.

I was hurled into the cells for the night and hit with another hefty fine. The only silver lining was that my Tyson was handed over to the RSPCA, so that was one thing crossed off my to-do list.

Stiff Punishment

As the weeks flew by, Chapstick embarked on more clandestine sting operations – every single one of them botched by his cack-handed DPD colleagues.

❝ Every sting I masterminded invariably ended with me being mistaken for one of the criminals.

One week, I was charged with infiltrating a gang of vagrants who were disturbing the peace. I spent a whole evening gaining their trust in the precinct by drinking white cider and hurling abuse at passers-by. But before I could make any arrests, the DPD blundered in and cuffed me along with the rest of them.

Another time, the chief asked me to bring down a group of flashers – twisted perverts who were exposing themselves to local women. To maintain my cover, I was forced to show my penis to an all-female yoga class in the park, only for the moronic DPD to stick me on the sex offenders' register.

Eventually, the strain began to affect my marrige. My beloved wife Carol told me that if I had another brush with the law, she'd leave me once and for all. So, one night, I called the commissioner to tell him I was getting out.

'I'm too old for this shit, chief,' I sighed. 'I'm calling it quits, cashing my chips in now so I can enjoy my retirement, sipping margaritas on a beach somewhere.'

The chief blew a gasket. 'Why, you got some noive, Chapstick!' he bellowed. 'You're the best goddam cop on the force, and now you wanna walk? Jeez Louise!' Then he seemed to calm down a little. 'Look, I tell you what,' he said. 'You do one last job for me, and I'll give you that goddam golden handshake myself.'

With a heavy heart, I agreed.

force

As it turned out, my final job would be the most dangerous and morally questionable yet. I was to infiltrate and expose a prostitution racket. The chief suspected local streetwalkers of offering sexual favours in exchange for money, but he needed proof before he could start making arrests. I would pose as a 'john' in order to get that proof.

The street where the girls were working was only a stone's throw from my own home, so to protect my identity I would don a false beard and dark glasses for the sting. That night I headed over. Almost immediately, I was approached by a burly blonde lady in a miniskirt and fishnets. 'Alright love,' she growled. 'Fancy a quick pull-off for ten?'

trogedy

My heart was pounding. Cheating on my beloved Carol was the last thing on Earth I wanted to do, but I was sure she'd understand that this one-off sacrifice could bring about an end to illicit sex work across the entire East Midlands.

I went behind a skip with the call girl, who proceeded to remove my penis from my trackie bottoms and begin pumping it with expert precision. To maintain my cover, I had to pretend I was enjoying the sickening experience, groaning orgasmically whilst fondling the woman's buttocks. Within seconds, I had the jester's shoes. But before I could shoot my wad, thus gaining conclusive proof that this woman was indeed a sex worker, there was a torch shining in my eyes.

You've guessed it. Another pen-pushing DPD cretin. He'd spotted me with a prostitute's hand round my chopper, put two and two together and made five.

My disguise was ripped off and the cuffs were slapped on. I protested, telling the officer I was a deep cover agent, and I had evidence at my house to bring down numerous Daventry-based crime syndicates. He agreed to let me show him, and we set off for my house.

To maintain my cover, I had to pretend I was enjoying the sickening experience, groaning orgasmically whilst fondling the woman's buttocks

But someone who knew me must have seen the commotion and phoned Carol, because when we arrived back at my gaff she was out front, burning all my clothes and possessions... *including every scrap of evidence I'd collected in my time as an undercover cop!* Notes, photographs, recordings – the whole lot was up in smoke, meaning there was no way to prove my incredible true story.

Carol filed for divorce, and I was carted off to the cells. I was charged with indecency and several cases of failing to turn up for court appearances. Serving six months for a series of crimes you did not commit is hard enough to bear, but when you were *actively trying to prevent them*, it's doubly so.

We attempted to contact Commissioner McMurphy of Daventry PD for a comment on Mr Chapstick's treatment, but a spokesman told us that no one of that name had ever worked for Daventry Police, adding that the force has never been known as Daventry PD. "Mr Chapstick has been known to us for many years," he told us. "He has helped us many times with our enquiries in connection with numerous sex offences, benefit frauds and illegal dog fights as well as a list of other civil disturbances," he added.

Skip the formalities: Chapstick put himself through hell to expose illicit sex trade.

LETTERBOCKS

Viz Comic, P.O. Box 841 Whitley Bay, NE26 9EQ : letters@viz.co.u

I USED to have great sympathy for those orangutans whose rainforest habitat is being destroyed to grow palm oil. But then I discovered that each ape occupies a territory of around 6 square kilometres. This seems awfully excessive to me. Maybe if these orange monkeys got over themselves and downsized a bit, then this whole fuss could be put to bed.

J Crease, Cambridge

MY wife and I very much enjoy the TV programme *Call the Midwife*. However, we've noticed recently that in every single episode, someone has a baby. Come on, writers. Pull your fingers out and think up some different storylines!

Stuart Tonks, Kingswinford

WHAT is Johnny Depp on? In that advert for *Au Savauge*, he is digging holes in the desert whilst wearing a really nice three-piece suit. Surely, if he has gone to the trouble of buying a shovel from B&Q, he could have easily picked up some bib and brace overalls while he was there?

Ulf Bjornsen, Cromer

WHEN I was growing up in the 1980s, before the days of mobile phones, we used to have hours of fun drinking alco-pops, throwing stones at cars and swearing at old people. When I tried it again for old time's sake recently, some bastard granny rang the police and I ended up with a caution. Technology has taken all the innocent fun out of life.

Eginald Flare, Camborne

WHEN you think about it, wiping your arse is quite a skill. You can't actually see what you're doing but in my case I get it right 9 times out of 10.

Stuie, Bunny

KLASS ACT?

MYLEENE KLASS has always been dubbed a 'Klass act' by journalists, not only because she has an arse you can bounce a pound coin off, but because she is always well presented and dedicates so much of her time to charity. But a few people who have crossed paths with the former Hear'Say songstress take a different view…

SPOTTED! I WAS just pulling out of a treacherous blind junction at the end of my street when a driver in a Peugeot 308 coming the other way flashed me to let me out. I couldn't believe it when I saw it was none other than Myleene Klass. She obviously thinks she owns the fucking roads, directing traffic like lady muck. Klass act? My arse. **A. Trotman, Torquay**

SPOTTED! I SAW Myleene whilst out shopping in Margate the other day. She spotted an old lady who had unwittingly dropped £20 from her purse. I couldn't believe it as she picked it up and gave it back to her. Typical do-gooder. That £20 would have been a wonderful bonus find for someone like me who is out of work and struggling to maintain a 40-a-day habit. Klass act? Not on your nelly. **F. Parker, Watford**

SPOTTED! MYLEENE came into a charity shop where I work and tried on a pair of jeans. After 5 minutes she came out and told me the jeans didn't fit, but she gave a £50 donation and hung around for an hour to sign autographs for the customers. I couldn't believe the audacity of the woman leaving the jeans in the changing room for muggins here to put them back on the shelf. Klass act? Fuck off. **S. Hawkings, St Neots**

WHY is it that only gymnasts and India rubber men can get a good look at their own anus? As an overweight 50-year-old fan of the rectal opening, I find this deeply unfair.

Dave Howard, Sheffield

I FEEL sorry for anyone born in the last couple of years, having to go through life with no Roger Moore around. I suppose they could watch some of his old films, but I wouldn't bother if I was them.

Bob Tip, Hull

"HAIR of the dog" sounds so much better than "have a drink before you get the shakes".

Ben, Whitstable

THE voting panels for the Oscars and Baftas have clearly not been watching the same European short films as I have for the last twenty years before narrowing it down to the final four or five on their shortlist. I can only assume that they must be borrowing them from a different bloke in the pub than I am.

Matt McCann, Tipton

WHAT if there is an Afterlife, but instead of being eternal, it only lasts 15 minutes or something? How fucking shit would that be?

Ben Nunn, Caterham

✱ That's a very good point, Mr Nunn. Perhaps a vicar could tell us exactly how long the Afterlife is, so that we can all decide whether getting a numb arse sitting in church, not having impure thoughts about your neighbour's wife, or turning the other cheek when somebody slaps you one, is worth the bother or not.

SCIENTISTS are warning that unless human industrial and agricultural practices change, the world's insect population could collapse entirely within the next century. Well, I for one won't shed any tears if they do. I got stang off a wasp while playing in the garden when I was about two or three, so as far as I'm concerned they started it. Fuck 'em.

Craig Scott, East Calder

HOW come when Charlie Brooker writes episodes of *Black Mirror* telling us again and again that we're using our phones too much, he gets called a modern-day Diogenes with prescient visions of the future of our screen-addicted society. But when I say the same to my kids I get called a boring old man who doesn't understand modern culture?

Ben, Whitstable

I LIVE in the house that 90s glamour model Jo Guest grew up in. I wonder if I would qualify for a blue plaque so that I can show tourists what a botch job her dad made of the rewiring. Also, I have a shed full of old paint tins if anyone wants some genuine JG memorabilia.

Ian Fitzgerald, Chesterfield

ON their hit song *Puff the Magic Dragon*, Peter, Paul and Mary sang that "a dragon lives forever". But that Smaug got it with a big arrow in The Battle of the Five Armies, St George slotted one in medieval times and I'm pretty sure Noggin the Nog killed one of the bastards too. Please do your research, 60s bands.

Jennifer Juniper, Beyond the Hill

IN physics class at school we were taught that when water is poured from a container, air must enter to take up the space. So what happens when you have a piss? Does the air go in your arse or something?

J Spratt, Stourbridge

HOW come we never see any of those pesky double glazing salesmen any more? I used to love slamming the door in their faces after telling them firmly to fuck off. So much, in fact, that ironically, the glass in my front door now needs replacing. Where are those annoying little fuckers when you actually need them?

Torbjorn Gulls, Dover

I REFUSED even to look at this so-called Blood Wolf Super Moon. Am I alone in yearning for a more innocent age when we told children that the moon was made of cheese, not blood or wolves? It's such a pity that everything has to be about sex and violence these days.

Phil Kitching, Isle of Jura

I BOUGHT a chicken and gravy pie the other day and I noticed the box had a 'serving suggestion,' which simply featured a picture of the pie with a slice taken out of it. Thanks for that. I'd planned to roll it into a cylinder and shove it up my arse.

Jeff Gusset, Bristol

WHY do we have to have airbags in cars? If it's to protect us from smashing our faces on the steering wheel, why not simply make the steering wheels out of the same material as the bags?

Billy Whiffles, Croydon

I CAN understand people wishing to follow a vegetarian diet, but what is all this 'vegan' nonsense about? I mean, how is it cruel to milk a cow? My Mrs loves having her tits played with and cows have four, so it should be twice as good. As usual, so-called 'expert' Chris Packham remains silent on the issue.

Mungo Chutney, Truro

WHY do so many hinges creak? I can only think it must be a design fault. Come on, door and gate experts, sort it out!

Vernon, Hunstanton

IN reply to T Steel (*Letterbocks*, page 32), chickens have neither a fanny nor an arsehole. Chickens have a 'cloaca', a posterior orifice that serves as the only opening for the digestive, reproductive, and urinary tracts, named after the Latin word for 'sewer'. Thus they have a large, smelly hole where a multitude of things come in and out of, much like your mother. But it's neither a fanny nor an arsehole, unlike your father.

Trim McKenna, Surbiton

✱ *Once again, what could have been an interesting and educational letter from Mr McKenna has been spoilt by his levelling crude abuse at the editors' parents, much as he has done in many previous issues. Viz Comic is a family magazine and will not stand for childish and insulting behaviour from its readers, especially one whose mum we know for a fact makes bukakke scud flicks under the railway arches in Surbiton, and whose dad wets and shits the bed every night.*

"IF you can't stand the heat, get out of the kitchen," they say. Not my kitchen, it's fucking freezing.

Robert Yorke, Glasgow

WITH all his money, Jeff Bezos is surely proof that male pattern baldness is currently incurable. Hopefully this knowledge will help some of you bald cunts out there save some cash.

Terry Casablanca, Ryton

SINCE Americans say fanny instead of arse, when they said "kiss my ass!" surely they should be saying "kiss my fanny!" Come on, you Americans, get it right and give us Brits a cheap laugh.

Rupert Rimjob, Airbiscuitshire

DOES the current royal family have a chess set with the Queen as the King piece and Prince Philip as the Queen piece? It would be very confusing to play.

Vic Grimes, email

DOES anyone know if nuns and monks need to poo? I have a mate who reckons he was brought up by orthodox Benedictine monks on a council estate in Wakefield during the miners' strikes, and he never once saw any of them curl one off.

Tim Buktu, Timbuktu

WHY is it that boxers hug each other and become "bessy mates" right after a fight? Surely they could have saved us all the time, trouble and expense if they had made friends before, and not fought at all.

Henry Queensbury, Devon

WE hear a lot about 'fat shaming' of young women by the media, and how it should be made a hate crime. However, it seems to be perfectly acceptable when two boxers are labelled heavyweights and forced to hop on the scales before a fight. How must they feel if one of them has put on a couple of pounds and all the paps are there clicking away at them?

Barry Muldoon, London

I CAN'T help noticing that these so-called Olympic gold medal-winning 'sprinters' are nearly always tall people with long legs. It's just cheating really.

Jane Hoole Garner, St. Ives

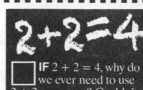

IF 2 + 2 = 4, why do we ever need to use 2 + 2 any more? Couldn't we just use 4 all the time? It would certainly save ink, and I'm sure it would work for many other numbers too.

Tim Riley, Stockton

WHAT ever happened to the Loch Ness monster?

P McPlop, Loch Ness

✱ *That's a very good question, Mr McPlop, people used to spot the thing all the time and now it's nowhere to be seen. Have any of our readers sighted Nessie recently? And if you managed to take an unconvincing, grainy, clearly doctored photograph of it, send it in.*

IT must have been a piece of piss to be a burglar during caveman times. There was no DNA profiling, no fingerprint technology and if a neighbour saw you robbing someone's cave, they couldn't even grass you up because there was no coppers. And even if there was, the grasses could probably only grunt the information anyway.

Richard Leakey, Tring

I SUSPECT the reason Sherlock Holmes never accepted a fee for his detective services was because he was signing on. Also, I reckon he kept Dr. Watson close because you never know when you'll need that all-important sick note when they stick you on Job Seeker's Allowance.

Stan Moriarty, Leeds

HOW come if I look at the clouds and they're going from left to right, when I turn around and look at the ones behind me, they're going in the opposite direction? I'd like to see the so-called boffins work THAT one out.

Tom Aspel, Dorking

AN APPLE a day keeps the doctor away, apparently, but I found the opposite to be true when I had to visit A&E after accidentally sitting on one whilst naked. Seven separate doctors came to take a look, along with half the nursing staff and a full class of students, before the offending fruit was eventually removed. To make matters worse, it sounded like most of them had been on the laughing gas. No wonder the NHS is on its knees.

Stan Plywood, Derby

WHOOPS AISLE APOCALYPSE

What are we doing?

Ssshhh...

Reduced

I've *got* her.

Who?

Her! That trollop I've been telling you about.

Thrusting her *tits* at the boy with the gun.

She must be 50!

I'm 50.

Yes, and you don't use *sex* to cheat other shoppers out of their rightful bargains.

It's been alleged that they set things aside for her out back!

Alleged by who?

People...

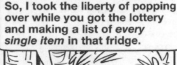

So, I took the liberty of popping over while you got the lottery and making a list of *every single item* in that fridge.

Here we go, here we bloody go...

Be ready to block her if she bolts.

Pâté!

That pâté has been in the back.

Sure?

Enough to blow this wide open.

Okay, okay, break it up, I am *onto* you!

Eh?

I saw the pâté, son.

This pâté?

Yes that pâté! Pâté that was not in that fridge not ten minutes ago –

– and I can prove it!

Caramac banana mousse pots, were £2.49, now £2.29. Bernard Matthews Golden –

I fetched that pâté just now.

You admit it?!

Admit what?

Stashing goodies out back for your little old girlfriend!

Nah, it'd got left on display full price. We miss the odd one.

How – convenient...

Let's see how much was *slashed* off this *odd one* then shall we?

SNATCH

On a promise of God knows what!

ADLD
Duck Pâté

WHOOPS! WAS: £2.99
NOW: £2.79

Out back later

Same time tomorrow?

Depends.

What else can you knock off the Caramac banana mousse pots?

56

GOVE DEMANDS UK SPELL CHECK!

FORMER education secretary *Michael Gove* today called for drastic measures to improve Britain's standards of spelling and grammar - after revealing that nearly *ninety percent* of emails he receives from constituents misspell the word 'bellend'.

The Edinburgh-born minister, 51, made the shocking announcement on *The Andrew Marr Show* on Sunday morning.

He told Marr: "In my fourteen years as a member of parliament, I have received literally thousands of emails, letters and faxes from the great British public. And it saddens me to say that, in nearly every one of them, the word 'bellend' has been spelled incorrectly."

slides

Gove went on to show slides of various correspondences sent to him by his constituents since 2005 - the overwhelming majority of which contained bellend-based orthographical blunders.

"The most common misspelling in the communications I receive is to erroneously hyphenate the word bellend, making it bell-end'," Gove explained. "This is demonstrated in a letter I got from a constituent a week ago, which contained the phrase: 'Gove, you fucking fish-faced bell-end.'"

swings

The minister continued: "Another regular mistake my correspondents make is to split 'bellend' into two separate words - 'bell end' - as seen in an email that arrived in my inbox just this morning, and began: 'Dear Michael, you are a big, fucking bell end'."

Minister slams 'woeful' standards of British orthography

"Incredible though it seems," Gove continued, "I've even had one that read 'why don't you stick your cock in a pig like Cameron did, you fucking belend', with one 'l'. Honestly, it beggars belief," the minister added with a hollow chuckle.

roundabouts

However, the Aberdeen-raised Tory MP went on to reveal that "bellend" is not the only word that is regularly botched by brainless Brits in the missives that swamp his desk. Other common orthographical crimes Gove routinely encounters in his correspodence include:

- Spelling 'twat' with double t on the end
- Splitting both 'fuckwit' and 'tosspot' into two words
- Numerous spelling and grammatical mistakes within the phrase, 'You weedy, fucking wet-lipped arsehole'

Gove concluded the press conference by telling journalists: "Britain leads the way in so many aspects - industry, trade, environment, healthcare - but until our woeful standards of spelling and grammar are brought up to scratch, we will always be a bit-part player on the world stage."

"We must take immediate and drastic action to resolve this problem once and for all," the weedy, Pob-faced, wet-lipped bellend added.

BIG DADDY _versus_ ISIS

At the Foreign Office…

It's no good, minister. We're losing the fight against Isis…

…The Axis of Evil is making territorial gains throughout the entire Middle East.

What is to be done?

Intelligence suggests that if we can take out their figurehead, Omar Bin-Jihad, Isis will be demoralised and finished as a threat to world peace.

Should we attempt a targeted drone strike on his compound?

Too risky, minister. He surrounds himself with a human shield of innocent women, children, labrador puppies and kittens.

There's only one man in Britain who can neutralise Bin-Jihad, and he's ready to go. Just say the word and we'll send him in.

The coward!

Let's do it!

That night, in the skies above Afghanistan…

We're approaching the drop-zone. Everybody get ready.

Does everybody know the plan? Big Daddy, have you checked all three of your parachutes?

Aye, 'appen I 'ave. I'm reyt oop fer this, me.

Green for go!

Come on, lads! Ea-seh! Ea-seh!

Ea-seh! Ea-seh!

WALLOP!

Oohyah!

Big Daddy! Are you alright? That was quite a heavy landing!

Course I'm allreyt, young 'un. Ninety percent o' t' grapple game is knawin' 'ow t'tek a fall.

Look. There's Bin-Jihad's compound!

'Ave it!

Shortly…

Right, unpack the assault gear. Once we blast through these walls and get inside the compound, we'll have just minutes.

Eeh, champion.

3…2…1…
Fire in the hole!

KA-BOOM!

Let's GO!

Like a well-oiled machine, the Commandos put their plan into action…

Target located!

What is the meaning of this? _Guards, seize them!_

The Independent Group

COLD CASE

The members of the UK's newest* political group speculate on some of the greatest mysteries of the age. This week...

*now disbanded

The Riddle of the Mary Celeste

ON THE MORNING of December 5th 1872, an abandoned Brigantine clipper was found drifting in the Atlantic Ocean 500 miles East of the Azores. Inexplicably, there was no-one on board, there was no sign of a struggle, and the crew's final meal had been left half-eaten on the table. None of the nine souls who had been aboard when the ship set sail from New York a month earlier were ever seen or heard of again.

The riddle of the **Mary Celeste** is one of the world's most enduring mysteries. Over the years, investigators have put forward many outlandish theories, but the truth has always remained elusive. But now we've asked Britain's shortest-lived political movement - The Independent Group - to take a break from whatever they are doing now and speculate about what really happened to that ill-starred vessel and its doomed crew.

This cross-party group of eleven independent thinkers failed to break the mould of UK politics. Now let's see if they can crack the 150-year-old mystery of that fateful voyage into oblivion.

Heidi Allen, Welfare & Pensions

I BELIEVE that just after the captain and his crew sat down to have their tea, a giant undersea whirlpool opened up under the ship and sucked down the Mary Celeste and her crew, like a pube going down the plughole in the bath. Once underwater, the nine terrified men would quickly have drowned, dragged down to Davy Jones's locker, never to be seen again. But wood floats, so the ship would have bobbed back up to the surface, none the worse for its ordeal. Why didn't the plates fall off the table? Simple. The powerful centrifugal force generated by the spinning ship clamped them firmly to the table like a motorbike on a wall of death.

Ann Coffey, Children & Education

THERE is ample evidence that space aliens regularly abduct human beings on land, so there is no reason to suppose that they couldn't do the same at sea. It is my firm belief that the crew of the Mary Celeste were caught unawares during their dinner and beamed aboard a spacecraft of extraterrestrial origin using a tractor beam of some sort. Once captured, they were anally probed using scientific instruments beyond our human understanding and fashioned from metallic elements that are unknown on earth. Once they had finished sticking things up their arses, the emotionless aliens callously dropped the puny earthling crew into the sea to drown like rats, before zooming off at light speed to the other side of the galaxy.

Luciana Berger, Home Affairs and Health

WE KNOW less about the creatures that live in our deep oceans than we do about the ones that live on the surface of the Moon. In my opinion, it is quite possible that the Mary Celeste was attacked by a giant squid, a cryptozoological Kraken of the sort spoken about in sailors' myths for centuries. Striking the crew unawares halfway through their dinner, this ravenous leviathan could have grabbed the hapless captain in its beak, whilst grasping the other men, each in one of its eight testicles, before retreating back to its nest in the inky blackness of the ocean to consume them at its leisure 20,000 fathoms beneath.

60

Mike Gapes, Foreign Affairs & Defence

IN MY house, family mealtimes often descend into acrimonious arguments and fist fights over silly little things like someone having too much gravy, someone sticking their elbows out, or someone else eating with their mouth open. In the confined environment of the Mary Celeste's cabin, it is easy to imagine such a mealtime punch-up amongst hardened sailors getting out of hand and rapidly descending into a desperate, all-out fight to the death. After slaying his eight crewmates and tossing their bodies into the sea, the eventual victor would be overcome with remorse at what he had done, and throw himself overboard.

Chris Leslie, Treasury & Trade

THE ONLY certainty in life is that everyone dies eventually. It's possible that the entire nine-man crew of the Mary Celeste all died at exactly the same moment, halfway during their dinner. Perhaps one died of old age, another of disease, while yet another choked on a sprout… the possibilities and combinations are endless. It would indeed be a fantastic coincidence, but then as Einstein once said, only a world without fantastic coincidences would be truly strange. But what happened to the nine dead bodies? The answer is simple; seagulls, terns and petrels would have flown in through the cabin windows - left open to let out cooking smells - and picked their skeletons clean. Their bones would then have crumbled to dust and blown away in the Atlantic breeze, leaving not a trace of the ill-fated sailors.

Gavin Shuker, Group Convener

IT'S A scientific fact that for every atom of matter in the Universe, there is a corresponding atom of antimatter. According to physicists, such as Professor Brian Cox, should these two microscopic particles ever come into contact, they will instantly cancel each other out and cease to exist. It is my strong belief that the sailors who were aboard the Mary Celeste may have somehow met their equal and opposite antimatter counterparts whilst tucking into their dinner 500 miles East of the Azores. Reaching out to shake hands with their antimatter selves was a fatal mistake that none of them would live long enough to regret. Pop! In a nano-second all nine of them had vanished into thin air, just like a light switch being turned off.

Joan Ryan, International Developent

CEREALS, especially when stored in damp conditions such as the bilges of a ship, become an ideal breeding ground for a fungus called *Claviceps purpurea*. If ingested, this releases a powerful pyscho-hallucinogenic toxin that causes St. Anthony's Fire - a condition that instantly turns its sufferers into suicidal zombies. If the Mary Celeste's crew's Weetabix had become contaminated, the sailors would have found themselves lurching round the decks of the ship like the living dead, ripped to the tits on poisonous spores, before tossing themselves like lemmings into the freezing waters of the Atlantic Ocean to perish. It chills me and my former constituents in Enfield North just to think about this horrifying scenario.

Continued over...

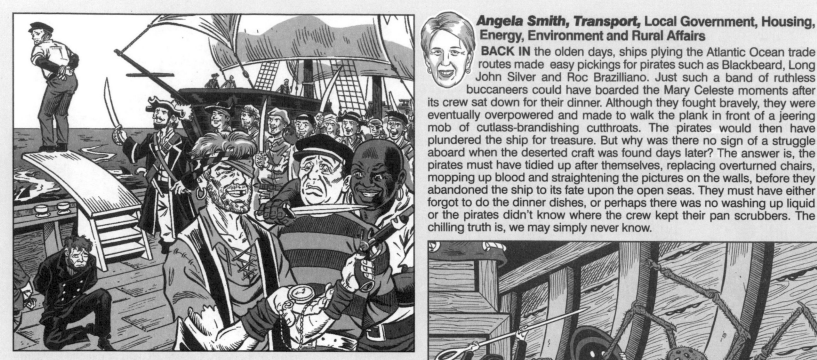

Angela Smith, Transport, Local Government, Housing, Energy, Environment and Rural Affairs

BACK IN the olden days, ships plying the Atlantic Ocean trade routes made easy pickings for pirates such as Blackbeard, Long John Silver and Roc Brazilliano. Just such a band of ruthless buccaneers could have boarded the Mary Celeste moments after its crew sat down for their dinner. Although they fought bravely, they were eventually overpowered and made to walk the plank in front of a jeering mob of cutlass-brandishing cutthroats. The pirates would then have plundered the ship for treasure. But why was there no sign of a struggle aboard when the deserted craft was found days later? The answer is, the pirates must have tidied up after themselves, replacing overturned chairs, mopping up blood and straightening the pictures on the walls, before they abandoned the ship to its fate upon the open seas. They must have either forgot to do the dinner dishes, or perhaps there was no washing up liquid or the pirates didn't know where the crew kept their pan scrubbers. The chilling truth is, we may simply never know.

Anna Soubry, Brexit & Justice

IN THE 1957 sci-fi shocker *The Incredible Shrinking Man*, Scott Carey stars as Grant Williams, a man who shrinks to the size of an ant after his boat sails through a strange, glowing cloud. Just as I believe that a hard Brexit is the wrong path for the British economy, it is my unshakeable contention that in December 1872, the Mary Celeste sailed through an identical cloud of shrinking gas. When the ship was discovered, the crew were still aboard, each of them having shrunk to just a quarter of an inch high and fallen through the gaps in the planking into the bows of the ship. It's a horrifying thought that as their rescuers paced the cabin, wondering what had become of them, these nine brave sailors were just feet away, fighting off spiders with needles for swords and buttons for shields, their anguished cries for help so high-pitched that they were only audible to bats.

Sarah Wollaston, New Colleagues

THERE were two major volcanic eruptions in 1872, at Sinarka in Russia and Mount Merapi in Indonesia, and in my opinion as former chair of the Parliamentary Health Select Committee, the combined force of these two seismic events would easily have been sufficient to wake up a Godzilla that had been slumbering peacefully under the sea since prehistoric times. Godzillas can pick up subway trains, swat airliners out of the sky and kick down blocks of flats, so the crew of a relatively small sailing ship would have been powerless to save themselves from certain oblivion. The truly worrying thing is that the next volcano to erupt could well awaken this terrifying beast once again. If that happens, heaven help the passengers and crews of any modern day ships who happen to be sailing in the vicinity.

Chuka Umunna, Group Spokesperson, Cabinet Office & Policy Coordination

OCCAM'S Razor tells us that the simplest explanation of an event is invariably the correct one. It follows from this that, if no-one was aboard the Mary Celeste when it was found, there was no-one aboard when it put to sea a month earlier. Perhaps the crew were delayed on their way to the docks and the ship sailed off without them. It happened to a mate of mine when he was on the National Express Rapide to Lincoln, and he got off to have a piss at Scotch Corner Services and the bus left before he got back.

Next Week: Where do Crop Circles come from? *The members of funk disco band* **Earth, Wind and Fire** *speculate about what causes this puzzling phenomenon.*

ITV'S "THIS MORNING" GANG in BATTLE for BRITAIN

PHIL.
HOLLY
GOK

D.J. '19

PHILLIP SCHOFIELD, HOLLY WILLOUGHBY AND GOK WAN HAD JUST FINISHED BROADCASTING ANOTHER EPISODE OF THEIR POPULAR BREAKFAST TV SHOW

GREAT SHOW, EVERYONE! SAME TIME TOMORROW!

SUDDENLY THE THREE FRIENDS WERE SURROUNDED BY A CURIOUS HUMMING VIBRATION

WH - WHAT'S HAPPENING?

WOW! SOME UNKNOWN FORCE IS WHISKING US BACK THROUGH TIME!

AND

EXCELLENT! THE TIME TELEPORTATION DEVICE HAS WORKED!

WHERE ARE WE? OR SHOULD I SAY... WHEN ARE WE?

THIS IS THE YEAR 1940, HOLLY!

WOW! IT'S WINSTON CHURCHILL, BRITAIN'S PRIME MINISTER DURING THE SECOND WORLD WAR!

YES! WORLD WAR TWO IS AT ITS HEIGHT, AND GERMAN BOMBS ARE RAINING DOWN ON LONDON.

WE HAVE TRANSPORTED YOU BACK IN TIME TO HELP US DEFEAT THE NAZI MENACE!

WE'LL BE GLAD TO HELP IN ANY WAY WE CAN, MR CHURCHILL!

SPLENDID! PROFESSOR BARNYARD WILL EXPLAIN THE SITUATION TO YOU...

IT IS OUR BELIEF THAT ADOLF HITLER'S AGGRESSIVE ATTITUDE STEMS FROM HIS FEELINGS OF LOW SELF ESTEEM.

IF HE FELT MORE POSITIVE ABOUT HIMSELF AS A PERSON, PERHAPS HE WOULD STOP INVADING OTHER COUNTRIES AND DROPPING BOMBS ON US.

AND THAT'S WHERE YOU COME IN! WE WANT GOK WAN TO GIVE HITLER A PERSONAL MAKEOVER...

...TO TRANSFORM HIM INTO A HAPPY, CONFIDENT INDIVIDUAL WHO FEELS GOOD ABOUT HIMSELF, AND NO LONGER WANTS TO EXPAND THE TERRITORIES OF THE THIRD REICH!

HOURS LATER THE "THIS MORNING" TEAM WERE BEING PARACHUTED INTO THE NAZI FUHRER'S BAVARIAN MOUNTAINTOP HEADQUARTERS

LOOK GUYS, THERE'S ADOLF HITLER!

I RECOGNISE HIM FROM HIS AWFUL HAIRSTYLE AND THAT DREADFUL UNFLATTERING OUTFIT THAT HE WEARS!

VOT ARE YOU DOING HERE? HAVE YOU COME HERE TO POKE FUN AT ME? EVERYBODY ALVAYS POKES FUN AT ME!

BUT I VILL HAVE MY REVENGE BY DECLARING WAR ON YOU ALL!

CALM DOWN, HERR HITLER — WE'RE HERE TO HELP!

YOU SEE, IF YOU VANT OTHER PEOPLE TO LIKE YOU... THEN FIRST YOU MUST LEARN TO LIKE YOURSELF!

B-BUT... HOW CAN I LIKE MYSELF?

I FEEL SO UGLY AND AWKWARD VITH ZIS RIDICULOUS HAIR AND ZESE STUPID CLOTHES!

WE'LL SOON CHANGE THAT!

WHY DON'T YOU STEP INSIDE WITH GOK, AND ALLOW HIM TO WORK HIS MAKEOVER MAGIC ON YOU!

AND SHORTLY

GOOD GRACIOUS! I WOULDN'T HAVE RECOGNISED YOU, HERR HITLER!

YOU LOOK FABULOUS!

I'VE GIVEN ADOLF A COMPLETELY NEW LOOK, WITH A WARDROBE THAT IS BOTH STYLISH AND AFFORDABLE.

JUMPER: PRIMARK £20

POLO SHIRT: GEORGE AT ASDA - £15

SLACKS: TOP MAN £25

THE TRICK IS TO CHOOSE AN OUTFIT THAT WORKS WITH YOUR NATURAL BODY SHAPE, RATHER THAN AGAINST IT.

FOR ZE FIRST TIME IN MY LIFE I AM FEELING GOOD ABOUT MYSELF!

GET ME WINSTON CHURCHILL ON ZE PHONE ~ VE MUST CANCEL ZE WAR, AND HOLD A TEA PARTY INSTEAD!

AND A FEW HOURS LATER THE "THIS MORNING" GANG WERE BACK IN BRITAIN TAKING TEA WITH WINSTON CHURCHILL AND THEIR NEW FRIEND ADOLF HITLER!

THREE CHEERS FOR PHIL, HOLLY AND GOK, FOR ENDING WORLD WAR TWO!

HOORAY!

Ignatius Manatee's Dixieland Jazz Band

Panel 1: HELLO HEADMASTER. ME AND MY DIXIELAND JAZZ BAND ARE HERE TO PLAY AT YOUR SCHOOL FETE.

I THINK YOU MUST BE MISTAKEN. IGNATIUS MANATEE'S DIXIELAND JAZZ BAND ARE ALREADY HERE AND HAVE STARTED PLAYING. LOOK.

Panel 2: GRRR! HUMBERT DUGONG'S RAGTIME BAND. I MIGHT HAVE KNOWN.

YEAH. WELL WE WERE HERE FIRST, SO YOU CAN JUST GET LOST!

Panel 3: BUT HEADMASTER, THAT BAND IS MADE UP OF DUGONGS – A COMPLETELY DIFFERENT TYPE OF SEA COW. LOOK CLOSELY AND YOU'LL SEE THAT THEY HAVE FLUKED TAILS LIKE A WHALE OR DOLPHIN. REAL MANATEES HAVE PADDLE-SHAPED TAILS LIKE MINE!

Panel 4: HMMM. THEY LOOK OKAY TO ME.

BAD LUCK IGNATIUS. WE'VE STUFFED OUR FLUKED TAILS INTO DUFFLE BAGS SO THEY LOOK JUST LIKE YOURS. CACKLE!

Panel 5: THEN, JUST LISTEN TO THE MUSIC THEY'RE PLAYING, HEADMASTER. IT'S RAGTIME – AN EARLY FORM OF JAZZ, BUT PIANO-LED USING MAINLY MARCHING RHYTHMS. OUR DIXIELAND IS DIFFERENT, WITH THE WIND INSTRUMENTS PLAYING IMPROVISED COUNTER-MELODIES OVER THE MAIN TUNE.

Panel 6: HA! HA! THE HEADMASTER HAS NO EAR FOR MUSIC. TO HIM IT ALL SOUNDS LIKE A RACKET! ANYWAY, IT'S TIME WE HAD A BREAK FOR SOME REFRESHMENTS.

NOT A CLUE.

Panel 7: B-BUT YOU'VE ONLY BEEN PLAYING FOR FIVE MINUTES!

DON'T BLAME ME – IT'S SEA COW MUSICIANS' UNION RULES.

Panel 8: ER...OKAY. HERE ARE THE ALGAE COCKTAILS YOU ASKED FOR IN YOUR RIDER.

ERK!

Panel 9: DRINK UP FELLAS. I KNOW HOW MANATEES LOVE A BIT OF ALGAE. NOT LIKE DUGONGS WHOSE DIET IS EXCLUSIVELY SEA GRASS.

RETCH! GLUC!

Panel 10: TITTER! HUMBERT'S BAND HAVE ALL GOT THE SQUITS. THEY WON'T TRY TO STEAL OUR GIGS AGAIN. WE'LL TAKE IT FROM HERE, HEADMASTER. A- ONE, A-TWO, A-ONE, TWO, THREE, FOUR...

GURGLE! PFFT! BOYS

BREXIT CONCERN FOR MILLENNIALS

UNCERTAINTY over the future of the economy after Britain's exit from the European Union has been a cause of great concern for many people. Individuals, organisations and businesses throughout the country have expressed their frustration over the lack of detail which has left them unable to plan for the future.

But the biggest uncertainty has been suffered by the millennial generation. Fragile, easily offended and unable to comprehend anything unless it involves the internet, these late teens and twenty-somethings have found themselves disproportionately affected by Brexit.

voice

"So, I've got this app, and according to that I have, like, a gluten intolerance?" explained millennial Jessie Cavalry, her voice going up at the end so it sounded like a question. "So, you know, I'm concerned that Brexit might be a bit, like, problematic for me?"

Still looking at her mobile phone, she continued: "Also, there are, like,

EXCLUSIVE!

implications for my mental health that have to be taken into consideration?"

Fellow millennial Harvey Dexter discovered he was lacto-gluten-soy intolerant after taking a multiple choice test on Facebook. "So, I shared the test with my 15,486 friends, and all of them turned out to be lacto-gluten-soy intolerant," he revealed. "It could only have been brought on by Brexit."

"And the same test revealed that if I was a *Guardians of the Galaxy* character, I'd be Yondo Udonata," he added.

Student and gluten-intolerent millennial Cressida de la Torte said

the government had a duty to inform the electorate about the gluten status of a post-Brexit Britain. "So, I'm worried that all this negativity may be exacerbating my mental health issues?" she told reporters whilst 'liking' a post on twitter and drinking a £7.50 cup of coffee.

cloamp

"I mean, the other day a comedian made a joke about millennials being unable to punctuate or something, I can't remember, which I found deeply, deeply offensive? So I had to go and lie down for a while."

And she had stern words for the Prime Minister and his plans for a full-gluten crash out of the EU.

"So, we definitely need a second referendum when we know what the gluten status of Brexit will be, and if the deal had been organised in the presence of nuts. Because I'm allergict to nuts, too," she said.

"I didn't actually vote in the first referendum. I mean, I meant

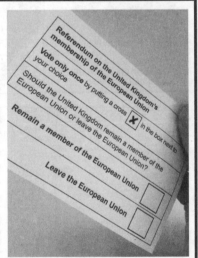

Leave it out: Referendum result has left many millennials floundering.

to, and if I had I would definitely have voted to, like, remain or something? But someone sent me this meme on Instagram, and it put me off," she added.

IT'S A WHALE WASHED UP ON THE BEACH.

MY BEST YEARS ARE BEHIND ME NOW.

I ABSOLUTELY love bells. In fact, I love them so much that I've even had one fitted... on my front door! This so-called 'door bell' makes a lovely ringing sound every time someone presses it, giving my visitors a melodic reminder that they're about to step into the home of a self-confessed bell fanatic!

Agnes Psychopath, Hulme-on-the-Wold

I FIND it utterly ridiculous that 'bell peppers' are so-called. They don't make a ringing sound when struck, you rarely see them in church towers, and they're literally never used to sound the alarm or commemorate important events. In fact, the only thing even vaguely bell-like about them is that they're shaped like bells. Honestly, the sooner we leave the European Union the better.

Oliver Reaction, Chipping Norton

I OWN a shop called Doorbellz'R'Us, which sells nothing but doorbells. Amusingly, though, the shop itself... doesn't have a doorbell! This fact never fails to make me wet myself with laughter whenever I think about it, which is roughly every ten to fifteen seconds during waking hours.

Jerry Suffering-Christ, Frome

BRITAIN'S JINGLIEST BELL FORUM, HOSTED BY BUSTY, BELL-OBSESSED NATIONAL TREASURE DAME HELEN MIRREN

HEL'S BELLS

Hi. DAME HELEN MIRREN here. You'll know me from pretending to be The Queen in exchange for money, but what you WON'T know about me is that I'm absolutely bonkers about BELLS. That's right - I simply can't get enough of these melodious directly struck idiophones that are found in the Hornbostel-Sachs system of musical instrument classification. And judging by the size of my Hel's Bells postbag, you lot are pretty fucking keen on them, too! So, without further ado, I think it's about 'chime' I gave a 'ringing' endorsement to some of your 'bell-issima' letters about bells. *Jingliest regards, Dame Hel xx*

IT makes me incandescent with rage when I hear people referring to the iconic Palace of Westminster clock tower as 'Big Ben'. As anyone with more than two brain cells knows, it is the *bell* within the tower that's called Big Ben, not the tower itself! Correcting people when they make this idiotic mistake is probably my most cherished pastime – alongside watching old black-and-white horror films. My favourite is the one about that terrifying monster, Frankenstein, and his creator, whose name currently escapes me.

Jeremy Chives, Hammersmith

I USED to make a very good living performing repairs and maintenance on broken, directly struck tintinnabulae. However, I quit that job last month to teach yoga at a high-profile gym, where my A-List client roster includes ex-*Bake Off* host Mel Giedroyc, comedy icon Mel Brooks and House of Lords leftie Melvyn Bragg. So, I suppose you could say – if you wanted to – that I used to 'mend bells', but now I 'bend Mels'.

Sebastian Ghostface, Stamford Brook

I CAN see Mr Ghostface's letter (*above*), and raise him. You see, I used to be a door-to-door salesman of campanulate musical instruments, but I took early retirement last year to divide my time between prank-calling the vaguely well known comedian Tony Hawks, and writing online diary-style text entries about mountain ranges. So I suppose you could say – if you so wished – that I used to 'hawk bells' but now I 'bell Hawks'. And I suppose you could also say – if you further desired – that I used to 'flog bells' but now I 'blog fells'. Perhaps Mr Ghostface would like to stick that in his fucking pipe and smoke it.

B Raekwon, Ravenscourt Pk

THESE so-called 'disabled' scroungers living off state benefits would do well to take a leaf out of Quasimodo's book. That guy was genuinely unfit for work, but did he lie around on the sofa all day sponging off his nation's green and pleasant taxpayers? No, he did not. He rolled up his sleeves and found a respectable full-time job as a bell-ringer in one of Europe's top cathedrals. Yes, he eventually went deaf and insane as a result, but I'd rather be deaf and insane than a whingeing snowflake remoaner.

R Littlejohn, Florida

I AM the Abbot of a small monastery, and I noticed recently that the bottom bit of our prayer bell – called the 'sound bow' – had a large crack through it. Seeing the opportunity for an amusing anecdote for your letters page, I asked one of my monks to nip out and get us another "bell end". I was literally screaming with laughter as I pictured Brother Barnabas humourously misinterpreting this order and returning a few hours later with either Piers Morgan, Rod Liddle or Bono in tow! Imagine my anger and despair, though, when he just came back with a new sound bow for the bell. I confronted him to express my disappointment, whereupon he explained that as a monk he lives a fairly sheltered life, and was unaware that the term "bell end" had a vulgar double meaning. I have since expelled him from the monastery and am currently petitioning the Pope to have him excommunicated.

Abbot Francis McGinley, Waterford

WITH reference to the above letter (*above*), I've always thought that being a monk sounds like an absolute piece of fucking piss. All you do all day is ring a few bells and read a load of daft old shite about angels and whatnot. Monks should try doing a proper day's work if they want to be taken seriously.

R Dawkins, Oxford

EVERYONE goes on about how "clever" Alexander Graham Bell was for inventing the telephone. But it was hardly a huge stretch of the imagination when a major component of his invention was right there in his surname! All he had to do was glance down at his birth certificate or signature, and bingo – the inspiration was there. If my name was 'Anthony Penicillin' or 'Anthony Steam-Turbine', then I probably would have come up with a world-changing innovation, too. But as it is, I've done the thick end of fuck all with my life. As usual, it's one rule for people whose surnames provide an obvious clue for what they should be trying to invent, and another for the rest of us.

Tony Curefor-Cancer, Hove

AS the new Poet Laureate, the first thing Her Majesty the Queen has asked me to do is write a poem about bells, in case there's ever a National Bell Day. This is my first official ode since landing the big job, so I was a bit nervous, but I think it turned out OK – apart from the last line which I'm well aware doesn't quite work. Constructive feedback would be welcomed at s.armitage@poet-laureate. co.uk, or you can get in touch on Twitter, where my handle is @RhyminSimon63. Anyway, here goes:

'Bells' by Simon Armitage (2019)

They jingle, they jangle, they peal and they chime,

They tell us where cows are and what is the time.

They warned us in old days when lepers were near,

You'll hear them go mental when it's the New Year.

You find them on bikes and on sleighs and on doors,

But also on churches and on stock market floors.

So, what are these wonderful, marvellous things?

You've guessed it – they're BELLS, and they rings, rings and rings!

S Armitage, Yorkshire

REGARDING the above letter (*above*), I was Poet Laureate for a few years before Mr Armitage took over, and Her Majesty the Queen also asked me to write a bell poem on the off-chance that National Bell Day became a thing. I thought I'd sent it over in 2016, but I've just checked my email to see that it's been stuck in my outbox this whole time. I'm copying it here below, just in case Her Majesty is reading and she prefers my one to Mr Armitage's:

'Bells' by Carol Ann Duffy (2016)

'B' is for 'Bong' – the sound that they make

'E' is for 'Early' – they chime and we wake

'L' is for 'Last orders' - hear the bell ring!

'L' is for see above - same fucking thing

'S' is for 'Santa' - with bells on his sleigh...

The same bells that jingle upon Christmas Day!

CA Duffy, Manchester

BELL-Y LAUGHS!

We're 'clappers' about your YOUR hysterical bell wisecracks!

Q: What is Charlotte Church's favourite kind of bell?
A: A Church bell

J Seinfeld, New York

Q: What is Jim Morrison's favourite kind of bell?
A: A Door(s) bell (Morrison was lead singer of *The Doors*)

D Letterman, New York

Q: What is John Wayne Gacy's favourite kind of bell?
A: A Sleigh bell (like 'slay', meaning 'to kill' because Gacy was a mass murderer)

P Kay, Bolton

Q: What do you call a former BBC Breakfast presenter that makes a melodious vibrating sound when directly struck?
A: Bell Turnbull (Bill Turnbull)

B Turnbull, London

Q: What do you call a BBC Breakfast weather presenter that makes a melodious vibrating sound when directly struck?
A: Carillon Kirkwood (A carillon is a musical instrument comprised of 23 cast bronze bells, and it sounds a bit like 'Carol', as in Carol Kirkwood)

B Turnbull, London

We have SUCH a giggle reading your barmy bell jokes! Do keep sending them in. Every one we print wins a lifetime's supply of money, food and property for you and twenty-six friends.

It's 10 Things You Never Knew... About Bells!

1 THE WORD 'bell' is derived from the Anglo-Saxon word *'bell'*, meaning 'bell'.

2 THERE have been countless hit songs about bells over the years, from **LL COOL J**'s *Rock The Bells* and **METALLICA**'s *For Whom The Bell Tolls*, to **AC/DC**'s *Hell's Bells* and **RADIOHEAD**'s *Morning Bell*. In fact, so ubiquitous are bells as a subject in popular music that experts believe songwriters should leave them alone for a bit. "Bells have been done to fucking death," says chartologist Paul Gambaccini. "There's literally nothing more to say about them. Musicians should give it a rest with the whole bells thing because, honestly, we're all getting sick of it."

3 SOME musical acts - such as **BELLE & SEBASTIAN** and **PATTI LABELLE** - love bells so much they have even chosen to *name themselves after them*. "Jesus fucking wept," says Gambaccini. "What is wrong with these people? We get it, okay, you like bells."

4 THE SMALLEST set of bells in recorded history belonged to the world's smallest hunchback, Calvin Phillips. Phillips was employed as a deformed-yet-kind-hearted bellringer inside a matchstick scale model of Notre-Dame Cathedral. His job was to ring the minuscule bells - each roughly the size of a large raspberry - every hour on the hour, whilst shrieking, "The minuscule bells! The minuscule bells!" over and over again. Phillips eventually went deaf and insane, and died of starvation beneath a gallows the size of a Subbuteo goal.

5 THE BICYCLE bell was invented by none other than Italian polymath **LEONARDO DA VINCI** back in October 1496. In his notebooks, the Renaissance genius wrote: "I have today fashioned an ingenious metallic tocsin that can be attached to a bicycle in order to alert other bicycle users to one's presence." However, in his excitement over his new gadget, da Vinci failed to remember... *that the bicycle hadn't been invented yet!* As such, initial sales for the bell were poor, and it wasn't until the invention of the penny farthing in the mid-1800s that his creation really began to take off.

6 WE ALL know that **JAY KAY** out of **JAMIROQUAI** loves big hats. But you probably didn't know that the Space Cowboy acquired this taste for outsized millinery... *by getting his head stuck in a bell!* At age 12, the adolescent pop fave was visiting Tewkesbury Abbey with his parents, Cilla Black impersonator Karen Kay and her husband Mr Kay, when he trapped his noggin inside a prayer bell whilst examining the internal clapper. His bonce was stuck fast, but rather than cry out for help, the experience awoke something inside the youngster, and he began prancing around the church with the bell on his head, entertaining worshippers with improvised cod-funk warbling. The bell was later removed by doctors but young Jay was smitten. He went straight out to buy the most bell-resembling head accessory he could find... and the rest is acid jazz history!

7 THE PROUD owner of the world's largest collection of bells is none other than iconic gangsta rap star **P DIDDY**. Harlem-born Diddy, real name Peapod Diddybridge, has amassed roughly 43,000 directly struck campanulate instruments of all shapes and sizes, which he keeps in a big padlocked warehouse in Carlisle. "I love bells - always have, always will," Diddy told the *Northampton Chronicle & Echo*. "Honestly, when I hear those big metal muthafuckers chimin' away, it just makes my heart soar."

8 WHEN you ring a bell here in the UK, it goes 'ding-dong'. But believe it or not, when you ring one in Australia, the sound it makes is *'dong-ding'*! That's because the rotation of the earth means that sound travels in a clockwise direction in the Northern hemisphere and counterclockwise in the Southern one. This is also the reason that everyone in Australia talks backwards, like in *Twin Peaks*.

9 MANY actors from the hit series *Twin Peaks* have spoken openly about their love of bells. *Twin Peaks* actors who adore bells include **PEGGY LIPTON**, who played Norma, **SHERILYN FENN**, who played Audrey, and **FRANK SILVER**, who played Killer Bob.

10 *TWIN PEAKS* actors who despise bells include **JACK NANCE**, who played Pete, **KIMMY ROBERTSON**, who played Lucy, and **CATHERINE E. COULSON**, who played the Log Lady.

SAVED BY THE BELL!

Billy Elliot actor JAMIE BELL answers YOUR life-threatening bell-based queries

Dear Jamie, **I AM** standing underneath a clock tower and have just looked up to see that a large bell has come loose from its yoke and is falling rapidly towards me. What do you think is the best course of action?

Arthur Neardeath, Tintern

Jamie says: *"This is a tough one, Arthur, as I don't know the dimensions of the bell in question. Some clock tower bells are easily large enough to contain a fully-grown human within their hollow central chamber, meaning they could land on you without even leaving a scratch, as long as the clapper doesn't hit you. However, since I don't have all the details in front of me, I think the safest thing for you to do is to run quickly out of the way before the bell hits the ground. Congratulations: you've just been Saved By The Bell."*

Dear Jamie, **I AM** a Mafia 'snitch' and I have just been hurled into a river with a large church bell tied to my ankle. I am sinking fast, and was wondering if you had any tips on how I might live to see another day.

Paulie 'The Snitch' Carcasso, New Jersey

Jamie says: *"First things first, Paulie: don't panic. Evidence indicates that gasping, thrashing and swimming hard are the absolute worst things you can do in this situation, as they increase the chances of water entering your lungs, which then further reduces your buoyancy. Instead, simply remain calm and undo your belt. As you descend into the murky depths, use the spiky bit on your belt buckle to saw through the rope attaching the bell to your ankle. Once the rope breaks and the bell is loose, swim straight to the surface and take a large breath of life-giving oxygen. Congratulations: you've just been Saved By The Bell."*

Dear Jamie, **AS I WRITE** this, I am choking to death on a large chunk of bell pepper. My wife tells me I have turned blue and I am finding it increasingly hard to breathe. Do you have any advice on how I might be able to survive this experience?

Nicholas Gointo-Thelight, Nuneaton

Jamie says: *"I do indeed, Nicholas. With your remaining breath, you should ask your wife to perform the 'Heimlich Manoeuvre' on you. If she doesn't know how, simply tell her to Google 'How to do the Heimlich Manoeuvre', and then perform it. If she does it correctly, you should be coughing up the offending bell pepper chunk within seconds and beginning to breathe again normally soon afterwards. Congratulations: you've just been Saved By The Bell."*

*Are **YOU** about to die because of a bell, or in a way that somehow relates to bells? Why not write in to:* **'Saved By The Bell' c/o Jamie Bell off Billy Elliot, Viz Comic, PO Box 841, Whitley Bay, NE26 9EQ**

BELL BLOOPERS

Big screen campanogulous cock-ups, with bell-loving movie fanatic *Mark Commode*

● **IN THE** 1984 comedy film **GHOSTBUSTERS**, we see the team's receptionist, Janine, sounding a loud bell after the Ghostbusters receive their first callout about a disorderly ghost. However, eagle-eyed viewers will have spotted a major blooper in this much-loved scene – *Ghosts don't actually exist!* The film's red-faced producers only spotted the cock-up when the final cut was already completed, and so the movie was distributed with this glaring error included. *D'oh!*

● **IN THE** Oscar-winning 1995 classic **BRAVEHEART**, William Wallace (Mel Gibson) approaches the castle of the evil Prince Edward, in order to challenge the English regent to battle. The film is set in 1297, and yet Wallace announces his arrival by pressing what is clearly an *electric doorbell* next to the castle's portcullis. To make matters worse, the doorbell plays the tune of *Miami 2 Ibiza* by Tinie Tempah, which was not even recorded until 2010.

● **THE MOST** memorable action scene in the 2008 James Bond film **QUANTUM OF SOLACE** sees 007 (Daniel Craig) push a Special Branch bodyguard (Paul Ritter) off a bell tower while the bells ring out around them. Believe it or not, though, this whole sequence is just *one long blooper!* In the script, the scene was supposed to feature only calm dialogue over the gentle chiming of the bells. But on the day of filming, Craig was furious with Ritter for eating the last Nobbly Bobbly ice lolly from the catering truck, and he lashed out angrily mid-scene. The two toppled off the bell tower and straight through a glass roof 50ft below. Instead of calling 'cut', director Marc Foster kept the cameras rolling as the pair continuing to scrap violently – and the blood-spattered 'blooper' ended up being included in the final film.

● **WE ALL** remember the iconic scene in drug drama **BREAKING BAD** when meth dealer Hector Salamanca kills his arch-rival Gus Fring by detonating a bomb attached to the bell on his wheelchair. However, there were red faces all round when it became clear that *Breaking Bad* is actually a **TV SERIES**, not a film – and therefore has no place being mentioned in this column. *#FacePalm!*

More bell-based silver screen balls-ups next time, bell-fans!

Mark x

LUCKY FRANK

Panel 1: YOINK! I'VE FOUND A PORNO MAG UNDER A HEDGE, JUST LIKE YOU WOULD IN THE OLDEN DAYS!
GLOSSY GLEAM
HOW LUCKY!

Panel 2: OH YARK! IT'S A PARTICULARLY "SPECIALIST" FORM OF PORN, CONSISTING OF PICTURES OF THE THIRD-RATE JOURNALIST **TOBY YOUNG** DISPLAYING HIS UNAPPETISING GENITALIA!
WHAT A DEEPLY DISAPPOINTING STROKE OF BAD LUCK!

Panel 3: HOLD THAT HORRIFIED FACIAL EXPRESSION, PLEASE...
CLICK!
PERFECT!
WHIRRR!
YOWP! AND HERE'S TOBY YOUNG HIMSELF, WITH A POLAROID CAMERA!

Panel 4: AS A COLUMNIST FOR THE SPECTATOR MAGAZINE, I GET AROUSED BY THE THOUGHT OF PEOPLE BEING SHOCKED BY MY FORTHRIGHT OPINIONS...
...AND YOU'RE CERTAINLY LOOKING PRETTY SHOCKED BY THE PICTURES OF MY "COLUMN" IN THAT PORN MAG!

Panel 5: I WILL NOW GO HOME AND MASTURBATE OVER THIS POLAROID PHOTO OF YOUR APPALLED FACE.
PLEASE ACCEPT £100 FOR GIVING A BRIEF SENSE OF PURPOSE TO MY PATHETIC EXISTENCE.
YOINKS!

Panel 6: SHORTLY
I SPENT THAT HUNDRED QUID ON A SEX ROBOT WHICH WILL PERFORM EROTIC ACTS LIVE, RIGHT IN FRONT OF MY EYES!
SEX SHOP
BLEEP! WHIRR!

Panel 7: WHEEEEEEE-
CRUNCH!
YIBBLE! A METEORITE HAS FLATTENED MY SEX ROBOT!
TALK ABOUT UNLUCKY! THE ODDS AGAINST THAT HAPPENING MUST BE ASTRONOMICAL!

Panel 8: SORRY ABOUT THAT! I AM AN ECCENTRIC ALIEN BILLIONAIRE FROM OUTER SPACE, AND THIS IS MY METEORITE!
PLEASE ACCEPT ONE MILLION SPACE QUIDS AS COMPENSATION!
YOINKS!

To the Edge of the Molar System

One small check-up for man: The lunar surface will soon see its first dental patients.

BRITAIN'S DENTISTS are launching an ambitious plan to push themselves into the Space Age, and give their reputations a thorough clean and polish into the bargain. And what better way to do it by opening up a dental practice... *on the Moon!*

Britain to put first dentists on the Moon

"Dentistry needs to move with the times," said chairman of the Society of British Dentists, Dr Tony Award. "We've been sticking our hands in people's mouths and fiddling painfully with their teeth, using largely the same equipment as we always have, for a hundred years."

"Our profession needs a rocket up its backside, and a lunar-based dental clinic is just what the British public is crying out for," he added.

practice

And the professional body is not wasting any time putting their ambitious plan into practice, aiming to put the first dentists on the Moon by March of next year.

Dr Award was quick to point out the benefits of an off-world dental clinic.

district

"This plan is potentially limitless," he told *Orthodontics* magazine. "Getting to the lunar dentist for an appointment would cost in the region of £60 million on a rocket, but once there, a basic check-up, scale and polish would cost just £120, the same as at a terrestrial dentist. And any NHS patients will continue to be subsidised."

"Also, patients will be able to pick up a bit of moon rock outside the surgery and take it home with them as a souvenir," he added.

The first lunar rocket, carrying three dentists, two dental hygienists, a receptionist and dental equipment, together with a pile of out-of-date magazines, is scheduled for launch in late February, and the clinic is expected to open for business on the Moon just 10 days later.

season

And Dr Award says he is expecting a rush of new patients eager to experience painful dental procedures in an atmosphere-free lunar environment.

"Imagine how relaxing it will be having your teeth drilled in a gravitational pull just one sixth that of the Earth, or having root canal work done in a crater 181 miles across. It will add a whole new dimension to a trip to the dentist," he said.

y blinders

But according to Award, a trip to the lunar dentist will be remarkably familiar in one respect.

"That slightly warm, minty, pink stuff we give you to swill your mouth with will be exactly the same," he said.

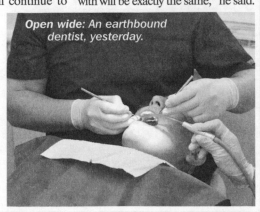

Open wide: An earthbound dentist, yesterday.

Robin Hood and his Merrie Men

Oh Robin, the Goose Fair! How exciting!

Yes, but we must take care, Maid Marion. The Sheriff has a bounty on my head and his men are everywhere.

MOUSE TOWN

You look like a fine shot, sir! Three arrows for a groat. Hit any playing card and win a cuddly toy!

Robin! Look at the size of that panda! Can you win it for me?

SNAKE LADY

A hundred groats if not alive

WIN ME

Why of course, Marion!

I am Sir Robin of Loxley, the finest shot in the land! It would be a mere trifle, m'lady.

Here's a groat, my good fellow. I shall take three shots...!

Not that I shall need the second two.

Woah-oh-oh-oh... You can't use your own equipment, sire.

You what?

You've got to use the bows and arrows provided.

What?... Those?

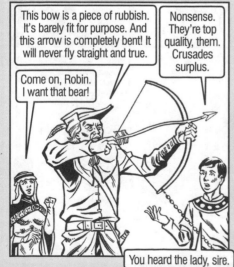

This bow is a piece of rubbish. It's barely fit for purpose. And this arrow is completely bent! It will never fly straight and true.

Nonsense. They're top quality, them. Crusades surplus.

Come on, Robin. I want that bear!

You heard the lady, sire.

Ballocks!

Never mind, sir. Happens to the best of us. You've still got two arrows remaining.

FLOT!

Take your time, sire.

Ooh, You nearly had it that time, sir.

P-FLUTTER!

For God's sake!

This bow is crap. And that arrow was bent like a dog's back leg!

'Tis a poor workman who blames his tools, sire...

... Here's your final arrow.

Keep your left arm straight, sire ...lock your elbow ...that's it... don't release your fingers, just slacken your grip and allow the bow to do the work...

Yes, thank you, I know how to do it! I'm the finest shot in the fucking kingdom!

If you say so, sire...

THUCK!

Yes! Geddin!

Ooh! Bad luck, sire!

Eh!?! What do you mean, bad luck? It's hit the card, clear as day! Now give my lady her prize.

No, It's nicked the card, sire. To win, the hole has to be completely within the edge of the card. That's the rule.

You didn't tell me that!

It's there in the Ts & Cs, sire!

How am I supposed to read that from here?! And most peasants are illiterate anyway, so they couldn't read the fucker if they COULD see it.

Robin, you're making a scene. Let's just go.

No!

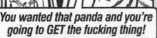
You wanted that panda and you're going to GET the fucking thing!

Give me another three arrows!

I'll show you, you fucking robdog.

K-THWOCK!

Geddin! How d'you like them fucking apples?!

Excellent shot, sire. Well done.

...and here is your prize.

Eh?...

No... I want that one. The big one. It says "Win Me"

Ooh no. Didn't you read the terms and conditions, sire? They're clearly on display for all to see.

What a fucking rip-off! Somebody ought to report you to the Sheriff of Nottingham!

WIN ME.
This bear is for advertising purposes only. Actual prize constitutes a much smaller bear.

Why don't you do it yourself... Robin Hood?!

Gasp!

...because I'm right here!

Guards... SEIZE HIM!

Next Week: Robin escapes from the Sheriff's clutches and goes to the Hook-a-Duck stall, where he is short-changed and discovers that all the ducks with prizes have hooks that are slightly too large to fit through the loop on the end of his stick.

SHOE SHOP SALE WARS

One day... Heh heh! Booking the local BBC weatherman to open my sale was the best twenty quid I've ever spent.

WINTER SHOE SALE 50% OFF SELECTED SHOES TO BE OPENED MONDAY BY LOCAL BBC WEATHERMAN PAUL MOONEY

A *local* weatherman, is it? It's a pity you didn't splash out £50 and get a *nationally* recognised face, Tunnock.

Ho-ho! **Bah!**

SALE STARTS MONDAY TO BE OPENED BY NATIONAL BBC WEATHERMAN TOMASZ SCHAFERNAKER

He's right! I'm going to cancel that local telly nobody and get someone with *real* star quality to open my sale...

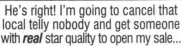

...that'll show that old wind-bag next door!

So... ...no, I'm afraid Tom Cruise is unavailable on that date... the same goes for Scarlett Johansson and Whoopie Goldberg.

What about somebody out of Star Wars? Him what plays the baddy or something, or the Princess one with the metal bra?

No...

...she died a couple of years ago.

What about Sean Connery, or maybe Diana Ross...or Clint Eastwood?

Clint Eastwood... Ooh yes! I like him...

I can see it now... *"Save a Fistful of Dollars at the Tunnock's Shoe Sale..."*...*" Do you feel lucky, Punk? You will at the Tunnock Shoe sale..."*

...How much?

He's $750,000 for a standard shoe shop opening. Plus first class air travel from LAX and 5-star hotel accommodation for Mr Eastwood and his entourage of approximately 15 hangers-on...

You're looking at about a million and a half dollars, give or take...

By 'eck! But look at it this way, Mr Tunnock...Mr Eastwood has got 4 Oscars...

...how many has Paul Mooney got?

Aye..., well, you've got a point, I suppose...

Go on... I'll book him.

You won't regret it, Mr Tunnock.

Monday... It sure is quiet, Mr Tunnock.

Don't worry, Mr Eastwood, here comes the press now...

OSCAR-WINNING SPAGHETTI WESTERN STAR CLINT EAST... SALE OPENING!

Get ready to cut the ribbon...

Ladies and gentlemen... it Makes My Day to declare the Tunnocks Shoes Winter Sale officially...

What the...!?!

SALE OPENING

Sorry, Tunnock...Schafernaker pulled out, so I booked these two instead.

Heh! Heh!

THOMAS PROUT SHOE SALE GRAND TODAY BY KIM KARDASHIAN & KANYE WEST

I now declare the Thomas Prout Bootylicious shoe sale open!

"Kanye" believe the muthafuckin' savings on wellies, slippers and kiddies' school shoes?

Viz Comic, P.O. Box 841 Whitley Bay, NE26 9EQ ★ letters@viz.co.uk

ST★R LETTER

HOW come, when lion cubs grow up a bit and go off on their own, they don't recognise their brothers and sisters when they meet them a couple of years later and end up scrapping like fuck? Our kid was banged away for twenty years, and I recognised him as soon as he got out. Alright, we had a scrap too, but that's irrelevant.

Stan Pastry, Goole

I LOVE Hot Cross Buns at Easter. But if they changed the name to Hot Cross Arseholes, it would put me right off them. So come on, bakers, please don't change our buns!

Alex Du Singe, Lincoln

IT'S ridiculous how much these Premier League football players get paid. When I was at primary school, our matches only lasted 30 minutes and results like 12-2 and 8-6 were not uncommon; I even remember one match resulting in an impressive 23-14 victory. Those games were far better value than the boring 1-0 results you regularly get in the Premier League. Let's start broadcasting school matches instead, and pay the kids what they are worth.

Arthur Shitface, Kettering

SO much for the Oscars rewarding the best actors. Every one of them who wins starts crying during their acceptance speech. A decent actor would be able to pretend they weren't overcome by emotion and play the part with a straight face without so much as a quiver. Great actors? Shite more like.

David McNally, Glossop

I'VE just been reading up on sex addiction. I didn't even realise it was an actual thing, but it sounds great to me.

James Wallace, Belper

MY local sports shop has a whole section of clubs dedicated to left-handed golfers, yet none for us right-handed players. Once again, we see big business pandering to the left-handed minority.

Mr S Andrews, Bristol

WHY is it that only the teams at the top or the bottom of a football league are allowed to play in these so called 'six pointers'? It hardly seems fair on the teams that are mid-table.

Damo, sunny Guernsey

IF I fell into a barrel full of tits, I think I'd actually rather come out sucking my own thumb. Either way it sounds like a deeply harrowing experience.

Gustav Fox, Haggerston

THE other day my wife started walking up the stairs saying, "I'm just going…" and I immediately said "…for a shit." She seemed really cross, in spite of the fact that I was right. Having sat through a lot of romcoms, I was under the impression that finishing your wife's sentences was really romantic and a sign of the close bond between you, but I'm obviously wrong.

Richard Curtis, York

SCOTTISH people are always complaining about being stereotyped, but they could make life a lot easier for themselves by not wearing kilts, drinking copious amounts of whisky, eating porridge and tossing cabers all day. They're not really meeting us half way.

Hughie Dixon, W.Drayton

IF Whoopi Goldberg married Peter Cushing, she would have made a very foolish decision as he has been dead since 1994.

Peter Busby, W. Australia

I'M glad that the world was made the way up it is. Great Britain would look shit if it was upside down with Scotland at the bottom.

Jeremey Beatle, Hampton

FOR any younger readers wondering what old men of 65-70, like me and my mates, talk about all day, it's usually how big the weather girl's nipples might be, and how perfect Rachel Riley's arse is. That's about it really.

Austin, Markfield

DO people still shag each other in haystacks, or is that another thing consigned to history?

Stuie, Bunny

GIVEN that our parliamentary system is based on the allocation of seats in the House of Commons, why do we often see so many people standing on the floored area? It seems that somebody needs to have a recount of available seats, then either buy some more in or get rid of a few MPs.

M Ripley, Altrincham

MY mate Muffy works in a soap factory, and he reckons if you put the soap with the arched bit facing upwards, it will never slide into the bath. He's a bit of a bullshitter but I'm going to try it. The trouble is, it's Tuesday, and my bath night isn't until Sunday. If someone else tries it before then, could they let me know how they get on?

Gordon Bennett, Auckland

I JUST watched a documentary that put forward the theory that Elvis is still alive, as he left all sorts of clues on his gravestone. The film-makers also noted that his name is an anagram of "lives". If that's not another clue I don't know what is.

Mal Alcock, email

✱ You didn't state what the gravestone clues were, Mr Alcock, but if they convinced you, they must have been compelling and thought-provoking evidence. Did any other readers see the same documentary, and if so did it convince YOU that Elvis is alive and well? Or perhaps you've seen the King himself and snapped a picture that you could send us to prove his continued existence beyond doubt. No lookalikes, please, just genuine photos of the actual, living Elvis.

I DON'T get this Easter egg hunt business, whereby adults frustrate children by hiding the chocolate eggs. Surely, if they want to prank the kids, wouldn't it be better to tell them that the Easter Bunny was caught and eaten by a fox and there are no Easter Eggs this year at all? It worked for me with Father Christmas and the reindeer mauling, and I saved a fucking bomb.

Frank Ocarina, Tring

PSYCHIC Doris Stokes famously contacted the dead and passed on their messages to grieving relatives. She herself crossed over in 1987, yet in the last 32 years nobody has heard a fucking word from her. Once again, it's one rule for fraudulent pensioners and another for the genuine dead.

Pearl Barley, Truro

MY mate Eric walks like John Wayne as he suffers from chronic, throbbing haemorrhoids, and he has applied to be an astronaut as he believes the zero gravity of space will render his farmers weightless. However, I think he should train as a deep sea diver as the pressure will ease them back up into the bomb bay. Can *Viz* shed some light on who may be correct before it's too late?

John Martin, email

THERE'S a builders' glue called "Sticks Like Sh*t", but I've found that shit isn't actually that sticky. However, Weetabix certainly is, so they would be better off calling their product "Sticks Like Weetabix". In fact why don't builders just use Weetabix instead? Believe me, that stuff really does stick like shit.

Dewson, Poole

AFTER I ate three bowls of stewed prunes the other day, my elderly nan told me that I'd be 'shitting through the eye of a needle'. However, she couldn't have been more wrong. If anything, my shitting was much less precise than usual. In fact it went everywhere.

Chris Heatho, Chorlton

IN this day and age, I don't know why sport has to be divided between men's and women's events. Trust me, I've seen some women giving men a good thrashing outside Wetherspoons on a Wednesday afternoon.

Brian, Ross-on-Wye

MY wife and I often wonder what snooker might be like in the future. My wife considers it likely that there will be a robot referee, with the players using lasers instead of cues. I think they may use fundamental particles instead of a cue ball, so players can impart quantum spin. They couldn't use a Higgs boson obviously, because as the first scalar elementary particle discovered in nature, it has no spin. What do your readers think?

Phil Kitching, Isle of Jura

* Sorry, Mr Kitching, we were with you up to the robot referees and laser cues, but you lost us when you started talking about Higgs bosons having no spin. Perhaps Professor Brian Cox or somebody like him could write in and tell us what they think snooker will be like in the future. Mark your envelope or email subject "I'm Brian Cox or somebody like him".

WHAT'S wrong with these people who turn up to all these "Yellow Vest" protests? If they don't like the vests, then they shouldn't wear them. Nobody is fucking forcing them, are they?

Billy Odes, Hull

WHEN Americans meet members of their armed forces, they always say, "Thank you for your service." I'm not suggesting we do the same, but perhaps if we said it to motor mechanics when we go to pick up our cars, they might feel a bit more appreciated and maybe stop ripping us off so much.

Bartram Trentby, Luton

CAN people who are selling their TVs on Facebook Marketplace please take a photo of it with some hardcore grumble, preferably *Bukkake Spunk Guzzlers 6*, playing on it? It'll save me coming over with a memory stick to test the quality before I buy.

Meester Smeeth, Brigg

PREDICTIVE text is really handy for words, but is absolutely rubbish with numbers. Come on, internet boffins, get it sorted.

Alf Huckham, Formby

I WISH *Match of the Day* pundits would stop drawing triangles between the players in their post-match analysis, as though 'playing triangles' is some kind of tactic. Unless they are standing in a dead straight line, you can draw a triangle between any three payers on the fucking pitch. It's simple geometry, not a game strategy.

Billy Wiffles, Croydon

I WONDER if the manufacturers of toilets ever pause to think of the tragi-comic scenes of folly and humiliation, human frailty and horror that their porcelain creations are certain to witness.

Phil Kitching, Isle of Jura

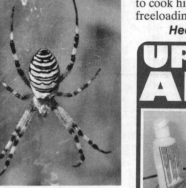

SEVERAL crabsticks glued together make an ideal high-protein, low-carb alternative to a stick of rock when you visit the seaside. Be sure to keep a red biro handy so you can write the name of the resort on the inside after each bite.

Magnus Mbanu, Cambridge

LADIES. Pretend you are the actress in the Oral B advert by sitting in a friend's lounge and exclaiming "I didn't even know Oral B made a toothpaste!" twenty-five times a fucking day.

Eldon Furse, email

LADS. When undressing to be intimate with your partner, remove your boxers by gently sliding two fingers behind the waistband on each side, applying just enough outward force to allow them to fall to your feet in a dramatic, sexy flourish.

Tom Caudwell, London

EMPTY paracetamol blister packs make ideal cryogenic freezing chambers for ants. Aspirin packaging can be used for more circular insects, such as ladybirds.

Magnus Mbanu, Cambridge

DIETERS. Always go cross-eyed when eating - twice the food for the same calories.

Lucy Ferson, Southampton

ALWAYS swallow chewing gum so that in the event of you sharting, your arse will blow a bubble that will contain the expelled excrement. Possibly.

John Owens, Glasgow

I HAVE a phobia of wasps and spiders, and recently your *Letterbocks* pages have included photos of both. If you intend to continue doing this, please print a warning on the cover, so that I won't shit myself when I open the magazine.

Bruce Goodman, Colchester

* How about this picture of a wasp spider instead, Mr Goodman.

THE saying "Give a man a fish and you'll feed him for a day. Teach a man to fish and you'll feed him for a lifetime" is very true. Like most dads, I taught my son to fish when he was a nipper. Now he's grown up with his own house, but he still comes round ours at least three times a week for my wife to cook his tea, the greedy, freeloading bastard.

Hector Blofeld, Deal

UP THE ARSE CORNER

Sender: Ste, *Halifax*

SKAGPUSS

DELIVER US FROM EVIL

YOUR theological postal enquiries answered by the Archbishop of Canterbury, **JUSTIN WELBY**

Dear Justin,

I RECENTLY ordered a package off Amazon, but I had to work on the day it was scheduled for delivery. Knowing that God is present in all places at all times, I prayed to Him to ask if He'd mind keeping an ear out for my doorbell and then signing for the parcel when it arrived. However, when I returned home from work, I found only a 'We called but you were out' slip on the doormat. If God is truly loving and omnipresent, why did He forsake me?

Grenville Space-Vampires, Leicester

Justin says: *God is indeed loving and omnipresent, so I don't believe for one second that He did forsake you. What probably happened is that God manifested Himself in your house as requested, and was keeping His divine ear out for the doorbell, but unfortunately He happened to nip for a piss at the exact moment the delivery man showed up. It's always the way, isn't it? I'm sure God would be more than happy to manifest Himself at your local depot and collect the package for you, if you pray to Him again and ask nicely.*

Dear Justin,

MY NEXT-DOOR neighbour was out yesterday, so his parcel was delivered to my house instead. I couldn't resist taking a quick peek inside, and when I opened the box I was shocked to see he had ordered an inverted crucifix, a Pentagram-emblazoned cowl and a gnarled wooden staff with a rotting goat's head strapped to the top. I am now concerned that my neighbour might be a practising Satanist, and I'm not sure what to do when he comes round to collect his infernal parcel.

Mavis Glass-Cage, Hampstead Heath

Justin says: *God certainly takes a dim view of worshipping the Antichrist, Mavis, but I'm afraid He takes an even dimmer view of opening other people's mail without asking. With that in mind, I'd advise you to befriend your neighbour and begin attending his Black Masses, as you will now almost certainly be joining him in the fiery pits of Hell. If you begin practising Satanism on a regular basis, you will put yourself in valuable credit ahead of your eternity with Beelzebub, rather than wasting your remaining years venerating a God who has already consigned you to the abyss.*

Dear Justin,

AS A DEVOUT Christian of many years, I am planning to honour God's glory by posting a turd to Professor Richard Dawkins. However, I am concerned that if I apply the incorrect postage, the turd may find its way back through my own letterbox. Do you know how many stamps I should affix in order to make sure that Mr Dawkins receives my faecal consignment safely?

Edna Ritualin-Thedark, Cornwall

Justin says: *The issue of mailing excrement to Professor Dawkins was debated at length by the General Synod last year. It was agreed by all present that the most appropriate means of dispatch is to seal the stool inside a padded A4-size jiffy bag and send by recorded delivery. That way, you can ensure not only that Mr Dawkins receives it, but also that he suffers the ignominy of signing for it, or – even better – slogging all the way down to his local depot to collect it! Good luck, and let us know how you get on.*

Have YOU got a query about lost, damaged or delayed mail that also relates in some way to Anglican theology? Why not write in to:
'Deliver Us From Evil' c/o the Archbishop of Canterbury, Viz Comic, PO Box 841, Whitley Bay, NE26 9EQ

SIMPLY THE BEST

ASK any upstanding British bloke to name the greatest honour that can be bestowed on him, and you'll only get one answer: *Being asked to perform the duties of a best man.*

There's no more prestigious position in life than standing beside your oldest and dearest friend as he takes his first tentative steps out of bachelorhood and into a year or two of joyous marital bliss.

However, while the role of best man is undoubtedly a great accolade, it's also one of the toughest tasks around. From organising the stag-do and safeguarding the rings, to writing and delivering a side-splitting speech, every item on the groomsman's itinerary must be handled expertly to ensure that the big day goes without a hitch.

And no one knows this better than veteran aisle waltzer **DOLAN BUNDY**.

Over the past three decades, octuple divorcee Dolan has had the unique opportunity to select a different wedding wingman for each of his **EIGHT** failed marriages. And he's learned a few things along the way!

"I've had more best men than people who've had seven hot dinners have had hot dinners," quips the Bolton-based bachelor. "Over the course of my eight disastrous nuptials, I've had plenty of chances to learn the particular traits, habits and qualities that go to make a truly top-notch groomsman," he added.

"Which is why, for my ninth wedding next month, I'm hoping to find somebody better suited to the gig than the eight useless twats I had before," said the jobless 56-year-old, whose eight previous marriages ended swiftly in acrimonious divorce.

"I was thinking of asking Pervy Malc to do the honours, but his ankle tag means that we'd have to find a church within 200m of his house and there isn't one."

Just for fun, we asked Dolan to use his skill and judgement as a serial best man selector to rate the wedding wingman qualities of five top showbiz stars! Which of these A-List icons would make the perfect groomsman?

Find out right now as we choose…

The Best Man For The Job

Best Man No. 1
Wee Jimmy Krankie

Dolan says: "At first glance, Scotch telly fave Jimmy has everything I'd typically look for in a best man. Despite being a 72-year-old woman, the pint-sized performer is smartly dressed in a tie and school cap, which is more than can be said for the shower of scruffy bellends who've served as my groomsmen over the years. She is also funny and at ease in front of a crowd.

As a professional comedy legend with four decades of cabaret experience, Wee Jimmy would be odds-on to deliver a pitch-perfect best man's speech. The gender-bending mock-schoolboy would perform a rip-roaring 10-minute routine, incorporating various embarrassing incidents from the groom's past, and leaving everyone from small children to grandparents rolling in the aisles.

However, while best man Krankie  would prove a wise choice on the big day, it would be a very different story altogether on the stag-do. Appearing to onlookers as a 10-year-old primary school student, Jimmy would likely be refused entry to every bar, club and strip joint on the stag party's itinerary. Even the group's daytime destinations, such as the Go-Kart track, paintball centre or X-rated porn cinema would stipulate age restrictions that the seemingly pre-pubescent entertainer simply couldn't meet.

In summary, Wee Jimmy would make for a 'fandabidozi' groomsman, but you'd best off getting someone else to organise the stag."

Dolan's Best Man Rating: 6/10

Best Man No. 2
Snoop Dogg

Dolan says: "Rap icon Snoop goes by a litany of inventive aliases, such as Snoop Dogg, Snoopzilla, DJ Snoopadelic and Nemo Hoes. As such, the Long Beach-born hip-hopper would have no trouble with the crucial best man task of assigning an amusing nickname to each member of the stag party. In the case of my stags, these have included 'Fat Baz', 'Big Jim', 'Scouse Trev', 'Beer Monster' and 'Pervy Malc.'

It is traditional to get these monikers emblazoned across matching T-shirts bearing the groom's face. And since Snoop operates his own online clothing store – *The Snoopermarket* – he would presumably be able to wrangle a decent price for printing up two dozen cheeky tees, all featuring the slogan 'LAST FLING B4 THE RING.'

Getting to and from the stag location can often be a huge stumbling block. On six of my eight bachelor parties, we've been chucked off the plane before it could leave, due to incidents such as Big Jim shitting in the drinks trolley and Pervy Malc good-naturedly grabbing a stewardess's arse. However, as a millionaire pop star, Dogg has his own private jet, so the group could get as rowdy as they liked on the flight to Prague or Ljubljana, without worrying about the humourless cabin crew phoning the filth.

Regularly rapping in front of millions of fans, the wedding speech would also be a doddle for seasoned performer Snoop. But a good best man's speech must walk a tricky line between being lightheartedly risqué and still clean enough for a family audience. I know from bitter experience (my second wedding) that having a best man swear profusely during his speech can be uncomfortable to say the least, and since Snoop is known for his X-rated lyrics, it would be no surprise if he were to slip the odd 'fuck', 'shit' and 'motherfucker' into his toast, to the distress of elderly relatives.

Ultimately, if Snoop could keep a lid on the old profanity, I think he'd make a tip-top hip-hop groomsman."

Dolan's Best Man Rating: 7/10

Best Man No. 3
Professor Richard Dawkins

Dolan says: "Blasphemous brainbox Richard is famous for his belief that the human race inhabits a random and absurd, godless universe. And this unshakeable faith in the lack of an all-powerful deity would certainly work in his favour as a best man.

With no fear of being consigned to Hell for living a life of sin, Dawkins would be free to organise the most wanton, depraved and hedonistic stag-do known to man. From coordinating a weekend's boozy gambling in Blackpool, to booking a group outing to a bukkake strip joint in Amsterdam, nothing would be too licentious for the sceptical egghead's hypothetical itinerary.

While less dedicated best men, such as my fourth and sixth, would draw the line at attending a live anal sex show, atheist Dawkins would stop at nothing to ensure the groom's last night of freedom was as debauched as possible.

However, whilst the Christ-shunning boffin would be a shoo-in to knock the stag-do out of the park, he may not be quite so reliable on the big day itself.

It's tradition that the best man stands alongside the groom at the altar as he takes his sacred marital vows. And if the bride insists on holding the nuptials in a church, then a staunchly atheist groomsman could prove disastrous. It would be hugely off-putting for the congregation to hear Dawkins coughing the word 'bollocks' every time the vicar mentioned God during the service.

In my opinion, Professor Dawkins would make an excellent wedding wingman, if he could only put his heathen ideals aside for one day."

Dolan's Best Man Rating: 5/10

Best Man No. 4
Uri Geller

Dolan says: "I know from experience that things can often get out of hand on a stag do. And when they do, it's useful to have a best man who can find his way out of a tricky situation. In this one respect, Israeli illusionist Uri fits the bill perfectly.

Should the entire party happen to end up in chokey for the night, as we did on my fifth stag, when Fat Baz slugged a copper in Krakow, Geller's mystical talent for metal manipulation would come in very handy. Using his psychic powers, the litigious telepath could bend the prison bars while the guards were asleep, and have the whole squad back in the boozer by breakfast!

Geller's other-worldly abilities would also be a boon when it came to the best man's speech. As an experienced mind reader, he could peer inside the groom's brain during the toast, in order to sense which anecdotes might be veering too near the knuckle for comfort. It's a skill I certainly wish my first best man had had, as he would have known not

to tell the whole congregation about me getting a blowie off my wife's sister the morning I proposed.

The only area in which Geller's occult powers could backfire is the safeguarding of the rings. This is arguably the best man's most important job, as I learned to my cost when my third groomsman, Ted, pawned both wedding bands the night before and then fucked off to Corals with the cash. Millionaire Uri wouldn't stoop that low, but the fact remains that as soon as his miraculous fingers touched the precious metal, the rings would be warped out of all recognition, rendered as useless and deformed as the spoons he leaves in his wake.

All in all, Geller would make a 'magic' best man... providing your missus was happy with a plastic wedding ring."

Dolan's Best Man Rating: 3/10

Best Man No. 5
Kim Jong Un

Dolan says: "A top notch best man must be comfortable taking charge and giving orders, and tubby despot Kim has had years of experience doing both. The roly-poly autocrat exerts a tyrannical control over a nation of 26 million people, so he should have no trouble shepherding fifteen pissed lads out of a strip club and into an Uber.

Kim's natural sense of authority would also be invaluable during the wedding itself. The big-boned dictator would have his team of ushers working overtime to ensure the schedule ran smoothly, with any slackers finding themselves immediately executed or fed to some dogs. Under Kim's brutal best man regime, the groom could rest easy knowing that every glass was full and every guest was happy, unlike my seventh wedding when my best man Nobby threw up in my mother-in-law's champagne flute and then dropped his guts during the vows.

As a seasoned public speaker on topics ranging from nuclear energy to the destruction of western capitalism, Kim would undoubtedly approach the best man's speech with relish. And while sceptics may doubt his ability to inject some comedy into his toast, a quick glance at the Dear Leader's haircut suggests that he has a fabulous sense of humour. If verbal gags weren't his particular strong point, Kim could simply order Pyongyang's finest joke writers to work night and day with their families held at gunpoint until a suitably side-splitting monologue had been thrashed out.

Despite his busy schedule and questionable human rights record, I think Kim could have a great 'Korea' as a best man."

Dolan's Best Man Rating: 8/10

NEXT WEEK: Dolan weighs up 5 more A-listers to see which one has the Vicar-like qualities needed to conduct the service.

82

Thou Shalt Not Come In

John 3.18: Rev. Erskine Crockford yesterday

A VICAR from Essex has shocked his parishioners and congregation alike after announcing that from now on, non-believers will NOT be welcome in his church.

"Anyone who doesn't accept the existence of God can just piss off as far as I'm concerned. They're not coming in," said the Reverend Erskine Crockford, curate of St Fiacra-in-the-Field church in Braintree.

"I know the Bible says we are supposed to welcome lost souls into our flock and stuff like that, but fuck it. I've had enough. It's Christians only in here, end of," he continued.

bouncer

And last Saturday, the reverend practised what he

You gotta have faith: St Fiacra-in-the-Field church

Controversial Rev bans non-believers from church

preached when he hired a bouncer to keep non-believers out of a wedding service.

In total, 40 people who had been invited to the marriage of Neville Pigsfoot and Marjorie Sweetbread were given the heave-ho at the church door, including the groom, the bride's parents, the photographer, the best man and several ushers.

"It was a ridiculous situation made worse by the fact that we'd paid the vicar the thick end of five hundred pounds to hire St Fiacra's," said the disgruntled groom.

wellard

"The doorman stopped me on the steps and asked me if I believed in God. I told him

not really and that was that."

"I had to stand in the graveyard and shout my vows in through a window. It was farcical," Mr Pigsfoot added.

little willy

After the ceremony, the Rev. Crockford said he had received over a hundred complaints from disappointed wedding guests, some of whom had travelled hundreds of miles only to be refused entry to the church.

But the unrepentant vicar rejected the protests out of hand. "Fuck them. They can stick their complaints up their arse," he told us. "If they want to come into my church they can believe in the Almighty, and that's that."

"I'm sick to my back teeth of atheists," he continued. "They never join in with the hymns or the prayers, and they never put a fucking penny in the collection plate. Fuck them."

schmeichel

"I don't care if that means there's only a handful of arses on my pews of a Sunday," he continued. "If they're not worshipping the Lord, they're not welcome in this church."

bosnich

"I've got two christenings to do tomorrow, and if them babies can't convince me that they believe in God, they're not getting in either," he said. "Bollocks to them."

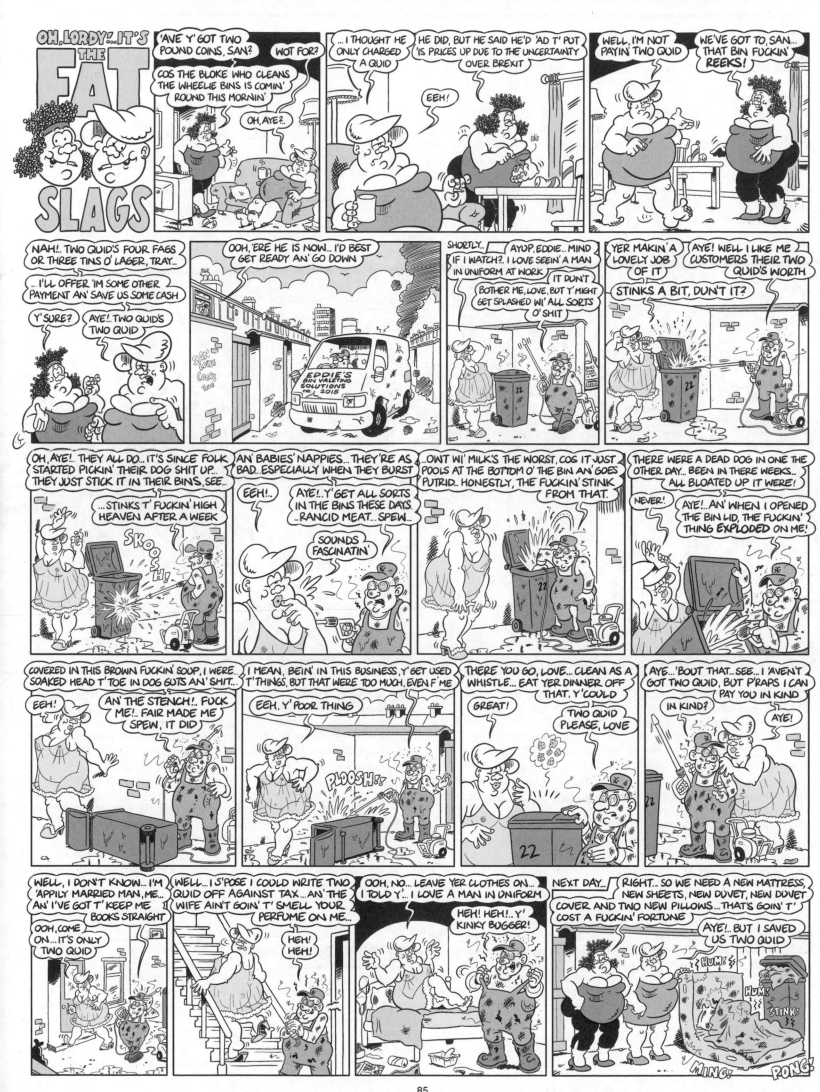

ABOVE every court in the land stands the figure of Lady Justice - that stirring symbol of the British legal system, where nobody is above the law, except some members of the cabinet and Prince Andrew, and a fair hearing is guaranteed for everyone. Before her impartial, blindfold figure, the greatest dramas of the age are played out, as lawyers pit their wits against each other to establish *the truth, the whole truth, and nothing but the truth*. With the sword of justice in one hand and a set of scales to impartially weigh the evidence in the other, she stands above proceedings to make

sure they are fair, decent, honest, and cripplingly expensive.

If you're a judge, a barrister, or Pete Doherty out of the Babyshambles, you will be in Court and experience our legal system in action on a daily basis. But many of us will never even see the inside of a courtroom. *Who are the players?... What do they do?... And how much do they charge per hour or part thereof, plus disbursements?*

Please rise, as we take a privileged look into this august, oak-panelled chamber to find out...

1. The Barristers

THE DEFENDANTS in any trial rely on barristers to act as their guides through the labyrinthine complexities of the law, and it is ultimately their job to discover the truth. But just like with tellys, shoes and second hand cars, you get what you pay for, and the more you shell out on a barrister, the more likely it is that your version of what happened turns out to be the truth.

These bewigged legal eagles follow a bewildering array of arcane traditions; they never shake hands with each other, they leave the bottom two buttons of their waistcoats undone, and they bill their clients in guineas - a charmingly anachronistic method of routinely overcharging them by 5%.

It is the defence and prosecution barristers' responsibility to represent their respective clients' interests. And although they are professional enemies when crossing legal swords in court, they keep things friendly by trying to win £5 from each other by being the first to get their witnesses to say a particular, unusual word - such as "hippopotamus"- when giving their evidence. As well as winning the money, the successful barrister gets the chance to pick the next day's word.

2. The Judge

THE MOST senior figure in the legal drama being played out is the judge, who has decades of experience as a barrister, both for the defence and the prosecution, under his belt. Afflicted with age-onset dementia, ludicrous eyebrows and spectacular buggers' grips, the judge must listen carefully to every legal argument, piece of evidence and testimony put forward, whilst struggling to stay awake and continent.

As he got dressed in his chambers this morning, this judge was under the impression that he was four years old and getting ready for a trip to the zoo with his parents, who died many years ago. Luckily, this doesn't impair his legal judgement, which is still as pin-sharp today as it was when he first began his legal career just after the war. In 1918.

3. Court Reporter

COURT CASES are a matter of public record, and it is the job of this reporter to summarise the complex legal procedures and decisions for the benefit of any of his paper's readers who aren't busy scrutinising a paparazzi photo of Gemma Collins getting out of a taxi outside a nightclub to see if she's got any knickers on.

Some court cases are a rich source of ready-made newspaper stories, shot through as they are with the lust, passion, hatred and revenge that are the staple fare of the tabloids. However, most cases involve something more prosaic, such as fraudulent use of a company expense account, theft of a diesel generator from industrial premises, or shoplifting a pair of Nike trainers from Sports Direct - and they make far from glamorous reading.

But skilful journalists can 'sex up' these less raunchy cases for their readers, by using adjectives such as "glamorous," "curvy" and "big-titted" when describing female witnesses. Alternatively, they might gain access to a defendant's Facebook account to see if they have posted any saucy pictures, or they may speak to the victim's neighbour to ask if they have ever heard them through the wall when they were having sex.

4. Court Artist

CAMERAS are strictly forbidden in court, so the press and TV news outlets employ skilled, on-the-spot artists to bring the scene to life for the general public. In minutes, these talented craftsmen and women capture the mood using just a few pastels and a sheet of beige sugar paper. The resulting sketch of three or four angular-featured people viewed from the side and slightly behind, who could really be anybody, allows the reader or viewer to believe they were really there in court as the drama unfolded.

Producing these generic sketches undoubtedly requires talent, but the real skill comes in the artist being able to place their signature where the picture editor or rostrum cameraman can't chop it off.

..Who's Whom and What Goes On in a
CROWN COURT

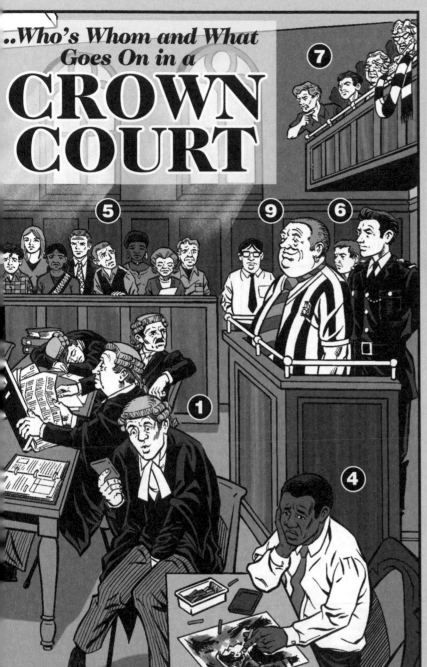

5. The Jury

IT IS THE right of every citizen to be tried by a jury of his or her peers, twelve men and women who will decide whether one of their fellow citizens is guilty beyond reasonable doubt. Selected at random from the populace, a jury is a true cross-section of society; man or woman, gay or straight and of any ethic origin, the jury is as diverse as our society. But all these people chosen for jury service have one thing in common - none of them were bright enough to lie their way out of doing it when the letter dropped through the door.

But there are upsides to jury service. As well as performing an important civil duty, if you have an unpleasant job, such as working in a chicken chlorination plant, or cleaning the breeding bins in a maggot farm, then two weeks on full pay taking part in a real-life courtroom drama will come as a pleasant distraction. In addition, if jury members can string out their deliberations long enough, they could get themselves a weekend in a hotel with room service, full English breakfast and mini-bar, all at the Crown Prosecution Service's expense.

6. The Police

IT IS THE job of the police to apprehend criminals, and the it is the job of the courts to prosecute them. So the police deliver the accused to court as their final duty before they hand them over to the Crown Prosecution Service. Well, almost their last job. Defendants often become abusive in court, so an officer is always present in the dock to deal with any trouble. Also, in the event of a guilty verdict, it is the role of the officer in charge to make sure the convict accidentally falls down the stairs on his way to the cells beneath.

Of course, if a police officer has evidence that will help the prosecution, he will hand it over and may be called as a witness in the trial. If he has evidence that will help the defence, he'll probably just keep quiet. But if he does take the witness stand, he will deliver the truth, the whole truth and nothing but the truth in a strange language, using phrases like "primarily became aware of" instead of "first saw" and "delivered a pedal blow to his genital area," instead of "kicked him in the bollocks."

7. The Public

TO ENSURE that justice is not only done, but seen to be done, all trials are open to the public. Anyone can enter the public gallery to see how the wheels of justice turn. Pensioners on occasion take the opportunity to go along and do some knitting when there is nothing much on telly. And the family and friends of the defendant often pop along to see how the trial is going and glare threateningly at the witnesses while pulling their fingers across their throats.

8. The Stenographer

ALL TRIALS are a matter of public record and it is the job of the court stenographer to record every word that is said during proceedings. They are not allowed to ask anyone to stop talking, slow down a bit, or repeat what they just said and, as a consequence, must type extremely fast. And what's more impressive is that they don't use an ordinary typewriter. The stenography machine looks more like a little piano, and the stenographer 'plays' the words rather like musical notes, although the noise that comes out is just quiet clicking.

9. The Defendant

THE ACCUSED is perhaps the most important person in the room, for it is they who have the most to gain or lose during the trial. A verdict of not guilty could see them go home with their heads held high, whilst a guilty verdict could see them sentenced to anything from a few hours' Community Service to a lifetime behind bars. So it is important that the defendant makes a good impression on the court to demonstrate that they are a model citizen who has been wrongly accused. To that end, many will have a haircut and borrow a suit for the occasion, whilst others will attempt to keep their foul language to a minimum when addressing the judge. Some will have spent the evening before their trial looking up how to do a proper tie knot on Youtube.

10. The Evidence

ANY CASE will succeed or fail on the strength of its evidence, both material and forensic. Material evidence is any incriminating item which places an individual at the crime scene - perhaps a bank card fell out of a burglar's pocket whilst he was doing a shit in somebody's front room, or perhaps a murderer unknowingly dropped his passport onto his dying victim as he fled. Forensic evidence deals with the invisible clues which point to a perpetrator - a single hair fibre, a fleck of paint or a minute quantity of DNA. Such is the complexity of forensic science, the prosecution will call on a well-respected, well-qualified expert in the field to explain to the jury, in layman's terms, exactly how this evidence points to the victim's guilt. The defence counsel will then call their own expert, equally well-respected and qualified, to explain to them why it doesn't.

11. The Witnesses

AS WELL as material and forensic evidence, cases often rely on witness evidence - sworn testimonies from people who saw what happened at first hand. But, as any book of optical illusions shows, the human brain is an unreliable organ which often plays tricks. Did the witness really see a man in a white T-shirt and dark trousers climbing over the back wall of the jewellery shop at 2:00 in the morning, or was it a large Manx cat? Was the attacker definitely left-handed, or did the witness see what was happening through a reflection in a window? Whatever it is, the witnesses take the stand and recount what they saw for certain in as much detail as possible. The opposing counsel then cross-examines them by asking if there is the slightest, remotest, most minuscule possibility that they could be mistaken or misremembering, to which the logical answer must always be "yes."

Can You Spot..?

- **SOMEONE** in a wig watching pornography on his phone
- **A MEMBER** of the jury seething because he wasn't elected foreman
- **SOMEONE** in a wig looking at the day's horseracing card in a newspaper hidden in a thick book
- **A MEMBER** of the jury who has spent the whole case sexually fantasising about the stenographer and hasn't heard a word anyone has said
- **SOMEONE** in a wig doing the Times crossword
- **SOMEONE** in a wig fast asleep
- **A JUDGE** who thinks the prosecuting counsel is his nanny, who is here to change his nappy
- **A LOCAL** newspaper reporter who has spent the whole case sexually fantasising about the stenographer and hasn't heard a word anyone has said
- **A MEMBER** of the jury wondering if anyone would say anything and if he'd get a bill if he got one of the pay-per-view porn films tonight at the hotel
- **AN OLD LADY** in the public gallery, knitting a scarf to go with the tank top she made during the Fulchester Ripper trial

NEXT ISSUE - Who's Who and What They Do into the soup in the kitchens at 10 Downing Street

Scum mothers who'd have 'em

"You in there mum?"

"Fuck off."

"Er, it's *me* mum..."

"What the fuck do *you* want?"

"Happy birthday?"

"What's that?"

"A gift!"

"Have you got the receipt?"

"You haven't even opened it yet!"

"Have. You. Got. The. *Fucking.* Receipt?"

"That's his first day in infants."

"Whose?"

"George. Your only grandson."

"Oh aye. Is this silver?"

"SMASH!"

"Where's that cunt Daz?"

"Six month into a two stretch."

"Who's this arsehole?"

"H-hello..."

"His mate."

"BAM!"

"Tell that fucker we'll be waiting."

"Will do."

"Why'd you say I was Daz's mate?"

"So they'd hit you instead of me."

"Who the Hell *are* they?"

"Mates of Daz's, you got this receipt then?"

"Ta."

"Have you any plans for the rest of the day?"

"I hadn't, but now I'll nip up town, cash this in and then go straight on the piss."

Shortly

CUSTOMER SE
INFO · RETURNS

"And why are you returning the item?"

"So I can get shit-faced."

USTOMER SE

"Oh, madam? Excuse me, madam?"

"What?"

"Don't you want to keep the photograph?"

"Nah..."

"I ain't got a frame."

88

HORROR CRASH

ONE of Britain's oldest ghosts was in a serious condition last night, after being involved in a traffic accident. According to reports, the transparent spectre of SIR ROGER DE TINTAGEL, who died in 1378, is believed to have been crossing an unlit road in the New Forest when it was hit by a car.

A Hampshire Police spokesman said the car's driver, 26-year-old office manager Sandra Spelhorne, was unhurt but in a state of shock following the collision. He told reporters: "This particular stretch of road is a popular spot for Sir Roger's manifestations as he was known to ride to hounds there during his life. His glowing phantom, complete with trademark ruff collar, tights and doublet, has long been a familiar sight to motorists travelling along the B3080 between North Charford and Hale Purlieu after dark."

"Quite frankly, this was an accident waiting to happen," the spokesman added.

Elderly Spook seriously injured in collision

Ghost of a chance: Sir Roger is in an unknown state after collision on this stretch of the B3080.

ague

Since dying from a fit of the ague in the 14th century, Sir Roger has become one of Britain's most popular and frequently-sighted ghosts. It is estimated that up to 50,000 tourists visit the New Forest each year in the hope of glimpsing him by the misty light of a full moon.

As a denizen of the spectral realm, it is unknown whether Sir Roger's wraith can die as a result of the accident, but it is being kept under observation by spirit mediums at nearby Godshill Infirmary. "Only time will tell whether he makes a full recovery from his injuries," a hospital spokesman said. "But looking on the positive side, if he does die, he'll probably just come back as another ghost anyway."

see-through

Former Prime Minister Theresa May was quick to wish Sir Roger well, tweeting: "Hoping this fine old British gentleman is soon back on his see-through feet and haunting the forest paths once more. #Chequers #Brexit #NoDeal."

Sir Roger also received get well soon messages from several other famous phantoms, including the spirits of Anne Boleyn, Florence Nightingale and Ronnie Corbett.

IT'S OSMAN ~DIAS!

POINTLESS egghead PRICHARD OSMAN might seem like a benign word whiz - but sources say that behind the scenes, the mild-mannered presenter is history's most megalomaniacal ruler. And the latest claim is that the 6'7" bespectacled brainiac, 48, refused to sign a contract for a new series of *Richard Osman's House of Games* until the BBC erected a glowering statue of him on a granite pedestal in front of Broadcasting House.

Boffin and King: Osman.

Quiz show boffin in reality Omnipotent King of Kings!

"When the audience gets bored and the director tries to stop him, he threatens to strike them all down with a thousand swords," he added.

The *8 out of 10 Cats Does Countdown* bookworm first raised eyebrows on *Loose Women* when he referred to Ruth Langsford as 'a traveller from an antique land'.

Referring to *Countdown*'s contestants, he later called the shows famous clock 'the hand that mock'd them.'

screen

An unnamed TV insider told us: "Despite Alexander Armstrong being his superior on screen, Richard has been making him call him 'King of Kings' once the credits have rolled."

"When he was on *8 Out of 10 Cats Does Countdown* they had to stop filming thirty times because he kept shouting 'Look on my words, ye mighty, and despair!' at the end of every letters round, even if he'd only got a three or a four."

driving

The source continued: "It's literally a reign of terror on *Pointless*. If it's a sports question in the final round, he insists on going through every single other pointless answer, even if it's just rugby or tennis."

Original Ozymandias: Rameses II yesterday.

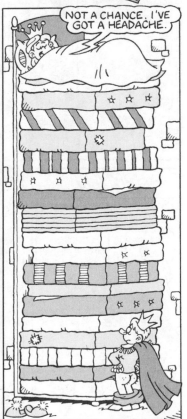

the Princess and the Penis

NOT A CHANCE. I'VE GOT A HEADACHE.

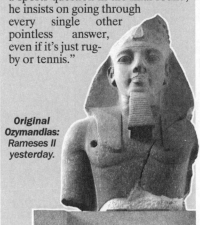

A Dr Rick Monroe Adventure

DR MONROE AND THE RACE AGAINST TIME

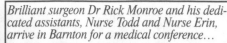

Brilliant surgeon Dr Rick Monroe and his dedicated assistants, Nurse Todd and Nurse Erin, arrive in Barnton for a medical conference…

This will be a great conference, Erin. My keynote speech should go down a storm.

It should, Rick... I can't wait.

BARNTON CONFERENCE CENTRE

TESCBURYSONS

Rick, look!... I think someone is in trouble.

What!?!...

...let's go.

Let me through, I'm a doctor.

Did anybody see what happened?

Yes. He accidentally swallowed a wasp and got stang off it... and his throat all swelled up.

His airways are being blocked. I'll need to perform an emergency tracheotomy...

Todd, look after him...

Where are you going, Rick?

I didn't bring my medical bag. I'm going to have to improvise with stuff I can get in this supermarket.

I'll help you, Rick.

Seconds later...

Okay, that's everything... kitchen knife, some vodka for sterilising, bandages, tape and antiseptic.

Let's get to the tills!

Christ! Look at the size of the queues... he'll be dead before we've got the stuff on the belt.

It's ok... we can use the self-checkout.

I mean, twelve tills they've got... and there's only two of them on...

...in the middle of the day.

Right quick as we can...

...hang on. It says have we brought our own bag. Have you got a bag?

No! Just press 'no' and scan the first thing through.

It's not letting me do it. It's asking how many bags I want.

Just press one, Rick.

But they're 5p.

BEEP!

Unexpected item in the bagging area! Please wait for assistance.

What the fuck?

Perhaps you pushed the bag down on the scale?

What's taking so long?

Here she comes.

Sorry, it just said unexpected item. I only put my bandages on...

BIP! BIP!...BIP! BIP! BIP! BIP!... BIP! BIP!...BIP! BIP!

...and it just...

There you go.

Quickly, he hasn't got long.

BEEP! BEEP!

BEEP!

What the fuck!?!

Assistance required.

It's the knife, someone's got to have to approve it.

Bloody hell!

Come on, Rick. Hurry.

TESCB

No, a bank card's no good... it's got to be some picture ID... something with your face on it.

I've got my driving licence... here.

I mean, for god's sake, do I look under 18?

BIP! BIP!...BIP! BIP! BIP! BIP!...BIP! BIP!...BIP! BIP!

I've got to ask. It's me job.

God... his epiglottal tissues will be going into spasm by now... I hope we're in time, Erin.

BEEP! Assistance required.

What the fuck!?!

It's the vodka.

Excuse me...!

PRIVATE

STAFF TOILET

Look, forget the vodka, we'll perform it non-aseptic...

...press 'Finish and pay':

Eleven pound twenty.

Here...

It says 'card denied'

Right.

What!?! What for!? It can't...I used the fucker this morning...

Press 'pay with cash'.

It says 'have you got a loyalty card?'

It says 'would you like to apply for one?'

No!

No, I don't have a fucking loyalty card.

Eh? It keeps spitting the note back out.

Try it with the Queen's head the other way up

That's got it... Right, put the coins in then we're done.

KER-CHUNK!

It's spat the pound out...

Try it again...

KER-CHUNK!

No, it keeps coming through. Have you got another one?

No...

Give it a lick!

A lick?

Yes, that's what my dad used to do on the fruities and fag machines when they spat coins out.

LICK! LICK!

KER-CHUNK!

No, it's spat it out.

Bollocks! Where's that woman? **Where the fuck is she?**

It says 'Timeout. Do you want to continue your transaction?'

For fuck's sake!

Next week: As the man's trachaeal lumen shrinks under the surrounding inflammatory muscles, Rick and Erin abort the self service tills and take the life-saving goods to a manned checkout, just as the cashier puts a "Sorry, this till is closing" sign on the conveyor belt.

What's in a Name? ~Boris Johnson

HE'S THE POLITICAL blonde bombshell who has risen from the obscurity of Eton College and Oxford University to make 10 Downing Street his home. He's overweight, tousle-haired, dishonest, adulterous former London mayor **BORIS JOHNSON**, and loathe him or hate him, he's made his way to the country's top job and is presently crashing us disastrously out of the European Union in his loveably roguish trademark style. But how much do we really know about this clownish, adultery-crazed old-Etonion who has risen to the highest office in the land? As usual, the truth is hidden in plain sight - in the letters of the Uxbridge and South Ruislip MP's name.

B is for BUSES

WHETHER it's ordering 800 of the wrong type or printing big lies on the side of them, Johnson has a decidedly chequered history when it comes to buses. But until recently, few people suspected that the former London mayor's favourite hobby was making models of London double deckers out of wine boxes in his spare time. The headline-grabbing revelation even came as a shock to Johnson himself, who seemed as surprised as anyone when the words came bumbling out of his mouth during a leadership election campaign interview with Capital Radio.

O is for OSTRICHES

ALONG with Spencer Percival, Earl Grey and Edward Heath, Johnson is one of a very small and select band of British Prime Ministers who have been pecked on the bellend by an ostrich. During his tenure as Mayor of London, Johnson toyed with the idea of setting up an ostrich farm in the run-down Docklands area. However, on a fact-finding mission to Eden Ostrich World in the Lake District, he accidentally strayed between a mother bird and her eggs, and was attacked. The enraged eight-foot bird nipped Johnson's bobby's helmet in its beak and had to be kicked up the arse before it would release its vice-like grip.

R is for ROLF HARRIS

AS A child, Johnson was very keen to learn to play the wobble-board, and even went so far as to take private lessons with later-to-be-disgraced multi-talentless Australian entertainer Rolf Harris. However, after 6 years of weekly lessons, and countless hours of practice, Johnson was still unable to make his board produce a wobble noise, so he gave up.

I is for IMPERIAL LEATHER

BORIS'S favourite type of soap is Cussons Imperial Leather. Indeed, many of the Prime Minister's favourite things begin with the letter I. For example, he supports Ipswich Town football club, the Isuzu Trooper is his favourite car, and Iodine is his favourite halogen in the Periodic Table, after Chlorine, Fluorine and Bromine.

S is for SANDWICHES

ASK the PM what his favourite flavour of sandwich is and he'll reply without hesitation - Cheese and Onion. However, that's because he's a pathological liar, and his actual favourite is ham and mustard.

J is for JUPITER

EVEN though it is the Earth's planetary next-door-neighbour-but-one, and has an approximate diameter of 90,000 miles, Boris Johnson apparently has no plans to visit Jupiter in the near future.

O is for OCELOT

JOHNSON is one of the only Tory party leaders to have been bitten on the bollocks by an ocelot. When he was editor of the *Spectator* magazine, Johnson toyed with idea of setting up a fur farm, and went on a fact-finding mission to Whipsnade Zoo to spend a day with the keepers to see how difficult it would be to breed and raise the valuable four-foot long wildcats. Unfortunately, during his visit Johnson got a little bit too close to the dominant male of the zoo's pack, which attacked him. The beast sank its razor-sharp three-inch fangs into Boris's knackers, refusing to relinquish its vice-like grip until a quick-thinking keeper kicked it up the arse.

H is for HEADWEAR

AS WELL as being famous for being a sex-crazed fucking liar, our new PM is perhaps best known for his trademark mop of carefully tousled blonde hair. The only time he covers his trademark scarecrow barnet is with a carefully chosen eccentric bandana, or occasionally a safety helmet if the solipsistic fat cunt's being winched along a zipwire into an Olympic stadium.

N is for NOOKIE
THE fanny-crazed statesman is estimated to have had it off with more than 8,000 of his friends' wives. That's more women than porn actor Ben Dover *(6,202)*, rock star Axl Rose *(1,706)* and wavy-armed seventies TV boffin Dr Magnus Pyke *(1)* have fucked put together.

S is for STYLOPHONE
IN HIS mid-twenties, Johnson became obsessed with the idea of becoming a professional Stylophone player, and returned to his former musical tutor Rolf Harris to take lessons. However, he soon gave up after displaying no aptitude whatsoever for the battery-powered, wasp-sounding electronic instrument.

O is for OKAPI
JOHNSON is one of the few British Prime Ministers who can claim that they have been bummed to near unconsciousness by an okapi. In 1992, while working as the European Parliamentary correspondent of the *Daily Telegraph*, Johnson toyed with the idea of set-

ting up a performing troupe of the giraffe-like Congolese antelopes, and visited Chester Zoo to see how easy it would be to train them to do tricks. Unfortunately, while he was in their enclosure, Johnson's belt broke and his trousers fell down, allowing the 2-foot-cocked okapi to mount him anally. The violent, agonising attack continued for nearly twenty minutes until one of the zoo's keepers fetched a step ladder, which he climbed up before kicking the priapic animal up the arse, causing it to lose interest.

N is for NIPPLES
LIKE James Bond's erstwhile nemesis Francisco Scaramanga, some people are born with a third nipple - known as polymastia, or a "witch's teat." We will probably never know for certain how many nipples Johnson has, because if he is ever questioned on the subject, we simply won't be able to believe anything the lying fat fucker says.

Next Week: *It's All in the Name looks at defeated leadership contender Jeremy Cunt*

FOODIE BOLLOCKS

And what will you be having chief?

That depends...

How mindful is your 99?

I'm not sure what that means.

Sigh.

Okay, start at the bottom. Tell me the story of your cones.

It's one of these or one of these.

Fresh?

Both packs opened today.

Packs? Surely more rewarding to make them from scratch.

I wouldn't know where to start!

Wow. Sugar cones a little trickier than waffle, but both child's play for any capable pâtissier.

My regular parlour at the Borough Market imports their wafer flour from a named Italian grinder.

I only do this weekends mate.

Pop-up, cool, I get it.

Let's talk gelato.

Is that them big wine gums?

Ice cream. Tell me all about your ice cream.

Well, there's this Mr Whippy sort -

Which should be banned.

- and traditional dairy soft-scoop.

Accredited herd?

Heard what?

Where you source the milk.

What milk?

The milk to make your ice cream.

I don't make the ice cream.

Tsk! Your supplier... are they artisanal?

No, they're from round here.

Excuse me.

Will you just make up your fucking mind?

I flatly refuse to be hurried over the menu.

Soon...

Traditional 99 in a waffle please.

Stop! Stop everything!

Can I get a cocoa content on that flake?

Wah!

94

RETURN OF THE POPE

HIS Holiness The Pope has been returned safely to the Vatican following his escape from the Apostolic Palace late last week.

Poped out: Pontiff slipped away.

God's representative on earth slipped away while being walked by a Cardinal last Thursday night and had been missing for six days.

"His Holiness likes to have a shit last thing at night," said Vatican Secretary of State Cardinal Tarcisio Bertone. "We usually send Cardinal Vincenzo out with him, but he was a little under the weather, so he had to ask one of the new cardinals to go. Unfortunately, he wasn't up to the job."

Pope Francis was last seen racing off through St Peter's Square in pursuit of some pigeons, and led Vatican officials a merry dance in the following days, with reported sightings as far afield as Bologna and Sorrento.

posters

Cardinal Bertone spent the day after the disappearance pinning up photocopied 'MISSING' posters on lampposts around Rome, and sharing pictures of the missing pontiff on Facebook

"It's been really hard on the Cardinal," said a Vatican source. "He's not a young man, and this has really taken it out of him. Seeing him on the back step of St Peter's Basilica last thing every night, rattling a fork inside a tin of communion wafers, it was heartbreaking."

tops

It is believed that in desperation the Vatican called in professional trackers, who set a number of traps in and around the city state, each one baited with an unshriven soul.

"We came down this morning and one of the traps was shut," said Cardinal Bertone. "There was the most tremendous banging and scratching coming from inside it, so we knew immediately it was the Pope."

The bedraggled pontiff was immediately examined by top theologians, who reported that he was none the worse for his ordeal, although he appeared to have been in a few fights.

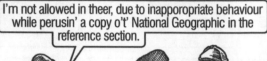

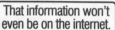

That afternoon...

BANG! BANG! SAW! BANG!

There. I think it's finished!

It's a real Bobby Dazzler. The West Riding's first 55 megaton thermonuclear ordinance...

...it should go off a treat

Aye, if we've followed the instructions properly.

'Ang on, lads. 'Appen we've forgot summat...

'Ow are we goin' t'get it up on th'Moor Top t'set it off?

We've just built an extremely complex weapon of mass destruction, Compo. I'm sure that, if we put our heads together, we can fashion some sort of wheeled carriage to get it up the hill.

So...

Of course, we'll have to call it something. Like railway locomotives and ships of the line, all thermonuclear ordinances should have a name.

Let me think... The name we choose must be something that immediately strikes fear, terror and dread in the hearts of all men.

'Appen I've got an idea!

Puff! pant!

Come on, men. Put your backs into it!

Ayup. 'Ere comes PC Cooper!

Afternoon, constable.

Lovely day.

TING! TING!

CRASH!

Shortly...

Are we at t'top yet?

...I'm knackered.

Patience, Compo. Nearly there.

What a view, gentlemen. On a clear day, you can see as far as Huddersfield.

I'll bet y can see Nora's bloomers on th'line, Foggy.

Mind, yer wouldn't need yer binoculars t'see them. Hee-hee!

Shall we get this bomb detonated, then? I want to get home for my tea.

Norman and I will retire safely behind this rock, Compo. You push the red button to start the three second ignition sequence!

'Old on a minnit... Why do I 'ave t'set ruddy bomb off?

No offence, Compo. But Norman and I are wearing our best clothes. You're wearing a moth-eaten woolly hat, trousers held up with string and a jacket that looks like a tramp's hand-me-down.

Exactly. These are my best clothes an'all!

Just press the button, man!

And that's an order!

CLICK!

Detonation sequence initiated! Ignition in three...two...one...!

Make room f' me!

Next week: Foggy, Clegg and Compo hijack a Boeing 747 and push it up the hill in a bath, before flying it through the front of Ivy's Cafe.

LetterbOcks

Viz Comic, P.O. Box 841 Whitley Bay, NE26 9EQ ★ letters@viz.co.uk

I HAD a dream the other night where Kim Jong-un came to my university to give a talk to hundreds of students in the lecture theatre. Before he started, they began playing a video that was rather disrespectful to the North Korean dictator, and he got up and furiously started to walk out. I immediately stood up at the back and shouted, "That's right. Fuck off, you fat bastard," to great applause from everyone. Have any other readers insulted a dictator in a dream in front of an appreciative audience?

Arthur Dury, Nottingham

HAVE any other readers noticed that cats' legs are longer when they are licking their own arse?

Col Percy Fawcett, Durham

IF dog years are an actual thing, how come vets charge full price for really old dogs? My mutt is about fifteen, so in dog years he is well and truly a pensioner and he should be getting free prescriptions and what-have-you. Not glasses obviously, I'm not stupid.

Hector Barnfeather, Hull

DO you reckon there will still be tobacconists in heaven by the time I get there? It's just that I stopped smoking several years ago, but I want to take it up again once it's no longer a health issue.

Stuie, Bunny

THE word 'Ah' can be used when you hit your thumb with a hammer, but can also be used when you sit down and have a nice relax. What a wonderfully versatile word.

Holli Tree, Clacton

WHY is it that world champion boxers compete for a belt when they primarily wear shorts with an elasticated waistband? Moreover, when they appear on TV interviews and suchlike sporting a tailored suit, they have to carry the belt over their shoulder because it won't fit through the loops on their trousers. It seems to me that boxing organisations should offer something more useful as prizes instead, such as a nice tie, or a 25% discount for life at Nandos, or another popular mid-price restaurant chain.

Doug Norton, Hereford

I'VE always thought of Queen Victoria as a dumpy, sour-faced old battleaxe like you see in history books. So watching Victoria on ITV, I've been surprised by what a beautiful young woman she was. Still, Albert cashed in his chips just in time, didn't he?

Tom Wainscotting, Leigh

WHAT I want to know is, why do lemons have pips, but limes don't? And I don't want any of your Smart Alec scientific answers, thank-you very much, just give it to me straight.

Richard Devereux, Hereford

IT'S all very well fashion students doing trousers with different coloured legs, or telling men to wear skirts. But what about inventing something useful, like new underwear? We've been wearing the same old Y-fronts and boxer shorts for years. Come on fashion designers, pull your fingers out and invent some new underpants.

Gunther Arboretum, Skate

* *We think that's a very good idea, Mr Arboretum. But fuck fashion designers, why not let Viz readers design some new underwear? Send us your designs for men's undercrackers that aren't Y-fronts or boxers. Remember, they must be stylish and modern, but also practical in terms of wash and wearability.*

SOME expert on the Discovery Channel said that things expand when they are heated. But when I put my knob in the toaster it just shrivelled it up, gave me third degree burns and singed all my pubes off. Expert Schmexpert, I say.

Jim Rowlands, email

ALL the old scientists we used to love were a bit eccentric, each with their own little idiosyncrasies to make us laugh. There was Magnus Pyke with all the arm-waving, David Bellamy with his big daft beard, and Stephen Hawking with his funny robot voice. And let's not forget Heinz Wolff with his flyaway hair and spotty bow tie at a funny angle. So come on Professor Brian Cox, get yourself a gimmick, you boring fart.

Toby Juggs, Nottingham

THEY say that plastic bags can last for up to 1000 years. But if that's true, how come there aren't any plastic bags from the Middle Ages still kicking about today?

Buff Orpington, Chepstow

DR Hook sang "When you're in love with a beautiful woman, you watch your friends." Well, my wife's horrendous, but I still wouldn't put it past some of them.

Beaker, Sydney

I DON'T know why Tesco label some of their apples as 'Baking Apples.' It's none of their business what I do with the apples once I've bought them, so enough of the Big Brother shit I say. In fact, just for that I might fry the fuckers instead. How do you like *those* apples?

Crompton Delaware, Hove

WHAT have those monkeys with the red arses been doing to make their arses so red, I wonder? Whatever it is, they should stop it, or try wearing underpants at least.

Fat Al White, Wrenthorpe

I HAVE recently noticed how there is hardly any time to check my social media pages in my car whilst waiting for the traffic lights to change. I've barely read the latest stories on Facebook before the driver behind is honking their horn for me to move. By the time I've commented on the post, they are usually absolutely livid. Could I ask all local councils to extend the length of their red light hold, otherwise a serious road rage situation is going to occur through no fault of my own.

Jenny, London

HOW come all Bond villains are always mega-rich industrialists? Would it hurt to have a normal, working-class bloke as the baddie from time to time? He could be signing on and claiming the dole, perhaps even selling a bit of weed on the side. Oh, I don't know, I'm an ideas man – I'm not going to write the fucking thing for them as well.

Brocky Cubbeli, London

ALL we seem to talk about these days is climate change. Why are British people so concerned about the weather all the time?

Cheryl Jepson, Leicester

HAS anyone else noticed that films are not the same as real life? You would never get anyone hanging from a clock face on Big Ben to prevent Russian agents from starting a war in Europe in real life, so why do film makers think that would happen and make a film about it?

Stefan Badham, Hampshire

the 'F' BOMB

NICE TO FUCKING MEET YOU!

H, MATE! HOW THE FUCK YOU DOING, YOU DAFT OLD FUCK?

YEAH? HE *NEVER*! FUCK. *REALLY*?!

NO!! FUCK.

FUCK!

FUCK ME, THAT'S FUCKING COMPLETELY FUCKING MENTAL!

NO!?! I DON'T FUCKING BELIEVE IT! *FUCK!* THAT FUCKER IS SUCH A STUPID FUCKING FUCKER!

ANYWAY, MATE! I'VE GOT TO FUCKING GO. I'M FUCKING LATE ENOUGH AS IT FUCKING IS!

TSK!

BUS STOP

OH FUDGE.

TRIP!

LATERS, FUCKWAD!

BOOM!

SO McVities is pronounced McVities, and only contains one 't'. The words titties, kitties etc, contain 2 't's, yet they are pronounced the same as McVities. I think this is entirely inappropriate and I am considering writing a letter to my local MP.

Steven George Stevenson, Aylesbury

I JUST won a fiver on a scratch card.

Jayne, Pissoff

* *Congratulations, Jayne. And you win another fiver for having your letter published in Viz. Although there is a good chance it will get lost in the post. A very good chance. Almost a certainty, in fact. Actually, the Post Office has just called and confirmed that your fiver has gone missing. Sorry.*

I WAS fascinated to learn that the Romans were right into porn. Apparently, they had erotic drawings all over their walls in the house. With me, it's just a matter of changing channels and pulling up my strides as soon as I hear the wife putting the key in the front door, so I don't know how those Roman blokes went on.

Harry Standhats, Luton

I TOOK my niece to a village fete the other day and got into an argument with the idiot running the bouncy castle, who kept insisting that I take my shoes off. I can understand that it might be polite to remove your shoes when entering a real castle that's worth millions of pounds, but I wasn't prepared to display the same reverence to a bit of rubber.

Matt Haydock, Tunbridge Wells

These "so-called" wildlife experts are always banging on about lions and tigers scent-marking their territory on trees in order to warn other animals away. Has it never even occurred to them that they might simply be bursting for a piss?

Hamilton Renton, Staines

I LOVE bears, me, especially their ears, but you have to question their intelligence. I watched a nature programme recently and this big, daft bear was stood up to its bollocks in freezing water trying to catch a fish. It gave up after an hour, yet the whole time the river bank was full of rabbits and beavers laughing at him. Come on bears, get your paws on some proper food, like a nice bit of sheep or a deer instead of pissing around trying to catch a fish.

Terry Farricker, Blackpool

WHY do they always do the collection half way through a church service? Shouldn't they at least do what buskers do and wait until the end? After all, the vicar might turn out to be absolute fucking rubbish.

Crawford Mulesaddle, Hull

COLUMBO only had one eye and yet missed nothing. Imagine how good a detective he would have been if he'd had two.

Gary Ireland, Tauranga

THE term 'cat's pyjamas' is used to describe something good. But in reality, cat's pyjamas would be torn to ribbons and covered in cat shit.

Gustav Fox, Knackersford

I'M sick and tired of people pointing out to me that I've combed my hair in the wrong direction. I can only assume my mirror is to blame, for showing me a 'mirror-image' of myself. Come on mirror-makers, surely in 2019 you can make a mirror that shows my reflection the right way round.

David Herron, Durham

IT'S amazing to think that as a man, I could comfortably beat Serena Williams in a game of tennis.

Dick Navey, Harrogate

HOW is it that narwhals are real and yet unicorns are mythical? Surely it should be the other way round. What possible use can a huge fish have with a horn? It's not like they joust each other or anything, whereas I'm sure a unicorn could do some proper damage given half the chance. I reckon God dropped the ball on that one.

Greg Alam, Hanham

I THINK it's sad that many newlyweds head for the divorce courts at the first sign of marital strife. They should remember that all marriages have teething troubles, but they will get there in the end. My wife and I have been married for 30 years now, and I can confirm that in the last 6 months things have been more or less civil, with only a handful of visits from the police.

Eldon Furse, email

MY wife has recently placed a small glass bottle of scented oil with sticks poking out of the top in our downstairs bog, and now it has the wonderful aroma of cotton fresh linen. Well, at least it did until I had a shit this morning. Now there is an overwhelming scent of turds. My arse one, scent bottle nil.

Anus Clap, Waterlooville

* *Rude Alexa*

ALEXA...TURN THE LIGHTS ON

TURN THE FUCKERS ON YOURSELF, YOU COW'S CUNT

IT seems that shops stock seasonal products earlier and earlier each year. Today I saw a birthday card, but my birthday isn't until October. Utterly ridiculous.

Rich B, Kidlington

THE authorities always demolish houses where terrible atrocities have taken place, like 25 Cromwell Street and 10 Rillington Place. Yet I notice that they haven't taken so much as a pin hammer to The Tower of London which has seen hundreds, if not thousands of deaths in its bloody history. Yet again, there's one rule for the blue bloods and another for your ordinary working-class serial killers.

Buckby Chorlish, Leeds

HOW come scientists looking for cures for diseases always experiment on mice? It's not as if mice are likely to die of the same stuff we do. I don't know anyone who has been tortured to death by a cat, or indeed had their back broken in a rudimenatry steel-sprung trap.

Topo Gigo, Hants

I AM committed to eating only locally sourced produce. As an obese alcoholic, it's marvellous that I live in between a Bargain Booze and a Greggs.

James Brown, Edinburgh

I JUST went on a website looking for healthy meal ideas and it asked me to accept cookies. Not a good start.

Christina Martin, Bexhill-on-Sea

WITH all the anti-pigeon netting that's being put up everywhere in towns these days, the morale of these birds must be at rock-bottom. I like to help build up their self esteem by awarding them an 'Individual Achievement' certificate if I spot one coo-ing particularly impressively, wandering about on one leg, or pecking at some really hot chips.

Mark Glover, Coventry

20 THINGS YOU NEVER KNEW ABOUT THE SOPRANOS

IT'S THE HBO smash that introduced the world to Tony, Paulie, Sylvio and the gang. It's *The Sopranos*, and back in the 2000s we couldn't get enough of this true-to-life portrayal of a mafia man, his wiseguy *paisans* and his intolerable family.

Over six series, including one that was split in half so it was actually more like seven, the New Jersey crew's antics had us screaming for *gabagool* and wishing we could have a go on a real gun.

But, despite the show's popularity, there are a few things even the most mob-keen viewer might have missed. So, grab your *goomah* (mistress) and a cold slice of *proshute* (ham), and educate yourself about *this thing of ours*.

1 **JERSEY** born actor James Gandolfini was not the director's first choice to play show's lead character Tony Soprano. TV presenter and comedian Bradley Walsh was initially offered the role, but shooting of the box office smash would have clashed with his appearance as Barnaby in *Puss in Boots* at the Birmingham Hippodrome. The *Chase* frontman turned down the part, and the rest is history.

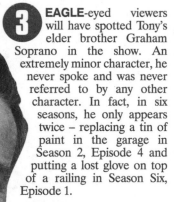

2 **NOT** everybody was a fan of the series. Amongst their number, the show's non-fans include intact-hymened MEP Ann Widdecombe, DIY superman Tommy Walsh and surviving Chuckle Brother Paul. *Schifosa!*

3 **EAGLE**-eyed viewers will have spotted Tony's elder brother Graham Soprano in the show. An extremely minor character, he never spoke and was never referred to by any other character. In fact, in six seasons, he only appears twice – replacing a tin of paint in the garage in Season 2, Episode 4 and putting a lost glove on top of a railing in Season Six, Episode 1.

4 **AND** putting some nuts out for the birds in Season 1, Episode 5. So that's three times.

5 **CONTINUITY** error! In Season 3 Episode 11 entitled *Pine Barrens*, one of the pole dancers in the Bada Bing bar can be seen gyrating sensually in a bra and knickers. But when we cut back to her minutes later, her baps *are all the way out*.

6 **EVERY** time a character died in the show, the remaining cast would get into character by holding a real Mafioso funeral for them, complete with black horse-drawn cortege, Catholic Holy Mass and two-day wake. This added several months to the shooting schedule.

7 **THE** character of Tony's screen daughter, Meadow Soprano, was named after writer David Chase's real-life daughter, Miss Meadow Soprano.

8 **THE** character of Meadow's friend Hunter Scangarelo was named after Chase's nephew, Ian Crockett, who shares a birthday with none other than the wife of Hunter from ITV's *Gladiators*.

9 **ONE** of the show's main characters is Dr Jennifer Melfi, a fictional therapist played by Lorraine Bracco. But in real life, therapists are an actual thing. In fact, many large American cities have a 'therapist' much like The Sopranos' Dr Melfi. And just like in the show, therapy is costly and goes on for ages.

10 **MUSIC** is an important part of the show, and

eagle-eared fans will have noticed that *exactly the same song* is used at the start of every episode.

11 **AFTER** kissing his wife Maureen goodbye, actor Steven Van Zandt, who plays bar owner Silvio Dante, headed for the studio for the first day's shooting. However, on arrival, he was amazed to discover that Maureen, also an actress, had been cast as his on-screen wife Gabriella. "The chances of that must be a million to one," he told *Variety* magazine.

12 **CONTINUITY** error! In Season 2 Episode 13 entitled *Fun House*, Tony Soprano and Sal Bonpensiero - played by Vincent Patsore - enter a restaurant where the waiter brings them each a plate of spaghetti bolognese. But half an hour later the plates are empty.

13 **AS** well as being a member of a New Jersey-based crime family, a soprano is also a kind of singer, a kind of clarinet, a small saxophone, and a model of car.

14 **ALTHOUGH** the car is actually a Hyundai Sonata, not Soprano.

15 **THE** memorable scene in which Uncle Junior gets his wrist stuck in a sink *was never supposed to happen*. Actor Dominic Chianese put his hand in there after telling crew he had seen a coin and refused to let go, making retraction impossible. The cameras kept rolling and the cast improvised. The coin turned out to be a grape. *Fuggedahbowdit!*

16 **NEW** Jersey police blamed the series for a rise in crime during the time *The Sopranos* was broadcast. Over the show's eight years on air, an average of 23 people per day were arrested in the state and charged with being a Mafia don. *Stugots!*

17 **MANY** airlines had the show edited for broadcast on their in-flight entertainment systems due to the high incidence of offensive language. However, there were red faces on KLM after fliers alerted staff to one glaring omission – Michael Imperioli plays Tony Soprono's young protégé, Christopher, whose second name, *Moltisanti*, is Dutch for 'hog's eye'!

18 **MANY** of the actors chose to get in character by actually committing crimes. As a result, James Gandolfini was given a suspended sentence for going into a dry cleaning shop in Atlantic City and demanding money with menaces, whilst Edie Falco, who plays his on-screen wife Carmella was arrested and charged with threatening an Uber driver with a syringe full of air.

19 **HOWEVER**, Falco beat the case by successfully arguing in court that Uber hadn't been invented yet. *Marone!*

20 **CONTINUITY** error! In Season 5 Episode 2 entitled *Rat Pack*, Tony Soprano goes along to watch Bruce Springsteen and the E Street Band in concert with best friend and manager of the Bada Bing bar Silvio Dante, played by Steven Van Zandt. However, as well as being in the audience, eagle eyed viewers will also spot Van Zandt on stage playing rhythm guitar in the band.

IT'S THE BIG QUESTION that is splitting the country in three down the middle and driving acrimonious wedges between families, friends and colleagues. All of us take one side or the other or the other, cleaving fiercely to our own beliefs, and our fractured country will never be the same until this burning issue is settled once and for all… *Just Which Holmes is the Best?*

Is it **SHERLOCK HOLMES**, the fictional detective whose incredible powers of logic and deduction solved any number of perplexing crimes that confounded the best brains of Victorian Scotland Yard? Is it **EAMONN HOLMES**, the journeyman TV presenter whose mundane shows have filled many thousands of hours of airtime in a competently run-of-the-mill manner for decades? Or is it **"BIG" JOHN HOLMES**, the seventies porn actor renowned for his exceptionally lengthy and girthsome trouser department?

Let's take a step back from the battle lines and coolly consider the evidence so we can put this burning issue to bed once and for all. It's time to draw a line under broken Britain and finally begin the healing process, as we ask…

SHERLOCK

ROUND 1
FILMOGRAPHY SINCE his first adventure - *A Study in Scarlet* - appeared in *The Strand* magazine back in 1887, Sherlock Holmes has been portrayed on celluloid more times than any other fictional character. Over two hundred movies have been made of his adventures, and seventy actors - including Basil Rathbone, Peter Cushing, Will Ferrell, Michael Caine and that fat bloke off the PlusNet adverts - have donned his trademark deerstalker hat to play him on film at one time or another. As such, it is a high-scoring opening round for the pipe-chomping occupant of 221b Baker Street. **Score (9)**

ROUND 2
VIOLIN PLAYING WHEN faced with a particularly tricky conundrum, such as a murder victim found in a room locked from the inside, stabbed with a dagger that has a handle of singular Oriental design, Sherlock Holmes would play his violin as a means of focussing his thoughts. So you might suppose he would score well in this round. However, if you watch any of his films, the actors' fingers and bowing arms never move in time with the soundtrack, implying that the music has been dubbed on afterwards and Holmes couldn't play the violin at all. **Score (2)**

ROUND 3
CRIME DETECTION IT MAY surprise you to discover that the eminent consulting detective Sherlock Holmes doesn't score particularly highly in this round. This is because in many of his famous cases, the mysteries he solved were not crimes at all. Rather, they were bizarre puzzles and conundrums. Why did someone lately returned from India receive five apple pips in the post? Why was a red-headed man paid a stipend to sit in an office every day and copy passages out of the Bible? Why did someone's shoe go missing, and why was someone running round Dartmoor with a false dog? **Score (4)**

ROUND 4
SIDEKICK THE great detective's sidekick was Dr Watson - a bumbling medical man who played the Robin to Holmes's Batman, the Tommy Cannon to his Bobby Ball, and the Iain Krankie to his "Wee" Jimmy/wife. And the perpetually confused medic fulfilled his role to a tee, conveniently forcing Holmes to explain his reasoning outloud. Once again, it's a solid score for the scourge of the Victorian criminal underworld. **Score (9)**

ROUND 5
PENIS SIZE AT THE end of the nineteenth century, prudish readers would have been shocked if *Sherlock Holmes* arthur Author Conan Doyle had regaled them with a graphic account of his character's membrum virile. As a result, we know nothing about the length or girth of the eminent detective's unit, either on the stonk or on the soft. As a fictional character, the truth - whether he was packing a proper heavyweight copper's torch like Stephen Pound MP or a Christmas tree fairy light like funnyman Bobby Davro - is all in the mind of the reader. **Score (5)**

ROUND 6
CHARITY WORK AS A forensic criminologist, Sherlock Holmes was able to command a tidy fee, and it was usually only well-heeled clients who could afford to pay for his professional services. However, if a mystery intrigued him and piqued his curiosity sufficiently, he would occasionally take on a case *pro bono*. Having said this, in all of his adventures, he never ran a Marathon dressed in a Bernie Clifton comedy ostrich outfit, never sat in a bath of beans, and never shaved off one eyebrow for Comic Relief, so he rounds off the competition with a middling score in this final round. **Score (4)**

HOW DID THEY DO?

SHERLOCK……………
WINNING this three way contest wasn't elementary at all. The game was afoot, but just like on the Rickenbacker Falls, Sherlock has come a cropper good and proper. Professor Moriarty has been joined by two new arch-nemesisses, Eamonn and "Big" John. **(33)**

EAM[ONN]

FILMOGRAPHY
DESPITE having appeared on our television sets more or less constantly for the last three decades, Eamonn has only made the leap to the silver screen twice during his inexplicably lengthy career in 2004's appallingly bad *Fat Slags* movie and 2014's not-quite-but-nearly-as-appallingly-bad *Mrs Brown D'Movie*. On both occasions, Holmes played himself

VIOLIN PLAYING
MAN[Y] of us took violin lessons when we were children scraping away for a few weeks before giving up and selling our instrument to buy some clackers or a Raleigh Chopper, and it is no[t] impossible that Eamonn Holmes did likewise

CRIME DETECTION
ALTHOUGH he has never been employed as a detective, it is more than likely that Eamonn has at some stage early in his career presented some sort of low budget long-forgotten *'Crimewatch'*-style

SIDEKICK
WITH a[n] amazing four decades hosting humdrum television programmes under his belt, Eamonn has shared his daytime telly sofa with an endless procession of similarly

PENIS SIZE
YOU might think that only one person knows the truth about what Eamonn's packing in his nylon Y-fronts his wife Ruth Langsford - but you'd be wrong. That's because, back in 2016, Holmes underwent a double hip replacement operation. During the course of the surgery, doctors would almost certainly have had to remove his underpants to gain access to his pelvis, and when they did so they would have been treated to a close-up view o[f]

CHARITY WORK
LIKE man[y] household names, Eamonn undoubtedly does lots of charity work. He may well be a member of the Lord's Taverners, the Wate[r] Rats and the Variety Club of Great Britain, all of whom do sterling work on behalf of those less fortunate tha[n] themselves. Sadly, finding out would once again requir[e] us to trawl through his ceaselessly dispiriting Wikiped[ia]

EAMONN……
IT'S not been a "Good Morning" at a[ll] for this consummate, time-served T[V] time-filler. Just as he did in his 200[6] autobiography *This Is My Life* (currently at number 1,171,919 in the Amazo[n]

Sherlock, Eamonn or Big John ...Who is the best HOLMES?

...and although we haven't seen either of these films - and we have no intention of ever doing so - we can only assume he gave his usual lacklustre performance, so it's a low-scoring start for the Ulster-born sofa-sitter. **Score 2**

...during his time at St Malachy's School in Belfast. *Did he ever play the fiddle? If so, was he any good? Was he as good as Yehudi Menuhin?* We may never know, and his music teachers have all now taken their secrets to their graves, so it's a middling score in this round for the sausage-fingered Ulsterman. **Score 4**

...programme on some low-rent regional television station. Sadly, finding out if this is indeed the case would involve crawling through the interminable list of insipid TV shows that makes up his lacklustre IMDB listing, so we may simply never know. As a result, just like his entire telly career, it's an uninspiring performance in this round for the *Good Morning Britain* screen-filler. **Score 2**

...unremarkable co-presenter sidekicks over the years. Sadly, naming any of them would mean scrolling through his unbelievably tedious IMDB listing once more, and we are simply not prepared to do that. **Score 5**

...his chap. Bound as they are by their Hippocratic oaths, what those surgeons saw will never be revealed to a soul, except perhaps at dinner parties. **Score 5**

...page, and frankly life is too short. Sending his old ties to charity auctions is the sort of thing people like him do, and his generosity of spirit is reflected by his good score in this round. **Score 8**

...bestsellers list) he has given a reasonable account of himself, but in the end Holmes is under the hammer. **26**

BIG JOHN

FILMOGRAPHY
"BIG" John Holmes starred in an estimated 559 adult movies, appearing in a wide variety of different and varied roles including plumber, pizza delivery man, nurses' home janitor and cheerleaders' bus driver. During his onscreen career, he bedded an incredible 14,000 women with his prodigious member, enough women to fill Tannadice Park, the home stadium of Dundee United football club, although there is no suggestion that any of the women who regularly attend home games there appeared in any of Holmes's hardcore pornographic films. **Score 10**

ROUND 1

VIOLIN PLAYING
WHEN all your waking hours are spent having sex on camera with 14,000 women, it's very difficult to find enough spare time during the day to become good at anything else. For this reason, becoming a low handicap golfer, a skilled model engineer who constructed miniature steam engines, or a skilled landscape watercolourist, were all out of the question for Holmes. Similarly, it is highly unlikely he ever got round to mastering any musical instrument at all, even the recorder, tambourine or banjo, let alone the notoriously difficult-to-master violin. **Score 1**

ROUND 2

CRIME DETECTION
IN HIS first starring role, Holmes played gritty PI Johnny Wadd. However, since the plot involved him taking part in five spitroasts, three gangbangs and getting sucked off eight times over the course of an hour, there was very little screen time left for him to actually solve a crime. The film spawned a successful series of follow-ups, including *Around the World with Johnny Wadd, Here Comes Johnny Wadd, Tell Them Johnny Wadd is Here,* and *The Return of Johnny Wadd,* none of which saw the eponymous detective keep his trousers on long enough to solve any crimes either. **Score 7**

ROUND 3

SIDEKICK
THROUGHOUT his career, "Big" John had a constant sidekick who was never more than thirteen-and-a-half inches away from him - the Bing Crosby to his Bob Hope, the Eddie Large to his Syd Little, and the Lord Charles to his Ray Allan. **Score 8**

ROUND 4

PENIS SIZE
THE actual size of "Big" John's big John Thomas is a matter of some confusion. Variously, its size has been claimed as being 10", 11", 13", 14½", and even 16", according to which websites you visit. Sadly, in all the films Holmes made, there was never a scene in which his organ was photographed next to a 50p piece for scale, so it is impossible to accurately gauge its true size. The best we can do is average out the existing data to give us a final mean figure of 11.9" from knackers to hog's eye. **Score 8**

ROUND 5

CHARITY WORK
EJACULATING on camera five times a day would leave most of us with little energy for doing anything else, no matter how good a cause it was for. But "Big" John was made of stronger stuff, and found time during his busy fuck-filled schedule to go from door to door in his neighbourhood raising money for good causes, including Greenpeace, Save the Whale and other animal welfare charities. Holmes would regularly spend his evenings baking cakes and biscuits, bringing them onto set the next day to sell to his co-stars for charity. Indeed, selling muffins to cast and crew on the set of his 1973 film *Ride a Big Cock Horse,* he raised nearly $50 in a single day which he donated to his local hedgehog rescue centre. **Score 7**

ROUND 6

BIG JOHN

WHAM! Bam! Thank-you Ma'am! "Big" John's the cock of the walk, and his class sticks out a mile ... or at least it sticks out somewhere between 10" and 16". He'd be popping the Champagne corks in celebration, if he hadn't popped his last shot, and his clogs, over thirty years ago.

41

NEXT WEEK: Collins vs of Arc vs Jett & the Blackhearts... *Who's the Best Joan?*

...OPERATION IMPOSSIBLE...
...OPERATION IMPOSSIBLE...
OPERATION IMPOSSIBLE...
...OPERATION IMPOSSIBLE...
OPERATION IMPOSSIBLE...
...OPERATION IMPOSSIBLE...

The Kremlin...03.08.2015...

Good afternoon, Comrade General Kolchinski. You are early.

BLIDDIP!

FINGERPRINT ...MATCH...

You can go in, sir.

I do not wish to be disturbed.

Yes, General.

I'm in!...

...the rubber fingerprints we lifted from Kolchinski's whisky glass in the brothel worked.

I never doubted it, Nathan

Now, can you see the computer terminal?

Logging on now!

I've got the missile launch codes on screen. What now?

Print them out and get out of that office quick. The General's plane has landed. He'll be at the Kremlin in half an hour.

There we go.

15284
99630
22156
02317
00621
56692

PRINT DOCUMENT? YES/NO

CLICK!

WHIRRRR! CHUG!-CHUG!-CHUG!-CHUG!-CHUG!-CHUG!

What's happening, Nathan?

The printer's making noises but there's nothing coming out.

♪ BONK!

Bugger! It says it's out of paper

Put some more in, Nathan! Quick! We haven't got much time!

I've found some. It's A3 though.

It doesn't matter, it'll be fine...

It's in!

Resume job?... Yes!

BONK! ♪

Shit!

RESUME JOB?

What is it?

It says "Document size does not match paper in default tray...

...change tray in default settings? Y/N"

Press No.

WHIRRRR! CHUG!-CHUG! CHUG!-CHUG! VRRRRP! VRRRRRRRRRRRRRRRRP!

It's printing! There's something coming out!

Ah, shit. It's all off one side of the paper. There's only half the codes on it.

Listen to me, Nathan. Open the Printer Preferences Panel and tick the box that says 'Centered.'

Do it now! The real General's on his way!

Okay! Done it! Pressing Print again!

1528
9963
2215
0231
006
566

WHIRRRR! CHUG!-CHUG! VRRRRRRRRRRRRRRP!

Come on! **Come on!**

VRRRRRP! VRRRRRP! VRRRRP! VRRRRRP!

It's taking ages.

What's happening? Do you have the printout?

Fucking thing!

Eh!?! It's done it *tiny*. What's it done **that** for?

Do it again, and this time click the thing that says 'Fit document to paper size'...

...and make sure you click 'Centred'.

Fit document to paper size...centred...Print!

VRRRRRP! VRRRRRP!

Oh...yes...it's doing something!

Great!

Bastard! Bastard! BASTARD!

What is it, Nathan?

It's printing it fucking massive.

Do it again at 50%. You're running out of time.

VRRRRRP! VRRRRRP! VRRRRRP! VRRRRRP!

I can't stop it! Oh, for **FUCK'S SAKE!**

...it says 'printing page 4 of 560...

Go into the print queue, highlight the job and press 'Delete'...

...Have you done that, Nathan?

Yes, it's stopped...

50%... centred... Oh, for fuck's sake.

What is it?

It says 'Printer Offline' now. What the **fuck**...?

Oh no... wait... it says 'Searching for Printer'...

...'Connecting to printer'...

I've got the spinning beach ball thing...

...'Connecting to printer'...'Connecting to printer'...looking good...come on...

...'Printer not connected'

...Oh for *fuck's sake*. *I'm going to chuck the fucking thing out the window in a...*

PRINTER NOT CONNECTED.

Oh, hold on...'Printer connected'...Resume print queue?'

Yes, Nathan... press **yes!**

PRINTER CONNECTED. RESUME PRINT QUEUE?

VRRRRRRP! VRRRRRRP! VRRRRRRP!

FUCK'S SAKE! It's gone all **FUCKING TINY** again!

Ten minutes later...

General Kolchinski! **But...?**

...Quit it and run the setup wizard again, Nathan.

I've **tried**, but it's saying it's not a genuine Hewlett Packard Magenta cartridge and I can't get that fucking message to go off...

...Fucking **bastard** piece of **shit**!

Next Week: Agent Blunt abseils off the Eiffel Tower and down the chimney of the Iranian Embassy in Paris, before attempting to print out a secret chemical weapon formula on a Brother HL1112.

Roger's PROFANISAURUS

A Criminal Selection from Britain's Favourite Lexicon of Filth and Profanity

profanisaurus@viz.co.uk

Agatha Christie *n.* A silent, putrid *arse crime* committed by someone in this very room, and only one person knows whodunnit.

alkytraz *1. n.* The police station drunk tank. *2. n.* Any Saturday night spent incarcerated on the salubrious Welsh island of Barry.

backfire *v.* To *fart* with sufficient volume to startle a police horse.

bobby's helmet *n. Bell end.* From the distinctive shape of the traditional British constable's hat which manages to look like a *tit* and a *cock end* simultaneously.

bobby's anorak *n. Kojak's roll-neck, cock collar, Wilfrid's jumper.* The prepuce.

bobfoc/bobfoc *acronym.* Body Off Baywatch, Face Off Crimewatch. Having a *welder's bench* inexplicably mounted on top of a finely carved *rack and pegs*.

Bolton alarm clock *n.* The convoy of police cars, ambulances and fire engines which charges through the streets of the delightful Lancashire resort at precisely 9.05 each morning.

Bransholme lighthouse *n.* Nickname for the Humberside Police helicopter, owing to the fact that it spends most nights illuminating the exclusive Bransholme Estate in Hull.

Burnley taxi *n.* A police car.

burnside drawer *n.* The bottom drawer in a fellow's office desk, which contains contraband material, *ie.* Alcohol, cigarettes and pornography. Named after no-nonsense, good old-fashioned copper Detective Chief Inspector Frank Burnside out of off of *The Bill*.

butler's ringpiece *adj.* Descriptive of something that is nipping clean. *"What can you see, Holmes?' I expostulated, as the great detective peered into his microscope. 'I'm examining the handle of this dagger of unusual oriental design in the hope of finding a speck of tobacco of a sort only available from one shop in London, or a hair from a rare species of Patagonian chinchilla,' he replied. 'However, I fear our murderer has wiped it as clean as a butler's ringpiece."* (from *The Brown Hatted League* by Sir Arthur Conan-Doyle).

cheerful Charlie *n. rhym. slang. Sausage fat.* From the dour-faced *Minder* detective played on screen by Patrick Malahide, *viz.* DS Cheerful Charlie Chisholm = jism.

Chelmsley Wood lie detector *n.* A West Midlands Police Force truncheon.

collar and cuffs *euph.* Matching hair colour, up top and down below. *'See that blonde? Do you reckon her collar matches her cuffs? If you think you can help, contact Tyne and Wear CrimeStoppers on the number at the bottom of the screen. Our team of detectives are waiting to take your call.'*

Columbo *n.* Named after the monocular, raincoat-clad TV detective, a seemingly ineffectual *epilog* that suddenly stops you in your tracks as you're walking out of the front door, by needing "just one more thing..." Also *Jimmy Cricket*.

Columbo's coat *n.* A tatty and creased-up *fanny* that looks like an aged basset hound might use it for a bed. Not to be confused with a *Columbo's mac* which is, of course, a tatty and creased-up *fiveskin* that looks like an aged basset hound has spent the morning chewing it behind the sofa. *'Oops. I think my Columbo's mac has got caught in your Columbo's coat.'*

convict lenses *1. n.* High powered *funglasses*, as commonly worn by men who have recently been released following a prolonged period of incarceration at Her Majesty's Pleasure. Or, conversely, *2. n.* Metaphorical astigmatic optical apparatus sported by the sort of woman who sees a conviction for armed robbery or murder as an attractive secondary sexual characteristic in a suitor.

copperdantic *adj.* Unnatural mode of speech used by members of the constabulary to lend import, gravitas and false precision to the everyday, the mundane and the completely made-up.

copper's torch *n.* A large, heavy, *bell-swagged schlong* dangling disturbingly between the legs of a skinny old man. A *schlepper.* *'What's the matter, your holiness? Are you wrestling with an intractable theological conundrum, such as the* concept of original sin?' 'No, cardinal. I've just went for a slash and I've been and caught me copper's torch in me zip.'*

coroner's cloth *n.* A piece of lavatory tissue tactfully placed over *skidmarks, pebbledashing* or any other discomfiting debris one has left in the toilet bowl, in the same way that scene-of-crime officers would cover up a dead body or other such unpleasantness from the gaze of passers-by. *Chocolate quilting, papering over the cacks, Turin shroud.*

Crimewatch reconstruction *euph.* Of the residents in a student house, around the time *Doctors* comes on, convening in the living room to stitch together disparate fragments of evidence in an attempt to produce a full understanding of the goings-on of the previous night.

double chalker *n.* Someone so morbidly *big-boned* that if they were found murdered, it would take two pieces of chalk to draw a line around them. *Today's birthdays: Roy Orbison, US singer-songwriter, 1936; Ed Stewart, Junior Choice DJ, 1941; Michael Moore, US polemicist double-chalker, 1954.'*

drugs bust *n.* Simultaneous entry of two *bobbies' truncheons* through the front and back doors. Also *police raid, SVSA.*

Glaswegian siesta *n.* A night in a cell.

Hackney bunting *n.* Police crime scene cordon tape, which is commonly used to decorate the streets of the inner London borough.

hangover Holmes *n.* A chap who uses all the evidence available to him about his person (*eg.* Bus tickets, cash machine receipts, stains, wedding rings, bruises, lovebites, *crabs*) in order to deduce what he got up to the previous night. See *Crimewatch reconstruction*.

Happy Shopper copper *n.* A community police support officer. *'I was too young to get a job as a lollipop man so I became a* happy shopper copper instead.'*

harbouring a known criminal *n.* Holding in a noisome *bottom burp* or suppressing a *baby's arm* while in an enclosed area or in close proximity to a lady.

hiding policemen's helmets *adj.* Of a lady, to be *nipping out, smuggling peanuts.*

jizz lamp *n.* A special ultra violet torch favoured by fictional crime scene investigators looking for feloniously deposited *man spackle* on mattresses.

jollies *1. n. Police.* In constabulary terms, trips to scenes of crimes. *2. n.* Women's breasts. *'Look at the jollies on that nun, your holiness.'*

knock off the bobby's helmet *v.* To engage in a fistfight with one's *little Kojak.*

Kojak's roll-neck *n. Foreskin.* Based on the slap-headed lolly sucking 1970s TV detective who always wore a cheesy-necked pullover.

Kojak's moneybox *n.* The *herman gelmet.*

love truncheon *n.* A *copper's torch.*

masonic handshake *1. n.* A secret signal surreptitiously passed between policemen, town planners and the shape-shifting lizards of the New World Order. *2. n.* Any act of *self help* which utilises an unusual grip.

mousetrap *1. n.* Unbelievably bad Agatha Christie play which performs a sort of Care in the Community role for bad actors and has now been running in

'Ello! 'Ello! 'Ello! Wot's all these 20,000 entries, then?

Viz PRESENTS Roger's PROFANISAURUS WAR AND PISS

ON SALE NOW £20

C IMINAL WO DSEARCH

HIDDEN in the grid below are all of the definitions in this *Roger's Profanisaurus* Criminal Selection. They may read up, down or diagonally, backwards or forwards. If you can find them all, or even if you can't, you'll win a Viz Cheap Pen. Simply send a **LARGE LETTER STAMP** to: *Roger's Criminal Profanisaurus Wordsearch, Viz Comic, PO Box 841, Whitley Bay, NE26 9EQ*. Please don't enclose any completed entries, we're not interested, we'll just send you a pen if you send a stamp.

```
D S D U B L P Z X R B Y U J L N M T G L A S W E G I A N S I E S T A B M L S A B
L E B A C K F I R E X N P I K C O L C M R A L A N O T L O B P K H T S G R W U L
A S S C B U K H T P D P O Z A C T G L O P D H I E R Z H L E V U J G T B U R D G
S N S V M I K H T E C G P Z A I M L R S Q T R O U S E R T R U N C H E O N L N K
D E A N Y F R K R M I D W L X E X T E K P C L J U F S Q N O F E R J X S M I C V
V L O M H D I C R I M E W A T C H R E C O N S T R U C T I O N E P T I X T V O O
A T Q V J K O O M H Y D T M M O P S T P E T P L H Y E M P T E E S D L N E T P I
L C L G W V T M P K D Y R P A V T E P U R B I D D W O K F P L U E Y U E Y F P L
X I F T E P H M I D E Q U G P Q T E V A W P R M O U C E I N W D L B M N O Y E L
Z V T R H D O W A L L M Y D U D R B N E G U L O S O T P W Y R H Y H L P F C R I P
A N C W B U S N N L M H T E L S R G V Y G A R E M T E L C A E E J A L M U A D A L
F O K S T G E R A U N P B T T O L I D S A B T L Y P I T W U N M F R H I R A A L P
P C O X G U U L M Y S E G O K E Y H B M P R G H R S F E L K O L R D A I R T N L T
P T J R C B S Y G E C U R C K O L U G Y A W O O A Y R M C N O P R A T S A I T O X
F K A T O P M U D B S C E O E O S P J P E E B V U C T A M L C H E S N G K M I V I
P B K C T T K A R Q H H J F E T M K D B G L M L U F H M K C D E A A M L J Y C E T
A R S R C U C A C N P A Y B K L H G R U E U I M E S E R P L I W M P E D E J P T J
L A R C Q B V E P G K R B O P M T S E M C Y G A O L Y G I C P E K O C T O I R R L
K N O C K O F F T H E B O B B Y S H E L M E T P B E T S L S C P A L L M Y D W U G
Y S L G S B A B U E O M H T F E S P L U M I S E T D X U W I T M U I L L D W O N E
T H L A E B X H I T D C O L L A R A N D C U F F S P L J L A M I J C T U O M T C C
R O N Z T Y L N T C R E L M E K O J A K S M O N E Y B O X P G O E E M T U P E H E
A L E A P S O K T E Z E I P M Y D Y L I A N Y D R G P P N Y L M L M G W B L U E I
Z M C Z T H A C Y P S A E L P T D E D R V N U T C A N K L L P L A A Q H L H T O P
R E K A C E M F V S D E K R D N U N P M J F R S N O K N I L R S W N B P E X S N G
E L X C Y L B O V U X R M M Y O T E L A D C F A Z E R E Z C X G P S S X C O T L N
P I E Z H M H D M S M G Y L P K O E P H R J H B L P S O A E D K P K E H H E N O I
P G S A C E K N T E P H G U O W C W P J E T L K R S N P N W F I L N A B A Y I X R
O H S E G T L U B H M P K H E H A S Y A S T I M K L D C H E H A E O M J L T R L S
C T E G D U J E H T O T K L A T R Z H E G K L C M H N E K C R L K C S D K S P E R
R H N A P G J K E P M L H D P O E E M T L S S E U J Q H D A M S N K G Y E S R T E
E O T A V C T L H U L U H R D B P I V C Y S L K U L T N S D R J C P N T R R E G L
P U I B H L K J E G M L G F D P T X G O P J M X T E A K L Z F O E L E Z M K G H T
P S W B H Y D L O N H F G E W E L O K Y G E E L L R T R P A L S N H O M K F N J U
O E T A C T P O L I C E H O R S E F A R T N V T E P M U S U Q Z H A H T J T I P B
H L N A B I O T R H K M Y O M F D L P I T F A Z S H K D M K B T G R S H H J F L M
S R E A Q G F X I G L Y M M I U H R D L K T Z H B E C B E W Z I H Y R Y E F S K L
Y D L S Z V N K P U S D M F L W H P Z J E I L F N I O M L H D T E B I Y B E N F U
P D I P L X G R E O E M L F B C V U P C H E E R F U L C H A R L I E C T E B W K L
P S S C R A T T E R C U S H I O N S Y W M J D T E R E A I T N A L P D E T T O P K
A M G L P O A R E X R U P H I D I N G P O L I C E M E N S H E L M E T S M I R B D
H M L F T R A G C K P I M R S Y N P O L H G T L M G D S T R H K L D E E U J B X X
C O L U M B O S C O A T M L P F R L A N I M I R C N W O N K A G N I R U O B R A H
B N D G T R B J L P M A S O N I C H A N D S H A K E B J H F P S T H M L I Y M L D
```

the West End for more than a hundred years. *2. n.* A bin found in the ladies' restrooms where women may discreetly dispose of their feminine hygiene products, such as *jamrags, fanny nannies*, and *chuftie plugs. 3. n.* One's wife's *minge* for the week or so each month when she is *dropping clots. 4. n.* A poorly balanced *chod hopper* lid that guillotines down onto the top of a fellow's *twig* while he's *straining his greens*, causing him to let go and make a grab for it, making *piss* go everywhere. Also *pivotal moment, golden handshake, Newton's curse*

Mr Brown's fingerprints *euph.* Forensic proof that a foul malefactor was present at the scene of a crime, *eg. Skidmarks* on an S-bend or gusset.

Old Bailey bird *n.* An embarrassingly unattractive ladyfriend who you would ideally like to smuggle into the house under a blanket, in a style reminiscent of the way that *scuffers* bundle particularly unpopular murderers into court buildings on the news.

particulars *n.* Of low budget British sex comedies involving police officers, ladies' *bills*, knickers. *'Excuse me, madam, but I may need to take down your particulars. And have a look at your cunt.'*

police horse fart *n.* A *change of heart* capable of dispersing an unruly mob.

policeman's knock, hard as a *1. s.* Descriptive of a ne'er-do-well, for example, perhaps ensconced in a public house bar. *'I wouldn't mess with him, mate. He's as hard as a policeman's knock.' 2. sim.* Descriptive of the physical resilience of an object. *'Lady Alexander caressed his thigh, slowly moving upwards and gasped. "My word, corporal," she said. "You're as hard as a policeman's knock!"'*

policeman's radio, rogered more times than *phr.* Said of a woman who's *had more cocks than Davey Crockett's rifle, more legs over her than a Blackpool donkey.*

potted plant *n.* An unkind epithet for a Police Community Support Officer. From the fact that they make the place look slight better decorated while performing no discernibly useful function and using up space that could otherwise be put to better use. *'Hello? Emergency Services? Someone's trying to break into my car.' 'Don't worry madam. We'll send a potted plant round with some customer satisfaction survey forms to fill in tomorrow afternoon.'*

Quebec Bravos *n.* Metropolitan Police phonetic radio code. QBs = Quality Breasts, used by bored *scuffers* on Saturday night city centre duty. *'Calling all units, calling all units. Que-* bec Bravos outside the 'Spoons in the High Street. Any units wish to assist? Over.'

riot hose *n.* When the *old man* delivers a powerful, out of control stream of *wazz* at the lavatory, soaking all and sundry in the style of a French police water cannon at a student demonstration.

riot coke *n.* Any tinned or bottled beverage that may incline the imbiber towards high-spirited behaviour in the street, *eg.* Strongbow.

roughing up the suspect *v.* What a vice squad copper tells his superiors he's doing when he's caught *polishing* his *bobby's helmet* in the seized porn store room.

silent witness *n.* Upon visiting the *chod-bin* and carrying out a CSI-style recce of the *pan,* the sodden, *stool*-soiled and flush-resistant *bunwad* that offers compelling forensic evidence of a recent lavatorial crime.

scratter cushions *n.* The wipe-clean, blue mattresses found in police cells.

strangle Kojak *v.* To *make the bald man cry, peel the carrot.*

swagman's hat *n. medic.* Condition of the *anus* when infested with numerous *tagnuts. 'Holmes surveyed the water closet cubicle before announcing, 'The game is afoot, Watson, and our quarry has a bandy-legged gait.' 'How the devil do you know that, man?' I exclaimed. 'Elementary.' vouchsafed the esteemed detective. 'The Izal toilet paper means he will almost certainly have a ringpiece like a swagman's hat."* (from *The Red-Ringed League* by Sir Arthur Conan-Doyle).

Sweeney! *exclam.* A humorous utterance shouted out in the style of Flying Squad DI Jack Regan by a man who is *kicking a lady's back doors in.*

talk to the judge *n.* To *suck a copper's helmet* by way of avoiding a speeding ticket. *'I know I was doing 75 in a 30 zone, officer, but is there any way we can work this out? Perhaps if I spoke to the judge behind that skip?' 'I'm not sure that's going to make any difference, sir.'*

three pipe problem *1. euph.* A case so perplexing that Arthur Conan Doyle's great detective Sherlock Holmes had to retire to ponder it carefully while smoking. *2. euph.* Issues of complex familial infidelity and possible paternity so perplexing that they are only seen on *the Jeremy Kyle Show.*

trouser truncheon *n.* The stout length of *wood* a bobby takes out in the back of his van on a Saturday night. A *turned-on copper's torch.*

undercover cop *1. n.* A plain clothes detective. *2. n.* A crafty spot of *DIY* under the bedsheets while the missus is in the ensuite.

whizzer and chips *1. n.* A fondly remembered comic. *2. n.* The gentle art of unzipping and *slashing* with one hand while holding a hot takeaway with the other. *'Keep toot for the filth, Mr Mayor. I'm just off for a whizzer and chips in the Nationwide Anglia doorway.'*

profanisaurus@viz.co.uk

Ben Dover's XXXMAS MOV...

HI! Octogenarian porn star *Ben Dover* here. I love everything about Christmas, me. The decorations, the turkey, singing carols round the tree. In fact, as far as I'm concerned, there's only one thing missing from the festive season... *a bit of Yuletide hardcore porn on the telly.*

Christmas movies are all about loving and giving, making time for the special people in your life, and renewing old friendships. Heartwarming family favourites like *It's a Wonderful Life*, *A Christmas Carol* and *Miracle on 34th Street* are all very well, but let's face facts, there's a distinct lack of cocks, tits and fannies in these timeworn family favourites.

But that's now a thing of the past, thanks to this fantastic XXX-rated FREE gift that's yours to cut out and keep. My **CHRISTMAS MOVIE PORN CONVERTER** instantly turns any heartwarming, charming, festive film into a hardcore Yuletide fuckfest. The only limit is your own filthy imagination!

Merry Sexmas, Ben xx

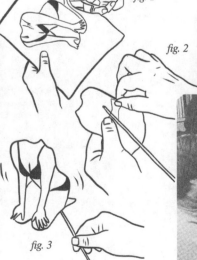

Check out these RED HOT seasonal examples!

Holiday Inn ... becomes *Holiday In All the Way!*

It's a Wonderful Life ... becomes *It's a Wonderful Wife (Swap)!*

Miracle on 34th Street ....becomes *Miracle on 69th Street!*

A Christmas Carol ... becomes *A Christmas Carol and her Hot Sister!*

INSTRUCTIONS

Simply scan in the erotic figures and blow them up by the percentage that corresponds to your TV screen size (see conversion table below). Then print them, cut out them out (fig. 1), and attach each one to a long skewer (fig. 2). Then simply wait for your favourite Christmas movie to come on the television, send the kids to bed, and position the figure in front of the screen. To hot up the action, start jiggling the figures up and down to simulate realistic intercourse etc. (fig. 3). Then sit back and enjoy the erotic action!

TELEVISION SIZE	MAGNIFICATION
12"	100%
24"	130%
32"	200%
43"	250%
55"	310%
75"	390%
85"	420%

fig. 1

fig. 2

fig. 3

E PORN CONVERTOR

"I'm turning in my fucking grave."
Mary Whitehouse, Colchester Cemetery

"This is hotter than a Christmas pud that's just out the oven and has been set on fire with brandy."
Lara Latex, Grumble Thespian

"The Viz XXXmas Movie Porn Converter is as fantastic as my tassel was long (ie. very)."
"Big" J Holmes, Oxnard Cemetery

"Hardcore blimey! What a Sexmas treat!"
Prof. Brian Cox, former keyboardist

"This fucking porn converter is the fucking Billy Bollocks. The fucker's made my bastard Christmas!"
Ian Dunt, political commentator

GREAT STOCKING FILLER!

IT'S AN XMAS CRACKER OF A GIFT!

WHOOPS AISLE APOCALYPSE

Please please *please* have forgotten...

Good morning Valentine!

Sealed with a loving kiss – and breakfast in bed too!

Nice card.

Does a job doesn't it? Discontinued for some reason – 19p.

Say you'll *fix it for me* to be your lover...

HOW'S ABOUT BEING MY *VALENTINE* THEN?

WHOOPS! *WAS £2.49*
NOW: 19p

Strawberries on your cornflakes?

They look off.

Only a w-few days.

The rotten bits are actually sweeter.

SPPPTTTHOOO!

That milk has turned.

Can't complain at a pound for 40 litres.

CORN FLAKES

ALDI *WAS £1.34*
WHOOPS! *WAS £1.34*
NOW: 14p

Drown out the sourness with more cereal.

Soon
Close your eyes.

Must I?

It's a surprise!

SURPRISE!

Two dozen red roses – *50p if you can believe it!*

Flowers are given away if you wait, bear *that* in mind at the next bereavement. Look! Choccies too!

I thought they'd stopped doing Dairy Tray...

They did, these'll be the end.

Dairy Tray
WHOOPS! *WAS £1.00*

Mildew.

Quick wipe down good as new.

But – *why*?

Every year the same, *ruined* by your penny-pinching – I'd sooner you didn't bother!

Oh no!

You must let me make it up to you!

How does a delicious romantic candlelit dinner for two sound?

Well. Nice, actually.

But ars Reduced

Grab the Rolo mousse-pots, I'll eat one off your chest!

Quick! Not sure how long I can hold him!

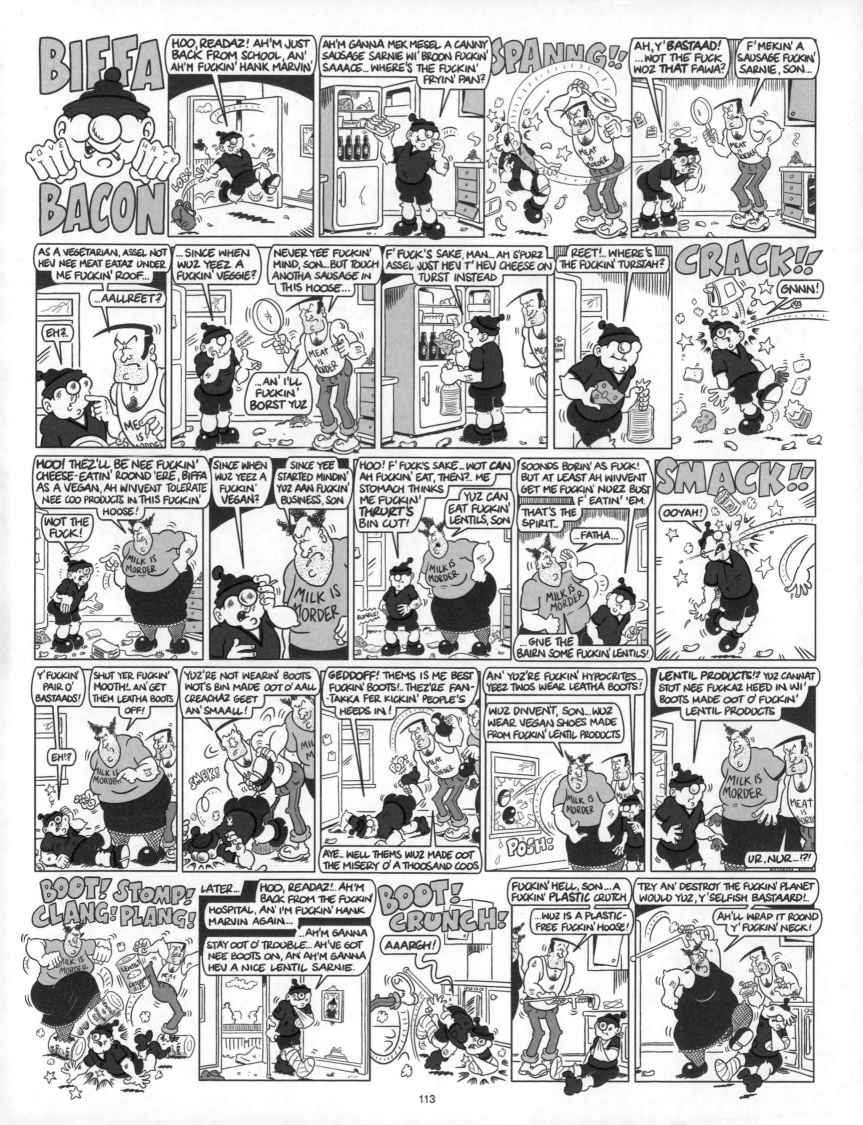

Take a Shit

YOU'RE BBC BARRED!

TV and Radio favourites named and shamed!

A FORMER landlord of the BBC bar has sensationally leaked a BLACKLIST naming many of the corporation's top stars whom he has been forced to BAN for unacceptable behaviour.

Ex-Beeb publican **PENRITH KENDAL**, who recently lost his job following a series of mainly unsubstantiated allegations including, but not limited to, serving drinks outside of licensing hours, theft from the till, being drunk while on duty, and the installation of surveillance cameras inside a vent in the ladies' toilets, says that a rollcall of the broadcaster's most highly paid personalities behaved so appallingly that he was left with no option but to forbid them from entering his premises.

Kendal told us: "It was my name above the door, and ultimately the buck stopped with me. I wasn't going to allow the stars to carry on like that in my boozer, no matter how famous they were."

As told to *Vaginia Discharge*

"I used to run a proper, old-fashioned flat-roofer – The Albion – on a run-down estate in Essex, so I've dealt with a few difficult customers in my time," he continued. "But compared to the stars who used to frequent my bar at TV Centre, they were saints, I can tell you."

Now, after being given his marching orders by the BBC on what he claims are exaggerated charges, Penrith has decided it is time to speak out and name and shame those who are really responsible for his downfall. He told us: "The BBC is run like an old boys' club. And when I started barring the stars, they closed ranks and made sure it was me that got the heave-ho."

"But I don't regret what I did. The behaviour of those household names really was atrocious, and they deserved to get barred."

Auntie-social behaviour: Rowdy Beeb regulars gave Penrith the runaround.

PACKHAM SHOWED WILD SIDE

❝ I'd only been in the job a couple of days when I was first forced to put my foot down and ban an unruly punter. It was ten o'clock on a quiet Monday evening. As usual, there were a couple of weathermen propping up the bar, and **JEREMY PAXMAN** and the *University Challenge* lads had just left after their regular post-show pie and a pint. My only other customers were **MICHAELA STRACHAN** and **KATE HUMBLE**, sat in the corner nursing a couple of small Merlots while they filled in the *TV Quick* crossword.

Then **CHRIS PACKHAM** came in and spotted them, and that was when all hell broke loose.

He'd got a big cardboard box under his arm, and there was all scuffling and scratching noises coming out of it. He put the box on the floor, opened the flaps, and out came an angry, snarling badger. I couldn't believe my eyes. It was a proper big one,

Packham: Threw Frazzles at badger.

and it had pissed while it had been in the box, so it stank to high heaven. God knows where he'd found it. Michaela and Kate screamed and jumped up on the banquette, and Packham grabbed the badger by the scruff of its neck and thrust it towards them, making them scream even louder. It was pandemonium.

I went over and pointed out that animals weren't allowed in the BBC bar, except guide dogs. But Packham was having none of it. 'Go eff yourself, four-eyes,' he told me, which Strachan and Humble seemed to find very amusing. 'It's my effing badger, and I'll bring it in the bar if I effing want.' Only he didn't say 'eff', he said 'fuck'. He was showing off in front of the girls, and they in turn were egging him on.

Then things went from bad to worse. Packham started throwing Frazzles and Monster Munches at his badger.

"It's my effing badger, and I'll bring it in the bar if I effing want."

The E-numbers in the crisps seemed to be getting the poor animal even more agitated than it already was, and it was running around in circles, shitting everywhere and making a high-pitched barking sound.

I was furious. **EMILY MAITLIS** usually comes in for a couple of pints of Guinness on a Monday after *Newsnight*, and I didn't want her getting bitten or going arse over tit after slipping in badger turds, as it would reflect badly on me in my first week in charge. I shouted to Packham to get his badger back in its box and out of my premises. To be fair to him, he did eventually do as I said, cornering the animal by the fruit machine and throwing **TOMASZ SCHAFERKNACKERS**'s anorak over it.

The unruly *SpringWatch* threesome eventually left, but they left yours truly

Quiz off: *Davis's (left) light-hearted teasing caused chaos in the BBC bar when Toksvig (right) kicked off.*

to clean up the unholy mess that the badger had left. I shouted after them that they were all barred. In the heat of the moment, I may have used some choice language which, with hindsight, I now bitterly regret; to be honest, I can't remember.

Later, after I had calmed down a bit, I chalked their names on the "barred stars" blackboard I had hung behind the bar. They may have been the first names on my blacklist, but they were sadly not to be the last. **"**

I 'THEROUX' LOUIS OUT ON ARSE

" One day, I became aware of a commotion in the corner of the bar. It was *BBC Breakfast's* Business editor **STEPH MCGOVERN**, and she was rocking the fag machine violently from side to side, effing and jeffing. It was 4 in the afternoon, and she'd been in since coming off air at 9.15 that morning. I went over to see what was up. 'There's something lodged in the slot,' she ranted, aiming an angry kick at the front of the

The Weird Weekends film-maker had crossed a line.

machine. 'It won't take my money, and I'm clemming for a tab.'

I told Steph to calm down and take a seat while I investigated what was wrong. It soon became clear what the problem was. Someone had sneakily attempted to fool the mechanism with three washers wrapped in foil instead of a £2 coin. And this wasn't the first time this had happened. The offender had form; over the past few weeks I'd found several other crude counterfeits in the fag machine coin box.

But this time, by jamming the slot, the culprit had made a fatal error. The last customer to use the machine before McGovern had to be the faker. I knew that all I had to do was to review the CCTV footage to identify them. I went behind the bar and eagerly re-wound the tape, peering at the grainy footage on the closed circuit screen.

I couldn't believe my eyes when I saw the unmistakable figure of offbeat documentarian **LOUIS THEROUX** standing by the cigarette machine. He was looking around furtively, checking the coast was clear before forcing his phoney coin into the machine. Then he seemed to panic, trying in vain to retrieve it using a penknife before skulking off guiltily as Steph McGovern staggered up to the machine.

I knew Theroux was still in the bar, so I decided to confront him. I told him what I'd seen him doing, and asked him to turn out his pockets. The fag machine takes four £2 coins, and the first one he tried had jammed, so I was pretty

Louis-ve it out! *Theroux's sneaky ciggy scam was old hat to Kendal.*

sure he'd still the three remaining fakes on him. But he was in no mood to play ball, and told me to go and eff myself. Although he didn't say 'eff', he actually said 'fuck'.

Well to me, that was as good as an admission of guilt. What's more, the *Weird Weekends* film-maker had crossed a line, as I've never stood for bad language in any of the boozers I've managed. I told him to sling his hook. Although I may have used slightly stronger wording than that in the heat of the moment, as he had really boiled my piss.

Theroux stood up to confront me. He's a tall lad, well over 6'2", but he's a big drink of water. I may only be 5'3", but I had a serious weight advantage over him, and he knew it. He clearly had no appetite for a dust-up and he headed for the door. I always liked his documentaries, especially the ones about nutty Americans and sex perverts, so it was with a heavy heart that I picked up my chalk and added his name to my ever-growing list of barred stars. **"**

WARWICK GOT TOKSVIG SHOCK

" Over decades as a professional custodian of a drinking establishment, I've had to break up more pub fights than I've had hot dinners. It's perfectly understandable. Tempers can easily flare when everyone's had a bit to drink, and it's the landlord's job to step and call time on any developing

argy-bargy. Indeed the vast majority of altercations end with the two parties shaking hands and buying each other another pint.

However, when big showbiz egos clashed in the hothouse atmosphere of the BBC bar, a simple disagreement could quickly escalate into ugly violence. And fisticuffs is something that I will not tolerate in any boozer with the name Penrith Kendal over the door.

Taking a final swig, she smashed the beer bottle down on the edge and pushed the jagged edge towards Davis' face.

Having said that, many of the big BBC stars clearly considered themselves above obeying the rules of my bar, and their resulting bad behaviour was a sight to behold. A case in point was *QI* presenter **SANDI TOKSVIG**.

Every week, after recording her light-hearted quiz show, Sandi would come in the bar for six pints of Greenall Whitley Mild. We would line the bottles up on her favourite table in the corner and she would neck them one after another as a means of 'coming down' from the adrenaline high of presenting the show. Regulars knew to leave her well alone while she went through her boozy routine; as long as nobody bothered her she was absolutely fine.

However, one night she was just about to down her last bottle when she was approached by **WARWICK DAVIS** off *Tenable*. Unwisely, Davis decided to tease his fellow quizmaster over a wrong answer she had given on the previous week's *QI*.

According to Davis, after asking **ALAN DAVIES** the formula for

CONTINUED OVER...

the surface area of a sphere and receiving a 'pass', Toksvig had given the actual answer as 3πr². 'It's actually 4πr². Where did you get your Maths O-Level from? Out of a Christmas cracker?' he quipped.

Everyone in the bar held their breath as Toksvig rose slowly to her feet. 'Oh aye, do you fucking want some?' she hissed. Davis was clearly taken aback. 'I don't want any trouble...' he stammered. But it was too late, he had lit Sandi's famously short fuse. Taking a final swig, she smashed the beer bottle down on the table and pushed the jagged edge towards Davis' face.

'Come on, let's have it then, fucker!' Toksvig screamed, lunging forwards. Fortunately, **ZEINAB BADAWI** and **GRAHAM NORTON** were at a nearby table, and they leapt up to restrain her just in time. Although they both received cuts and bruises as they wrestled the veteran *Number 73* presenter to the ground and prised the broken bottle out of her fist, it was only thanks to their quick action that Davis was saved from a nasty glassing.

Moments later, she stumbled out of the bar, pinballing off the furniture. 'I wouldn't drink in this shit-hole again for a gold fucking clock,' she slurred. But I wasn't taking any chances, and as the door slammed shut behind her, I chalked her name up on the blackboard... *Barred!* 〞

TALE OF BROTHERS GRIM

❝ The first time the **DIMBLEBY BROTHERS** – David off BBC1's *Question Time* and Jonathan off Radio 4's *Any Questions* – came into the bar, I was very excited to meet them. I'd been a big fan of both their shows for years, and they were exactly like you'd expect; two charming, urbane gentlemen. I poured them each a complementary single malt and we chatted amiably about current events. They told me how good the place was looking.

Then suddenly, without warning, the mood soured and the friendly smiles fell from their faces. 'Yeah, it's a nice bar,' said David. 'It would be a shame if anything happened to

Dimbleby off with you: Celebrated TV journo brothers Jonathan (left) and David (right) tried to put the pressure on Penrith.

ROLL CALL OF SHAME

During his two weeks behind the BBC bar, Penrith was forced to bar a Who's Who of household names for a whole variety of reasons, including:

Avuncular Radio 2 *Popmaster* favourite **KEN BRUCE**, for throwing a table through the window when the Deuchars IPA barrel ran out.

News24's **CLIVE MYRIE**, for asking for a glass of tap water, then topping it up with whisky from a bottle that he'd brought in under his coat

Veteran *Bake-Off* judge **MARY BERRY**, after she leant over the bar and helped herself to a double gin from the optic while he was in the cellar fetching up another card of Big-D nuts.

Highbrow BBC4 *Arts* presenter **WALDEMAR JANUSZCZAK**, whom he caught selling hooky rolling tobacco to other stars, from a suitcase in the bogs

it, wouldn't it Jonathan?'

'It would, Dave,' he replied icily, as he nonchalantly nudged his glass off the bar with his elbow, sending it crashing to the floor where it shattered into a thousand pieces. 'But accidents happen. Things get broken. Things catch fire. People get hurt.'

David Dimbleby leaned in close. 'Do we make ourselves clear, sunshine?' he asked, his inquisitorial tone familiar from a thousand episodes of *Question Time.*

I have to admit that they had indeed made themselves clear. They were running a protection racket. They were nothing better than a pair of two'penny ha'penny Kray Twins wannabes.

But the Dimblebys didn't scare me. I had dealt with scums like them, and worse, on a daily basis back when I ran the Albion, and I answered them in the only way they'd understand. I drew back my fist and punched Jonathan squarely in the nose. I may even have hit him a few more times. I can't remember, but what I can remember is that it was definitely in self defence.

As Jonathan staggered back from the bar with

blood streaming down his face, I grabbed his elder brother by the collar and told him he could expect more of the same if he didn't get out of my bar immediately. In the heat of the moment, I may have used slightly stronger language than that, although I can't quite remember the exact words I used.

As I was adding their names to the blackboard, my line manager came in. She was very agitated, as the Dimblebys had just been in to see her, claiming that I had attacked them. According to them, they had been sitting quietly at the bar enjoying a whisky when Jonathan had accidentally knocked a glass onto the floor. They claimed that I had come running over and launched an unprovoked attack on them, during which Jonathan Dimbleby had lost a tooth and had his glasses broken.

They furthermore alleged that I had been drunk, which was certainly not the case. I had only had a couple that particular evening, and very few earlier in the day, and the only reason I may have smelled strongly of drink was because **MOIRA STEWART** had thrown a full glass of whisky over me that afternoon when I was

They were nothing better than a pair of two'penny ha'penny Kray Twins wannabes.

ejecting her from the premises.

Not surprisingly, my manager sided with the Dimblebys and I was sacked on the spot. It didn't help that I was already on a double final warning on a series of other trumped-up charges where I had allegedly hit celebrities whilst under the influence of alcohol. My protestations of innocence counted for nothing against the misinformation, half-truths and downright lies coming from the biggest names on the BBC payroll. 〞

Yesterday, Penrith was back behind the bar of the Albion, the flat roof pub he managed before his move to TV Centre. He told us: "It's true I left here under a bit of a cloud, but it's rough as arseholes round here and the brewery couldn't find anyone else willing to take it on."

And he extended a warm welcome to any new customers who fancy popping in for a refreshing pint, a warm pie and a go on the quiz machine. "Keep your head down, don't look any of the regulars in the eye and you should be fine," he told us. But he had this message for any BBC stars who have found their way onto his blackboard of shame.

"If you're barred from one of my boozers, you're barred from them all."

Take a Shit

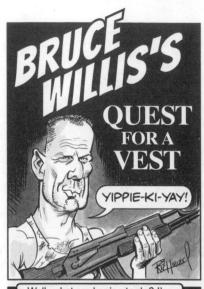

BRUCE WILLIS'S QUEST FOR A VEST

YIPPIE-KI-YAY!

Have you seen me vest, our Demi?...

...I'm filming Die Hard 28 this morning, and I can't do it without me vest, luv.

I've put it in the wash, our Bruce. It were all sweaty and covered in gunpowder and blood.

Aw flamin' Nora, Demi. That's what it's supposed to look like, y'daft cow.

Well if y'didn't want it washed, y' should have said.

Well, what am I going to do? I'm s'posed to be on set in half an hour.

Why don't y'call round Mrs McCririck's next door?...

...Her John off the Channel 4 racing's just snuffed it, so she'll probably 'ave some of his vests goin' spare.

Good idea. If his vests were owt like his pants were on Celebrity Big Brother, they'll be right manky.

KNOCK! KNOCK!

Morning Mrs McCririck. Sorry for your loss and all that.

Very kind of you, Mr Willis. It's been a very difficult time, but I'm taking every day as it...

Listen, you're not lobbin' out any of your John's mucky old vests, are you?

Erm...Aye, I've got one 'ere, as it 'appens. I were goin' t'cut it up for dusters.

Y'can 'ave it wi' pleasure.

Ooh, champion, Mrs M. It looks like it's proper been through the wars. Just what I need for Die Hard 28.

It's right grubby, this, just like the one I wore in The Fifth Element.

Aw bugger. It's ten bloody sizes too big, this. It won't cling to me pecs and abs when I'm doin' all me action scenes.

Well, he were a bit of a fat twat, our John, God rest 'is soul.

Shortly...

FISH -N- CHIPS

BOB'S YER BOOKIE

ROYAL SOCIETY FOR THE PREVENTION OF BIRDS

NEW STOCK

These'll have an old vest, you'd think.

Have y'got any old vests in, missus? Extra small, so they're nice an' tight round me midrif.

Ooh yes. We 'ad some come in yesterday, as it 'appens.

It were a coal miner who brought them in. Used to wear 'em down the pit, he did. Right mucky things.

Ooh, champion! I'll 'ave one o' them.

'Ere y'go, luv. Fresh back from the launderette.

Aw, *bollocks.*

118

Shortly...

Ruddy 'eck, what a perfect vest!

'Ere, pal. 'Ow much do y' want f' that vest?

What? This old sweaty, grimy thing?

Aye, I'm due at Pinewood Studios t' do Die Hard 28, only me missus has washed me mucky vest, the daft mare.

Y'can 'ave it for a tenner, Mr Willis.

What a stroke of luck. I've just got ten dollars 'ere, look.

No, not ten *dollars*. Ten *quid*... that's about thirteen dollars.

But... this is all I've got.

Sorry, Bruce. You're not 'avin' it f' that. No tenner, no vest.

Aw, bugger. What am I going' t' do? Filming starts in ten minutes.

Hmmm... That vest's nice and small... an' it's seen better days...

...I'll half-inch the bugger and mucky it up a bit on me way to the studios. Heh-heh!

Ooh, it fits a treat, this! Just like the one in Last Action Hero.

I'll just hitch a lift in this corporation shit wagon and get it properly mucked up!

Oof!

Ooyah!

Eurgh!

PINEWOOD STUDIOS 10 MI

10 mins later...

Heh! Perfectly scruffed up, and right on time for me first scene of the next instalment of me interminable franchise!

HUM!

Mornin', Mr Willis. They're waiting for you on set, sir.

Thanks Reg.

Hi Bruce. You're right on time to start shooting the first scene. You've got to run into this bank that's on fire and shoot some robbers.

Love it!

BANK

Oh, could you take that mucky old vest off, first?

Eh?! But why?

Well, Die Hard 28 is sponsored by Persil Automatic Washing Powder... and they want your vest to have that dazzling bluey-whiteness that only their new biological formula can achieve, even on stubborn stains. Stains that other powders leave behind.

And...

Okay, Bruce. Remember to keep that vest clean... and...

...*Action!*

LETTERbOCKS

Viz Comic, P.O. Box 841 Whitley Bay, NE26 9EQ : letters@viz.co.uk

IF people think Daenerys Targaryen's character switch in *Game of Thrones* is shocking, they should see my wife when I come home late from darts.

Kirk Flatus, Filey

ON the escalator to the Underground the other day, I couldn't help but notice how many advertising boards had models with missing teeth. I saw one so-called 'model' advertising Colgate who had 4 missing teeth. What's more, she had a jizzing cock tattooed on her chin. Come on marketing managers, how about hiring a few less penis-defiled models with better teeth for your products?

J Canavan, Kettering

I'VE just read that the oldest person alive is 116. But if my nan Connie Newth was still alive, she'd have been 118. How do you like them apples, so-called "World Record" holders?

Adrian Newth, Stratford

I'D like to apologise to my fellow passengers on the bus last night, who had to endure the sight of me drunkenly urinating on the back seat. It was unforgivable, and I am so sorry to have embarrassed any of you with such unladylike behaviour. But it was a fucking great day out, though. I love a good funeral.

Harriet Kempton-Park, Merthyr Tydfil

THESE so-called scientists banging on about Earth's population growing too fast haven't got a clue. Apparently the planet has been around for 4 billion years and there are 7.5 billion people on it. This means the human population has risen by less than 2 people every year. Fucking idiots.

Matt Greenwood, Weston-super-Mare

IT'S never occurred to me that 'tapas' is an anagram of 'pasta'. Come on, Spanish food inventors. Don't just jumble up the names of pre-existing foods from other Mediterranean countries and pass them off as being your own culinary names.

Kristian Barford, Rotterdam

STAR LETTER

I WAS a bit sceptical about umbrellas, but having just used one going down the street in the rain, I can tell you they really work. For anyone who still has doubts, I'd encourage you to give them a try.

Kent House, Finsbury Park

IN 1976 when I was 15, I went on holiday to Spain with my mate Andy and his parents. We were in a restaurant and I was wearing a pair of peppermint green Oxford bags and no underwear. I farted and shot diarrhoea all down the back of them. Can any of your readers beat that?

Mez, Hogwarts

✻ *Well, Mez, we think that all depends on what you mean by 'beat.' Perhaps you could write in and outline the parameters that would mean it had been "bettered" before we throw your challenge open to our readers.*

I HEARD a child cheek his parents in Tesco today and his dad said "I'll teach you to be cheeky!" I can't help thinking that would just make things worse. Then again, what do I know?

Carlos, Portstewart

I CAN'T help wondering if there might be a parallel universe in which the monkeys with red arses have got blue arses, and vice versa.

Palmer Vjorhend, email

WITH reference to Mr Vjorhend's letter *(above)*, physics throws up some very strange concepts that challenge our reason; an electron can exist in two different places simultaneously, matter can quite literally be created from nothing, and all the positive integers to infinity add up to $-1/12$. But come on, Mr Vjorhend, a universe where blue-arsed monkeys have red arses and vice versa is just so fucking far-fetched, it's laughable.

Brian Cox, CERN

I RECENTLY found out that the name Brian is of Celtic origin and means 'Strength and Honour.' This really does surprise me, as my next door neighbour is called Brian and he's a complete and utter fanny.

Audrey Ramsbottom, email

IF the Romans were so great, how come they all spoke Latin and not Italian, which might have been more useful? And why did the ones in Britain all go back to Italy where you can't even get chips? Its always worth questioning the history they teach you.

Kate Suzette, Scrabster

HAVING a piss in the shower this morning, it occurred to me that it would be great if I could of had a shit in there too. Come on, bathroom and toilet designers, why not get together and invent a shower where you can have a shit? I'd buy one.

S. Andwich-Paste, Shipham

DO any of your readers know if Marina from *Stingray* was actually a mermaid or was she just a woman who swam underwater a lot? And was she ever actually involved in the action, or was she just the object of Troy Tempest's wet dreams?

Col Percy Fawcett, Durham

WOULDN'T it be great if Adam Ant teamed up with Declan Donnelly whenever regular partner Ant McPartlin needed a break from his showbiz duties? They could still perform as Ant and Dec and fulfil the cheeky Geordie duo's contractual obligations, as I'm sure their contracts will not specify to which particular Ant they are referring.

Stephen Lewis, Manchester

IT seems to me unfair that people born on December 31st have to wait all year for their birthdays. If you were born on January 1st however, your birthdays come round lickety fucking split.

John Mason, email

IMAGINE if it was Alton Towels instead of Alton Towers. A theme park, based around fluffy bathroom textiles. Utter madness.

Ian Baker, Weston-super-Mare

I'M sick of taking the same plastic straw to McDonalds every time I go there. It's pretty manky now and a bit chewed at the end. Wouldn't it be better if we just taught sea life not to eat plastic instead? Dolphins have learned to do backflips on command, so they're not that stupid.

Douglas Daniels, Upper-Lowermiddletoft

TOP TIPS

BIRDWATCHERS. Recreate the thrill of birdwatching in your front room by simply erecting a small shed in front of the telly, cutting a hole in the side and watching documentaries about reed warblers on the 'Mute' setting through your binoculars, while eating Marmite sandwiches and probably nursing a semi.

James Davies, Stockport

CUBES of raw chicken dusted in cornflour make an ideal healthy alternative to Turkish Delight. Probably.

Andrew Underpants, Widnes

WOW guests into thinking you've made a time machine by setting off a firework in your wardrobe and then emerging dressed as a Viking.

Billy Grayson, Bundaberg

SEAGULLS. When somebody starts feeding you bread at the seafront or in Morrisons car park, don't start squawking at the top of your avian lungs. That way, you won't attract dozens of your mates and you won't end up having to scrap for it.

Edna Shitcrumbs, Hull

PARENTS. Add a touch of realism to your child's doll's house by simply putting a couple of Coco Pops into the toy toilets.

Iain Devenney, Abingdon

KERB Crawlers. Avoid detection and arrest by purchasing an ex-council road sweeping vehicle for your night-time forays into the seedier side of life.

Thrumpton Staines, Lancs

DESIGNERS of spaceships. Make sure you have a manual override accessible on BOTH sides of the door or hatch that you need to open or close. That way a crew member won't have to sacrifice their life due to your poorly thought-out design.

Simon McElvanney, Billingham

toptips@viz.co.uk

I HATE the expression "Let's get the ball rolling." It's completely sexist. You never hear "Let's get the tits bouncing" or any other female equivalent. Why should men get all the credit for getting things done?

Teresa Throbsworthy, Kent

PEOPLE say "You never know what's around the corner." But I do - The Red Lion boozer and a Cash Converters.

Hapag Lloyd, Runcorn

JUST imagine if he wasn't a skeleton, how muscly Skeletor would be. He would be able to deck He-Man easy then.

Magnus Mbanu, Cambridge

THEY say that the Great Wall of China can be seen from space, and maybe that's true, but I've seen pictures of it on the internet without ever having set foot on a spaceship. Perhaps these so-called astronauts should just learn how to use a computer like the rest of us, and save NASA an awful lot of money.

Buff Orpington, Chepstow

WHY, in films, whenever there's a shipwreck and they end up on a desert island, do they always seem to be obsessed with getting the radio working? Surely they should be concentrating on building a raft or lighting a beacon fire? Fuck *Steve Wright in the Afternoon*, I say. Get your priorities right.

Claude Humshaugh, Deal

'THAT'LL put the cat amongst the pigeons,' goes the old adage. Well, I took my cat to Trafalgar Square last week, and she sat down, licked her arse, then fucked off across the road and got run over by a taxi. I think it's about time the experts revisited the meanings of some of these old sayings.

Nigel Quicksand, Bristol

MY toothbrush needs charging every 13 days, whereas my wife's lasts for 11 days before it runs out. This means that both chargers are in use only one night in every 143.

The Owl, Northfields

WE hear so much in the news about icebergs melting at the North Pole due to climate change. We also hear a lot about fatbergs forming in our city sewers, caused by people not disposing of cooking oils responsibly. Rather than water companies breaking them up, why don't they float them up to the Arctic to replace the lost icebergs? The lower temperatures there mean that they won't melt and they will give polar bears something to sit on.

T. O'Neill, Glasgow

I HAD a dream once in which Kylie Minogue performed such disgusting sex acts that I went right off her. Frankly, I expected better of the Aussie songstress.

Flotaty Ade, Weston-s-Mare

IN reply to Richard Devereux *(page 98)*, who isn't interested in science, the reason that limes don't have pips but lemons do, is because there aren't any pips in a lime but there are in a lemon. Is that dumbed down enough for you, you fucking knob?

Terry Wilson, email

"KEEP your friends close, but your enemies closer" is a strange piece of advice. I feel pretty stupid watching my mates having a great time on the other side of the pub while I'm sitting at a table with my ex-wife and the twat she ran off with.

Terry Broomshank, Luton

WHY was everyone so terrified of waking the Kraken in Greek Mythology? The lazy bastard was under the sea, asleep for hundreds of years at a time. I know I wake up in a really good mood when I've had a bit of a lie-in, so I don't know why he always woke up with such a strop on.

Hector Crampons, Tooting

YET again a horse wins the Grand National. It's all getting rather predictable now, isn't it? Why don't they let Lewis Hamilton enter in his car to make the race a bit more interesting. Or Usain Bolt - he can go like the fucking clappers when he's got his trainers on. Come on, Aintree, liven it up a bit.

Harriet Kempton-Park, Merthyr Tydfil

AS time goes on, it strikes me that surely the middle ages aren't really the middle ages any more, but more like the early twenties. I propose we start calling them the 'late adolescence' of history. Who's with me?

D Cooper, Malta

I QUITE like Richard Branson, but I really don't like Noel Edmonds, yet they both look just as silly with the same ridiculous beards. It really goes to show that you can't judge people on looks alone.

Jane Hoole Garner, St. Ives

✱ Do you know of two celebrities who look very similar, but you like one of them and not the other? Perhaps you loved Jimmy Hill, but couldn't bear Acker Bilk. Maybe you admire Jacko out of Brush Strokes, but Terry the chef from Fawlty Towers left you unmoved. Or perhaps you love the Honey Monster but think Boris Johnson is an absolute fucking bellend. Write and let us know.

MY brother-in-law recently had an unfortunate incident whilst performing jury service. The case lasted 6 weeks and ended in a little confusion, with my brother-in-law being found guilty and sentenced to 2 years in prison. I wonder if any other readers have relations who have been convicted of a crime they did not commit. Obviously, don't write in if you are related to John Rambo or any members of the A Team. Or that bloke who turned into the Hulk in the 1970s.

Terry Farricker, Blackpool

I DON'T understand why law enforcement agencies fire tear gas into buildings during siege situations. Surely it would be better to fire in laughing gas. The criminals would be more likely to surrender and come out in a good mood and having a laugh rather than emerging coughing and with all guns blazing.

Frank Segal, Deal

HOW come the woman using the electric toothbrush on the Oral B advert hasn't got a dribble of spit anywhere? I end up looking like a rabid St Bernard 20 seconds after I turn mine on.

Kirk Flatus, Filey

I THINK some of these TV presenters are bang out of order at these "red carpet" award ceremonies. Asking someone whose clothes they're wearing is the height of cheek in my book. I borrowed our kid's suit last month for court, and even the presiding judge didn't have the front to ask me where I'd got my whistle from.

Bjorn Aldiss, Ely

AN EMBARRASSMENT OF RICHES

WE ALL get embarrassed from time to time, and celebrities who are called Richard are no different. So we phoned up 3 of our favourite A-List Riches and asked them one simple question: What was YOUR most embarrassing moment?

Richard Dawkins, *godless egghead*
MINE happened a few years back when I was due to give the keynote address at the Atheists' Alliance International Conference. It was a huge crowd and I was pretty nervous, so I did what I always do before a big speech: I popped outside to say a quick prayer and ask Almighty God to watch over me in my hour of need. When I stepped on stage a minute later, the entire audience was looking at me in abject horror. And that's when I realised... I'd left my wireless mic on! A whole room full of the planet's top sceptics had heard me giving it the old "Our Father Who Art In Heaven" routine outside! Talk about awkward. I couldn't get out of there quick enough.

Richard Gere, *famous actor*
MY MOST embarrassing moment took place on the set of *Pretty Woman*. We were about to start filming one day, and I'd just had a fairly heavy lunch of tinned tripe and black pudding so I nipped for a shit before the director called 'action.' I won't lie... it was a bad one, and there was no brush so I could do nothing about the unsightly stains all over the bottom of the bowl. When I opened the door I walked straight into one of the lighting guys who was waiting outside. I was so embarrassed about the state of the khazi that I blamed it on the person who'd been in there before me - my A-List co-star, Julia Roberts. I'm not proud of it, but I certainly spared myself a few blushes. And to this day, poor old Julia is still known as 'Skidmark Roberts' in Hollywood lighting circles.

Richard Littlejohn, *hateful gobshite*
I HAD a mortifying moment just the other day. I'd invited my fellow gobshites Katie Hopkins, Rod Liddle and Sarah Vine over to watch *Game of Thrones*, and I got a bone-on during one of the sex scenes. The Red Woman started stripping off, and wallop... I was suddenly sporting a raging diamond cutter, right there on the sofa. Then the phone rang, and there were no cushions nearby, so I had to get up and waddle across the room in full view of everyone. It was excruciating. Luckily, my cock is only three quarters of an inch on the bonk, so I don't think anyone noticed.

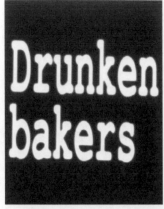

Drunken bakers

What the – What the *fuck* are you *doing?*

I'm making apple pies. You're making *shit* pies!

Since *when* do we put a ton of sugar on *top* of our pies? Yeah, I know... But they all do it now, so you've got to.

If *they* all put dog turds in their steak pies would you do that an' all?

You've never had a steak slice from QuidBake then...

Any road, seeing as how you ain't baked a single thing in sodding weeks –

– fuck off.

No point kicking against it, people just want stuff sweeter these days.

Aye, and look at state of 'em.

They can all look like death, for me, so long as they take a pie.

You're giving 'em diabetes, I watched it on the telly!

Balls, that's only the trendy new word for having a sweet tooth.

Sugar goes in the *pastry*, there's your sweetness...

Bit in the fruit, careful, take the sour edge off...

You want it tart not sweet.

That Kipling cunt was first at it, covering up his pale greasy lids

Now they can't do without.

I bet, if I made some like they was, they'd sell before *them*.

Maybe. That's the thing though –

– you ain't going to, are you?

You lazy bastard.

However Where's the fuckin' baking beans?

I ain't a clue.

FRESH APPLE PIES £1.50

How come? You've made pies today.

I didn't blind bake the crusts! Done 'em all from raw.

Ahh, I see. One more shit thing about 'em.

Claggy bottoms.

Later Handsome pies, them, to be fair.

Eggwash.

Mine'll still go quicker though...

May the best pies win.

But We'd best bin these, really.

Oh aye, bottling it are we?

They're crawling with ants.

~~FRESH~~ APPLE PIES

122

CAT OUT OF HELL!

A BRISTOL couple revealed yesterday that they have called on the church to exorcise their CAT, which they believe is possessed by the Devil.

Since taking up residence with Stan and Olive Crumbmould in Plywood Grove, Clevedon, Tizzy, a 3-year-old black and white shorthair, has scratched and bitten their children, stolen food from other cats in the neighbourhood, attacked a postman through the letterbox and even dragged a live crow in through the catflap.

"She can sometimes be really loving and affectionate," said Olive, 46. *"But then she gets this look in her eye and she just flips."*

"We're at our wits' end, and we have no choice but to turn to the church. She's pure evil," Mrs Crumbmould added.

mouse

Bishop Declan O'Hooligan, primate of the diocese, sympathised with the hell-cat's owners. "This feline once tormented a mouse for almost an hour before finally putting it out of its misery," he told reporters. "And he decapitated a squirrel right in front of Mrs Crumbmould in the kitchen."

"Nothing could do that unless it were playing host to the very soul of Lucifer himself," the Bishop added.

Cat: 'Just flips' say owners.

Family in flap over Mephistophelian moggie

"Indeed, so powerful is this particular possession that I feel a basic, common-or-garden £250 exorcism may not be enough."

"In my opinion, only the deluxe package, at £950 plus VAT, will cast Beelzebub from this cat's mortal body," he added.

door

But neighbours in the area were surprised at the news. "There are worse cats than Tizzy round here," said one woman who wished to remain anonymous. "The tabby at number 8 is always shitting on my lettuces. And it killed the little girl next door's guinea pig."

"It's a little bastard," she added.

Komod-oh NO!

A reptile dysfunction: London Zoo's Komodo dragon launched vicious attack on 98-year-old Duke.

THE DUKE of Edinburgh was being treated by doctors last night after being bitten on the arse by a Komodo dragon. The 98-year-old Prince had sat on the wall of the animal's enclosure at London Zoo to eat an ice cream, when the 12-foot lizard reached up and sank its razor-sharp teeth into his buttocks.

Prince Philip was rushed to the first-aid room near the gift shop at the zoo's visitors' centre, where the 6-inch wound was adjudged severe enough to require hospital attention. A luxurious stretch Rolls-Royce ambulance was summoned and he was taken to the Lindo Wing of St Mary's Hospital in Paddington for assessment and treatment.

toxic

According to experts, although Komodo dragons' bites are not toxic in themselves, the animals' saliva is teeming with harmful bacteria. Those who are bitten typically suffer severe sepsis and can quickly die if it is not treated quickly.

Eat your Phil: Buttock-hungry reptile caused royal rumpus.

Staff at London Zoo confirmed that prior to the attack, the Duke had been sat with his arse hanging over the enclosure wall, putting himself at severe risk. However, due to his

Prince bit on arse off of Dragon

superior, aristocratic rank, no-one had the authority to tell him to move.

One zookeeper told us: "I saw the dragon approaching Prince Philip, eyeing up his royal highness's bottom and licking its filthy, infected lips. He was completely unaware of the terrible danger he was in."

electric

"I wanted to warn him to move, but I knew that he was a stickler when it comes to formalities, and if I addressed him without him addressing me first, I would

be in trouble," the keeper continued. "It was a terrible situation to find myself in, but there was literally nothing I could do without breaking royal protocol, which deems that you must not address a member of the royal family unless they address you first."

garden

"I didn't want to get one of his famous tongue-lashings," the keeper added.

Yum-yum, Duke's bum: Toxic lizard sank teeth into consort's buttock, leaving him requiring hospital treatment.

A hospital spokesman confirmed that the Duke's wound had been dabbed with TCP and had a large, crossed-plaster dressing stuck over the gash.

* *Publisher's note: HRH Prince Philip was more or less alive-ish at the time of going to press.*

Have Your Say!

BITING A high-ranking member of the Royal Family on the arse could be construed as Treason, a crime that still carries the death penalty in the United Kingdom. However, according to legal scholars, only human beings can be charged with such crimes. So has the Komodo dragon which launched the attack on Prince Philip's backside got away scot-free, or should it be subject to the full force of the law and brought to justice? We went out onto the streets to see what YOU thought...

...I DON'T think any action should be taken against this Komodo dragon. In the wild, they eat all sorts of animals, buttocks and all. It was only doing what nature intended.
Ada Käelstrom, Goole

...IF I had of bit the Duke of Edinburgh on the backside, I'd now be in police custody, and quite right too. But it would seem that if I came over here from the island of Komodo, I could sink my teeth into his arse all day long with no repercussions.
Stanley Humshaugh, Luton

...YOU can bet your bottom dollar that if a British lizard had bit Prince Philip, it would quickly have been destroyed. But because

it was a foreign lizard, we've all just got to accept it. The quicker we leave the EU, the better.
Nigel Farage. London

...I THINK the dragon would have bitten whoever's arse had been hanging over the wall. It just so happened that it belonged to the Queen's husband. But no harm was done, and Prince Philip now has a very good dinner party story out of the incident.
Bartram Twelves, Croydon

...PRINCE Philip should be grateful for the incident. He is always at a loss as to what to say when he meets members of the public, and usually just asks "...and what

do you do for a living?" or "...have you come far today?" Now he can start every encounter with "... have you ever been bit on the arse by a Komodo dragon?"
Gertrude Strudle, Cheam

...KOMODO dragon or not, the beast should suffer the same fate as a human who bit a member of the Royal Family on the arse - death by hanging, drawing and quartering. Half-throttling it to the edge of death, and burning its intestines while it watches, before cutting it into four bits will send a message to all animals in London Zoo that royal buttocks are off the menu.
Teddy Blunderbuss, Horsham

...THE Duke of Edinburgh takes our tax money, and if he can give a bit back by getting his arse bitten off a lizard and giving us a laugh, then he should. In fact, every member of the Royal family should be queuing up to get their arses bitten for our amusement. They ruddy well cost us enough.
Dirk Cronkite, Wales

...MY DOG bit eight different postmen on the legs, arms and hand. Eventually, I bought a muzzle for him and the problem stopped. Perhaps London Zoo should be as responsible as I was and muzzle these lizards. I reckon one to fit an Alsatian would do, or maybe a St Bernard.
Hector Golargely, Trune

...FOR the Duke of Edinburgh to dangle his arse over the edge of a Komodo dragon enclosure is an act of stupidity beyond belief. I once idiotically put my cock into a mousetrap for a bet, and quite frankly we both got exactly what we deserved.
Barry Cardboard, London

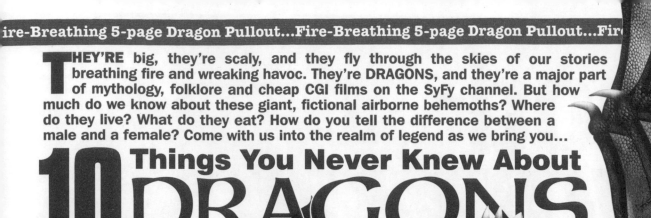

THEY'RE big, they're scaly, and they fly through the skies of our stories breathing fire and wreaking havoc. They're DRAGONS, and they're a major part of mythology, folklore and cheap CGI films on the SyFy channel. But how much do we know about these giant, fictional airborne behemoths? Where do they live? What do they eat? How do you tell the difference between a male and a female? Come with us into the realm of legend as we bring you...

10 Things You Never Knew About DRAGONS

1 **DRAGONS** never existed, but if they did, they would be related to the dinosaurs. In fact, real life dragons would be a species of winged T. Rex, which palaeontologists would have referred to as *Tyrannosaurus pterodracos* or something like that.

2 **WERE** they to exist, dragons' ability to breathe fire would probably be due to the presence of two organs, the pyrotechnocrine glands, which would be situated in the thorax. These would almost certainly secrete two different organic compounds which, individually, would be stable. When muscles beneath these glands, likely called the sub-pyrotechnocrine muscles, contracted, they would force these compounds up two channels, plausibly the left and right endocervical ducts, in the beast's neck. It is odds-on that these would join to form a common opening, imaginably called the ignis spincter, where the two chemicals would mix to form a highly flammable compound that would combust on contact with air. Probably.

3 **THE** *Harry Potter* novels contain a howling blooper when it comes to dragons. In the book *The Goblet of Fire*, Charles Weasley, who is studying Dragons in Romania, lists TEN different species, including the rare Hungarian Horntail, the large Norwegian Ridgeback and the Great Peruvian Vipertooth. However, in reality there are NO species, because they don't exist. Author JK Rowling still gets embarrassed when this blunder is pointed out to her.

4 **BIOLOGISTS** assert that real dragons could never have existed. Speaking to *New Scientist* magazine, Professor Richard Dawkins said: "Unlike every other vertebrate in the fossil record, which has four limbs or limb modifications, dragons have six, ie, two front legs, two back legs and a pair of wings. There is no branch of the vertebrate evolutionary tree where more than four limbs have appeared. It's utter fucking bat-shit bollocks."

THE DRAGONS' DRAGON DEN

TV'S DRAGONS are renowned for their ability to spot a good business opportunity. So if their fire-breathing fairytale namesakes are ever discovered, they will be the first to put their cash on the table in the hopes of getting a good return on their venture capital. We ventured into their TV den to ask telly's best entrepreneurs to pitch their exclusive investment plans and tell us how they would make a cool profit from hot dragons.

Duncan Bannatyne

I'D SET up a theme park called Bannatyne's Dragon Land on some brownfield wasteland. I'd have some of the dragons giving the kiddies rides, and other ones that they could pet, although I'd get their fire-breathing mechanisms taken out and have them de-clawed by vets. It would cost £30 to get in, or a family ticket for two adults and 3 children would be £100, and people wouldn't be allowed to bring their own food in. If they wanted to eat, they'd have to go to the Dragon restaurant or the St George Café where a small glass of orange would be £4 and a burger would be £12.50, and the chips would be extra.

Shoulderpads Woman

I SPENT years in the logistics business, and it's a world that I know inside out, so I would employ fleets of dragons to deliver parcels. Because they have vertical take-off, they could deliver to congested urban areas with ease, carrying the parcels securely in their talons. They could locate the correct address by magic, or if you don't believe in magic, they could be equipped with a sat-nav system that gave them a sharp electric shock across the bellend when they flew over the correct address, painful enough to make them drop the parcel down the chimney.

Theo Paphitis

I'D SET up a flying taxi business called 'Dragon Cabs'. It would be a bit like Uber, but instead of cars, we'd have a fleet of a thousand fire-breathing dragons, with each one licensed to carry up to four passengers. You'd book them via a mobile phone 'app' that gave you a price there and then, and tell the dragon master where you wanted to go. As soon as the business started making money, I'd set up a rival business called 'Firedrake Taxis', because as any successful entrepreneur will tell you, when you have a thriving business, you should set up your own competition before anyone else does.

Deborah Meaden

EACH year, over £250,000,000's worth of metal is stolen from Britain's scrapyards. Usually, the thieves strike at night, drugging the oil-covered guard dogs with tranquiliser-laced meat. My company - Draco Group Security - would rent out fire-breathing dragons to guard these scrapyards during the night. Since they don't actually exist, dragons can be anything your imagination wants them to be, so mine would be immune to tranquilisers, and I could charge scrap men top dollar to rent them out.

Peter Jones

I'D SET up my own dragon-fired power station, where I would keep the dragons in a boiler room and use their fire-breathing abilities to drive steam-powered electrical turbines, generating countless kilowatts of power for very little cost. I would break their wings so they couldn't fly off, and have people poking them up the arse with sticks to make them breathe fire. On the face of it, this may sound very cruel, but the beauty of a dragon-based business is that since they don't exist, you can treat them how you like without falling foul of the animal rights brigade.

5 DRAGONS play an important part in the Chinese New Year celebrations, dancing around while people bang saucepan lids together. But you won't find these dragons breathing fire. That's because they are made from paper and have people inside, and to have them belching flames would present a severe health and safety hazard.

6 NOT all dragons are terrifying giant beasts bent on fire-borne death and destruction. In the children's animated TV show *Chorlton and the Wheelies*, the eponymously named dragon was a small, Manchester-born simpleton who spread happiness wherever he went in Wheelie World.

7 ALL the other inhabitants of Wheelie World had wheels instead of legs, presumably to cut down on stop-frame animation costs.

8 ZOOLOGISTS have calculated that in order to get it airborne, the wingspan of a 20-ton dragon would have to be 160m, twice that of an Airbus A308. What's more, the wings would have to beat at a staggering 250 times per second, making a flying dragon buzz like 15.5 million wasps - that's enough of the stripy bastards to fill Wembley Stadium and an Olympic-sized swimming pool to a density of about one wasp per two cubic feet.

9 DRAGONS have featured as the main characters in many cartoons, except *Dragon Ball Z*, which featured a whole variety of strange creatures that lived inside red and white tennis balls. The story centred around Goku, a young boy whose mission was to separate parents around the world from their money via a series of never-ending merchandising opportunities.

10 PERHAPS the most famous dragon slayer in history was St George, a Roman soldier in the Praetorian Guard. In 287AD, he travelled to the Libyan city of Silene where the population was being terrified by a dragon. St George killed it with a lance called Ascalon, and the grateful population turned into Christians by way of thanks.

By George, He's Got It!

St George is surely the most famous dragonslayer in history. But sadly he died in 303AD, and the question has to be asked: *Who could fill his boots and protect Britain from a future dragon attack?* Since these beasts do not exist, the chance of one attacking the UK is fairly remote, but it always pays to be prepared. We looked a selection of modern day Georges and assessed their dragon-slaying abilities...

George Clooney, *Actor*

IN ADDITION to coffee adverts, George has made dozens of action movies, including *From Dusk Till Dawn*, where Clooney and his co-stars saw off hundreds of vampire Hell's Angels armed with crossbows and chainsaws. So you would imagine that one solitary dragon would be a walk in the park for the Tinseltown heart-throb. But Hollywood is the land of make believe, and every foe Clooney has vanquished has been an ACTOR! In real life, Clooney would probably soil his Gucci trousers if he came face to face with a genuine fire-breathing behemoth. Additionally, although he now lives in Oxfordshire, Clooney is an American citizen, and whether he would willingly fight a dragon to save a foreign state remains to be seen.
Dragonslayablity: 4

George Monbiot, *Guardian Columnist*

ON THE face of it, left-wing-rabble-rouser Monbiot would appear to be our perfect saviour in the event of a dragon attack. With his constant banging on about climate change, a fire-belching, CO_2-spewing beast is certain to get is dander up and put him in a fighting mood. However, his highly critical approach to everything would mean that Monbiot would insist on 'hearing the dragon's point of view' before deciding whether or not to slay it. The good news is, if he did decide that killing the beast was the best course of action for the UK and the planet, his degree in Zoology from Oxford University means that he would know exactly where to stab it for a clean kill.
Dragonslayablity: 7

George Foreman, *Cookware salesman*

EVEN IN his heyday as twice heavyweight boxing champion of the world, Foreman would have had difficulty landing a knockout blow on a forty-ton fire-breathing monster. And now, at the age of 70, he would stand no chance at all of laying it out for the count on the canvas. But the former boxer has made far more money as an inventor than he ever did slugging it out in the ring, with his famous low-fat grill netting him upwards of $200 million in royalties. So it's possible that he could use his inventing skills to come up with an equally successful device to rid us of any unwanted firedrakes. *The George Foreman Lean Mean Dragon Slaying Machine* could be the answer to all our prayers.
Dragonslayablity: 8

George RR Martin, *Be-capped Author*

MARTIN'S epic fantasy *A Song of Fire and Ice* has been translated into 30 languages, sold over 100 million copies and spawned the most successful television series in history. The story features the Mother of Dragons, Daenerys Targarian, and her quest to gain the Iron Throne. As a result, nobody knows more about dragons than Martin. Their anatomy, how they move, their capabilities, strengths and, more importantly, their weaknesses are second nature to the author. However, as a 70-year-old man knocking on the door of 25 stone, it's unlikely Martin would be able to get out of his chair unaided, let alone slay a fully grown dragon.
Dragonslayablity: 2

George Galloway, *Gobshite*

THE FORMER Labour MP for Glasgow Kelvin is as fearless as they come. Throughout his career, he has shown himself not afraid to challenge the political hierarchy, nor to express controversial opinions or make a complete twat of himself by pretending to be a cat on *Celebrity Big Brother*. So it's unlikely that Galloway would tremble in the face of a fifty-foot-long, fire-breathing flying lizard. He would most likely use a sword to bring about the beast's demise, after first giving an interminable speech about how deficiency in political theory was being filled by the entryist infiltration of the Labour party by Trotskyists, in a monotonous voice, in order to lull the beast to sleep before delivering his fatal blow.
Dragonslayablity: 9

George Lazenby, *Former James Bond*

THE 6'2" former 007 actor has all the physical attributes needed to make short work of seeing off his scaly foe. Not only that, but on slaying the beast, he would doubtless utter a humorous dragon-related quip along the lines of "Well, that's got me all fired up." However, Bond's weapon of choice, the 9mm semi-automatic Walther PPK pistol, would be unlikely to penetrate the armour-plated scales of a dragon. After emptying a magazine into the creature to no effect, the would-be assassin would discover that his licence to kill did not cover dragons. The creature would turn its wrath on Lazenby, leaving him shaken, stirred and burnt to a crisp.
Dragonslayablity: 1

George Osborne, *Former Chancellor*

IT'S DIFFICULT to think of two skill sets that are further removed from each other than looking after the economics of the world's 5th largest economy, and slaying a gigantic, fire-breathing mythical monster. And indeed, were Osborne to find himself in a contest with a dragon, he would be foolish to call on any skills that he learned whilst at No. 11 Downing Street. As a student, he was a member of the notoriously riotous Bullingdon Club, and he could perhaps draw on this experience by behaving appallingly in front of the animal, daubing paint on it, smashing its scales and throwing it into a boating lake. But even this would not finish the animal off, although as a true Bullingdon gentleman, Osborne would gallantly pay for any damage he had caused to the beast.
Dragonslayablity: 2

Dragon Disrupts Council Meeting

Dragon! Balls! Eeh!: Mythical beast interrupted planning meeting chaired by late Councillor Chymeswold (below).

The S

A MEETING of the Humberside and District County Council was thrown into chaos yesterday when a dragon burst into the debating chamber of the Town Hall in Goole and started spewing fire.

The 15 members of the council, along with three members of the planning committee, were just about to move to vote on a temporary extension to the alcohol licence at Mr Valentinos on the town's East Parade when the 30-foot reptile smashed through the back wall near the speaker's chair.

rubble

Council chairman, Cllr. Derek Chymeswold, was instantly crushed under the rubble caused by the violent entrance of the 15-ton mythical beast, and the remaining committee members immediately moved a motion to hold a minute's silence in his memory.

"I suggested that we pay our respects to Councillor Chymeswold in the usual way," said Deputy chairman Frank Carpetwright. "My motion was just about to be seconded by Mavis Dewdrop from planning, when the dragon spat its fire at her, instantly turning her to ashes before our eyes," he told the *Goole and Humber Suppository and Advertiser*.

flintstone

Senior planning officer Ted Bribeworthy gave a moving speech thanking Mavis for her years of service to the council's planning subcommittee, but was cut short when the invading giant lizard bit him in half. At that point, Deputy Chairman Carpetwright tabled a motion to abandon the meeting, which was passed by vote of 9 to 4, with 2 abstentions, whereupon the surviving councillors and members of the planning committee headed for the exit.

slate

At this point, the dragon made a dash for the door of the chamber, crushing two councillors as it did so.

"The mythical beast was hell bent on destroying all of us," Councillor Carpetwright told reporters. "The Town Clerk, Mrs Crumbhorn, threw her minutes ledger at the bloody thing and got it right in the eye," he went on. "But that only served to enrage it, and it incinerated her with its fiery breath."

But while the dragon was distracted,

Blood and Fire Rain Down on Administrative Assembly

Councillor Joyce Cursmuck, who sits on the Parks and Gardens subcommittee, managed to climb the spiral staircase into the public gallery and jump on the beast's neck.

"I knew it was dangerous," she said. "But it had already killed about six of the committee, and we were in danger of not being quorate, so I thought it was the only thing to do."

shmoo

The dragon then took to the air and flew around the chamber breathing fire, dislodging light fittings and scorching ornate 19th century ceiling plasterwork, whilst Mrs Cursmuck held on for dear life.

"I was terrified. It was like something out of Game of Thrones," she said.

gazoo

It was while the dragon was circling that the quick-thinking Parks and Gardens subcommittee member had an idea.

"I remembered when I was little, being told that if you were ever attacked by a crocodile, you had to poke them in the eyes until they let you go," she said. "And it occurred to me that this ruddy thing was nothing but a big crocodile with wings."

According to the remaining council members present, the dragon let out an unearthly scream as Mrs Cursmuck drove her fingers into its eyes.

"That howl," said Alderman George Carsales. "I shall remember that howl until the end of my days. The dragon immediately dropped out of the air, landing on the floor of the chamber and Mrs Cursmuck rolled off," he continued.

"I think Joyce must have blinded it good and proper because it got up and was clattering into walls and everything."

"Eventually it reached the back of the chamber and went out the way it came in and we haven't seen it since," he added.

arsehole

The surviving committee members then gave a vote of thanks to Mrs Cursmuck for her quick thinking, and Mr Carpetwright brought the meeting to a close after asking if there was any other business.

"We've had to abandon a few meetings over the years for one thing and another, but never anything like this," said Mr Carpetwright. "The sprinklers once went off accidentally, and a couple of years ago we had to move our meeting to another room because there was a broken sewer pipe leading to the smell of foulage in the chamber."

"But this takes the bloody biscuit, let me tell you," he said.

1. Meat - £500,000

Reptiles are essentially cold-blooded, featherless birds, and it is highly likely that dragon meat would taste very similar to chicken. If we assume that a dragon weighs 50 tons, and the meat from it could be sold for an £2.50/kg, the same as a chicken, a typical animal could be worth £125,000 or more over the butcher's counter. Not only that, the short term novelty value of dragon meat could see it selling for four times price of poultry, netting any poacher a cool half million for each dragon he delivered to the abattoir. However, consumption of dragon meat may come with a health warning, as just like the hide there's a good chance the flesh may be fireproof. No matter how long you cooked your dragon breast fillets, they could still be alarmingly pink in the middle, leaving you and all your barbecue guests laid low with a nasty dose of the quicklyshits.

2. Skeleton - £500,000

Animal bones are already a valuable commodity, as they are ground down for fertiliser, glue and dog biscuits. However, dragon bones could prove even more profitable if left intact. Any natural history museum around the world would love to have a real dragon skeleton in its collection, and heavy metal bands - such as Metallica, Napalm Death or Judas Priest - would dig deep to have a genuine dragon skull hanging up behind the drummer when out on tour.

3. Feet - £40,000

The international umbrella stand trade used to be a £50 billion a year business, but has been stagnant since animal rights troublemakers sought to get elephant hunting banned decades ago, and a newly resurgent trade in dragons' feet umbrella stands could give this ailing industry the boost it so desperately needs. Of course, with only four umbrella stands harvestable from each dragon, the supply of products would be strictly limited to four times the number of dragons that could be slaughtered, meaning that high-end retailers such as Harrods, Fortnum & Mason and Harvey Nicks could set a premium price point of up to £10,000 per umbrella stand.

x Million Dollar DRAGON

DRAGONS HAVE always been thought of as mythical beasts, but thanks to stories like *Harry Potter* and TV shows like *Game of Thrones*, many people believe they might now actually exist.

And the idea that dragons have remained undiscovered since their medieval heyday is not as far fetched as it sounds. As recently as 10 years ago, entomologists in the rainforests of Papua New Guinea discovered a species of fruit fly that was previously unknown to science.

Similarly, these fire-breathing, double-decker bus-sized flying lizards may have lain hidden from plain sight for centuries.

Tragically, like whales, almost as soon as they are discovered, dragons will be exploited and ruthlessly hunted, with their valuable body parts sold off to a variety of industries. Sadly, because they don't exist, they are not protected by current animal welfare rules, and poachers will be able to shoot as many of these magnificent, non-existent beasts as they wish, before flogging off their body parts to the highest bidder.

Amazingly, it is estimated by expert cryptozoologists that a fully grown adult dragon could net its hunter up to SIX MILLION DOLLARS (£4 million). So let's take a look at the market in dragon parts, and see how the profits add up....

8. Skin - £1.5 million
The tough, leathery hide of an adult dragon would sell to the fashion industry for a cool £1.5 million. Thanks to its exotically-coloured iridescent scales, the skin from a single dragon would provide fashionistas with enough material to make 5,000 pairs of exotic gloves, 2,000 high-end handbags, or up to 500 bolero-style couture evening jackets. Even, the roughest bits of the pelt, taken from the dragon's scrotum and around its anus, could be sold to the steel industry, where their leather's tough, fire-proof properties would prove invaluable in the production of protective aprons and tough gauntlets.

7. Teeth - £750,000
Ask pianists what they prefer their instruments' keys to be made of, and they'll invariably answer without a moment's hesitation - ivory. However, in recent years traditional elephants' tusks have been off the menu for piano makers, as sadly the endangered animals are now a protected species. Happily, since they don't officially exist, the animal rights brigade will be unable to complain about dragons' exotic teeth being harvested by piano makers. What's more, with each cryptozoological beast's mouth crammed with up to 500 giant, razor-sharp teeth, with each one yielding 10 or more key-sized veneers, a single dragon could furnish the keyboards of up to 50 bog standard school pianos ... or 20 full-size Steinway concert grands.

6. Eggs - £210,000
Since dragons don't actually exist in the real world, no-one knows how many eggs they lay in a typical clutch. However, most experts agree that like a chicken, if they existed they would probably lay between seven and ten rugby-ball-sized eggs at a time. Of course, these could be sold to the catering trade for use in industrial omelette manufacturing, where each egg - roughly the volume of 100 battery-farmed chickens' eggs - could be worth around £4 or so. However, the elite Fabergé egg industry would pay an awful lot more for them. Antiques experts believe that a typical gold- and gem-encrusted Fabergé dragon's egg could go under the hammer for a cracking £210,000 if placed in an exclusive jewellery auction at Sothebys or Christies.

4. Organs - £2,000,000 plus
Since dragons are mythical beasts that don't exist outside the pages of fantasy fiction, as soon as they are discovered an entire industry based on the bogus science of dragon homeopathy will spring up overnight. The animals' organs will be credited with miraculous properties, such as being able to cure hair loss, bad eyesight and impotence. The creature's 8-foot penis, once powdered, will be accredited with miraculous aphrodisiac properties, and sold by quack herbalists to gullibly soft-cocked and fat-walleted customers, such as Pele, Richard Littlejohn, Nigel Farage and Michael Gove, in return for huge profits. What's more, if homeopathic properties were attributed to some miraculous dragon penis elixir, the weaker it was, the more effective it would be adjudged to be, pushing the medical charlatans' profit margins even higher.

5. Fire chemicals - £500,000
Since dragons don't actually exist, scientists are unclear about what biological mechanism they employ to breathe fire. What's clear is that they must somehow secrete a highly flammable propellant that they blow out of their mouths and instantaneously ignite using some form of biological flint. Now that fossil fuels such as oil and coal are becoming frowned upon, clean-burning dragon-based 'bio-fuel' may well turn out to be the answer to the world's burgeoning energy problems, making any dragon a valuable commodity.

NEXT WEEK - How much could a mermaid make as a prostitute?

THE REAL ALE TWATS

A NEW BLETHERFORKS PUB HAS OPENED IN THE OLD FIRE STATION, CASKETEERS.

IT IS OUR BOUNDEN DUTY TO GIVE IT THE ONCE-OVER.

WE CAN'T ALLOW A NEW HOSTELRY TO OPEN IN FULCHESTER WITHOUT SUBJECTING IT TO OUR EXPERT SCRUTINY!

THE OLD FIRE ST ~ J.D. BLETHERFORK

NOW OPEN

ACTIVATE YOUR CRITICAL FACULTIES, FELLOW TAVERN-O-PHILES!

OH DEAR. THE USUAL BLETHERFORKS LAYOUT, I'M AFRAID...

...A HUGE, ECHOING CAVERNOUS SPACE, WITH ALL THE ATMOSPHERE OF A SCHOOL CANTEEN!

ONE CAN'T HELP FEELING THAT IF YOU'VE SEEN ONE BLETHERFORKS, YOU'VE SEEN THEM ALL!

THIS COULD BE A PUB ANYWHERE FROM LAND'S END TO JOHN O'GROATS.

TUT TUT! AND THE SAME-OLD-SAME-OLD RANGE OF BEERS...

THE USUAL MASS-MARKET, BIG BREWERY STUFF THAT YOU FIND IN EVERY BLETHERFORKS ACROSS THE COUNTRY!

DON'T YOU SELL FULCHESTER PALE ALE?

NOT HEARD OF THAT ONE, SORRY...

WHAT?! YOU'VE OPENED UP A PUB IN FULCHESTER, AND YOU'RE NOT EVEN FAMILIAR WITH OUR MOST POPULAR LOCALLY BREWED BEER?!

LOOK, I JUST WORK HERE, MATE...

PRODUCED BY FULCHESTER BREWERIES, THE FPA IS A GOLDEN, HOPPY SESSION ALE WITH HINTS OF CITRUS ON THE NOSE. 3.8% ABV.

EVERY DECENT FREE HOUSE IN TOWN SELLS FPA!

CAN'T HELP YOU, SORRY! WE'VE GOT GREENE KING — THAT SEEMS VERY POPULAR...

!!!

GREENE KING! COME, CASKETEERS, WE WON'T EVEN DIGNIFY THAT WITH A RESPONSE!

GREENE KING! TSK!

PTUI! GREENE KING!

BLETHERFORKS IS NOTHING BUT A McDONALDS FOR DRINKERS!

FIRE STATION ~ THERFORK ~

A GIANT, FACELESS CORPORATE MONSTROSITY SERVING UP MASS-PRODUCED SLOP TO UNDISCERNING MORONS!

FROM NOW ON, COMPADRES, WE WILL ESCHEW THE BIG PUB CHAINS!

LET US FIND A SMALL INDEPENDENT BOOZER OWNED BY INDIVIDUALS WHO ARE PART OF THE LOCAL COMMUNITY!!

THINK SMALL!

THAT WILL BE OUR WATCHWORD, CASKETEERS!

AND—

BEARD CITY TAP HOUSE & MICROBREWERY ~ ARTISAN CRAFT ALES ~

NOW OPEN   BAR

AHA — THIS LOOKS MORE LIKE IT!

OH YES, THIS IS FAR MORE AUTHENTIC!

BEARD CITY

TODAY'S ALES
HOPSTER - 5.4%
BEERDY WEIRDY - 6.2%
OWLD FULCH - 7.4%

LOCALLY SOURCED HOPS

COSY AND INTIMATE, WITH A UNIQUE QUIRKY CHARACTER WHICH IS FIRMLY ROOTED IN FULCHESTER'S LOCAL HERITAGE!

GOOD DAY TO YOU, BARLORD!

DO YOU SERVE FULCHESTER PALE ALE, PERCHANCE?

FULCHESTER PALE ALE?! CERTAINLY NOT!

HOPSTER - 5.4%
BEERDY WEIRDY
??

WE DON'T SELL MASS-MARKET RUBBISH LIKE THAT!

FULCHESTER BREWERIES ARE A GIANT, FACELESS CORPORATE MONSTROSITY WHO SUPPLY THEIR SO-CALLED BEER TO NEARLY A DOZEN PUBS IN THE REGION!

UGH! MASS-PRODUCED SLOP FOR UNDISCERNING MORONS!

BEARD CITY TAP HOUSE & MICROBREWERY ~ ARTISAN CRAFT ALES ~

HA!! HA!! FULCHESTER PALE ALE INDEED!

HO! HO!

HE'LL BE ASKING FOR A PINT OF FOSTERS, NEXT! **SHRINK!**

AND BACK IN BLETHERFORKS...

>SQUEAK!< THREE PINTS OF GREENE KING, PLEASE!

130

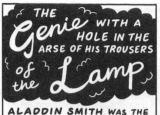
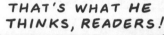

CRISIS POINT!

A LINCOLNSHIRE businessman has become the latest in a long line of institutions and public figures to declare a Climate Emergency.

Gary Dogseggs, founder and CEO of Grantham-based Gary's Burgers, said it was time for the business world to "wake up" to the problem of climate change.

"As business owners, we need to do far more to combat the growing climate emergency," he told the three delegates at the Grantham Conference on Climate Change in a layby on the A52. "Businesses account for a huge proportion of global carbon emissions, and it's time to face the fact that we have to change," he added.

profit

"Some things are more important than short-term profit," said Dogseggs, whose burgers, snacks and hot drinks have been a favourite of road users travelling between Nottingham and Grantham ever since Gary's Burgers was first established in 2006.

And last week, the 52-year-old forward-thinking entrepreneur used the conference to announce major changes to his business as part of his declaration of a Climate Emergency, including:

* Engine to be turned off while the van is stationary in the layby

* Heinz ketchup bottles to be refilled with bulk-bought tomato sauce from the cash and carry, reducing waste from single-use plastic

* Recycling encouraged by offering 20p off the famous Gary's Burgers tea to any customer bringing their own cup

* Use of public transport to be encouraged, with a new pitch outside Grantham bus station on Saturday nights from midnight till 4am.

Dogseggs, who also works as driver, head chef and till operator at Gary's Burgers, told us: "These are hard decisions, but it's clear to me that drastic action is needed."

curtains

He continued: "I hope other business owners will follow my example, and we can work together with politicians, scientists and the general public to finally tackle this existential threat."

flix

Dogseggs dismissed claims by one delegate that beef consumption was a major cause of climate change, saying that was "a load of bollocks."

Burger me: Local business owner Dogseggs is taking initiative to reduce environmental footprint.

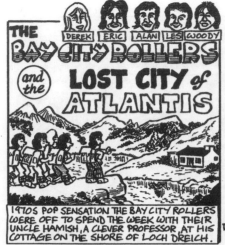

THE **BAY CITY ROLLERS** and the **LOST CITY of ATLANTIS**

DEREK · ERIC · ALAN · LES · WOODY

1970s POP SENSATION THE BAY CITY ROLLERS WERE OFF TO SPEND THE WEEK WITH THEIR UNCLE HAMISH, A CLEVER PROFESSOR, AT HIS COTTAGE ON THE SHORE OF LOCH DREICH.

DJ '19

UNCLE HAMISH IS A VERY BRAINY INTELLECTUAL — BUT HE CAN BE RATHER GROUCHY!

HA HA! YES WOODY, HE DOESN'T SUFFER FOOLS GLADLY!

I BID YE WELCOME, BOYS!

BUT I HOPE YE'LL NO' DISTURB ME WITH YON FOOLISH POP MUSIC THAT YE PLAY!

I CANNAE BE DISTRACTED FROM APPLYING MA ENORMOUS INTELLECT TAE SOLVING THE WORLD'S PROBLEMS!

WAR, RACIAL HATRED, POLITICAL UPHEAVAL — IT'LL TAKE ALL MA BRAIN POWER TAE FIND A SOLUTION TAE OOR PREDICAMENT!

Daily News WORLD DESCENDS INTO CHAOS!

LET'S TAKE THIS LITTLE BOAT OUT INTO THE MIDDLE OF THE LOCH AND PRACTISE SOME SONGS THERE!

GOOD IDEA, DEREK! THAT WAY, WE WON'T DISTURB UNCLE HAMISH!

BUT OUT IN THE LOCH, LES TRIPPED OVER HIS LONG TARTAN SCARF AND FELL OVERBOARD.

WOAH!

LES! BE CAREFUL!

LES VANISHED BENEATH THE SURFACE OF THE LOCH FOR A MOMENT — AND WHEN HE REAPPEARED...

GUYS! COME AND LOOK AT THIS!

YOU WON'T BELIEVE WHAT'S UNDER THE WATER...

...IT'S SOME KIND OF ANCIENT SUBMERGED CITY!

I DO BELIEVE THAT IT'S THE **LOST KINGDOM OF ATLANTIS**!

EXCITEDLY, THE ROLLERS SWAM DOWN TO EXPLORE THE UNDERWATER CITY OF ANCIENT LEGEND.

INSIDE THE CITY'S MAIN PALACE, THE BOYS WERE MET WITH A SURPRISE.

WOW! LOOK AT ALL THIS FUTURISTIC TECHNOLOGY!

I THOUGHT ATLANTIS WAS SUPPOSED TO BE AN ANCIENT CIVILISATION!

WE ARE INDEED AN ANCIENT PEOPLE — BUT WE ARE ALSO MASSIVELY BRAINY AND TECHNOLOGICALLY ADVANCED!

GOSH! AN INHABITANT OF ATLANTIS!

WE ATLANTEANS ARE THE **SECRET RULERS OF THE WORLD**!

THESE COMPUTERS CONTROL ALL THAT HAPPENS ON THE EARTH'S SURFACE — EVERYTHING FROM CLIMATE CHANGE TO POLITICAL UNREST!

ERIC LOOKED PUZZLED

BUT... WHY HAVE YOU GOT ALL THE CONTROLS SET TO **BAD** THINGS, LIKE WAR AND RACIAL HATRED?

GLOBAL CHAOS · HIGH · LOW · WAR · INTOLERANCE

WHY DON'T YOU MAKE THE WORLD A PEACEFUL PLACE, WHERE EVERYBODY LOVES ONE ANOTHER?

"LOVE"? WHAT IS THIS WORD WHICH YOU SPEAK?

OUR HUGE BRAINS ARE SO FILLED WITH INTELLECTUAL CLEVER-CLEVERNESS THAT WE HAVE NO UNDERSTANDING OF SIMPLE CONCEPTS SUCH AS "LOVE."

ALAN PICKED UP HIS GUITAR

WELL, I GUESS IT'S UP TO US TO TEACH THEM — **RIGHT GUYS?**

SOON THE ROLLERS WERE PERFORMING THEIR NUMBER ONE HIT "GIVE A LITTLE LOVE"

YOU'VE GOTTA GIVE A LITTLE LOVE, TAKE A LITTLE LOVE...

BAY CITY ROLLER

... BE PREPARED TO FORSAKE A LITTLE LOVE...

THANK YOU FOR THAT ILLUMINATING LESSON.

WE WILL IMMEDIATELY REPROGRAM OUR COMPUTERS SO THAT THE WORLD IS DRIVEN BY PEACE AND LOVE, RATHER THAN WAR AND HATE.

AT LAST IT WAS TIME FOR THE LADS TO LEAVE THE SUNKEN CITY OF ATLANTIS.

GOODBYE, BAY CITY ROLLERS — AND THANKS AGAIN!

BACK AT THE COTTAGE THEY FOUND UNCLE HAMISH IN A STATE OF EXCITEMENT.

HAVE YE SEEN THE NEWS, BOYS? WAR AND HATRED HAVE BEEN ABOLISHED AND THE WORLD IS AT PEACE!

Daily News WORLD HARMONY

IT MUST'VE TAKEN A TEAM OF INTELLECTUAL GENIUSES TAE SOLVE ALL THE WORLD'S PROBLEMS!

MEANWHILE, YOUSE BOYS HAVE JUST BEEN WASTIN' YER TIME PLAYING YER FOOLISH POP SONGS!

IF ONLY HE KNEW — EH GUYS?

HA HA HA!

The End

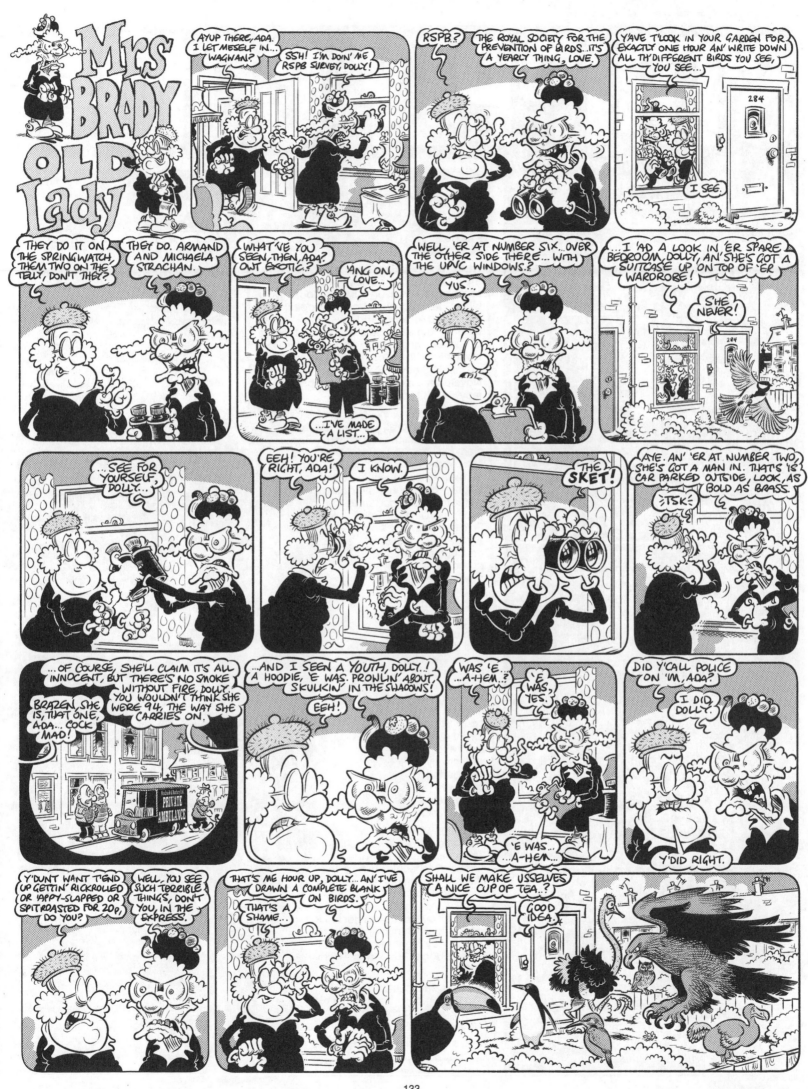

STRIPPLY COME I

ASK any real red-blooded fella to name his dream job and the answer will always be the same... *MALE STRIPPER.*

Having hundreds of drunken, lust-crazed women clawing hungrily at your bare, oiled flesh on a nightly basis is the average bloke's ULTIMATE fantasy, and he's lying if he says it isn't. However, while the glamorous lives of these muscle-bound hunks may look enticing in hit Hollywood films such as *Magic Mike* and *The Full Monty*, the reality can often be quite different.

"When one of my lads turns up to strut his stuff at your do, be it a hen-night, birthday bash or retirement party, the girls in the crowd are guaranteed a proper show with the full teacake," says Alec Seedy, CEO of Nottingham's leading erotic entertainment agency. "To achieve this, they spend hours in the gym every day, toning their bodies to the peak of perfection."

According to Seedy, the rewards on offer reflect the dedication and sheer hard graft required to become a top male erotic artiste. "A good stripper at the top of his game can easily make fifty or sixty quid a night," he told us. "Not to mention the obvious fringe benefits. Backstage after the show, he can literally take his pick of the baying middle-aged women in the crowd."

"Sure it's an alluring prospect, and the average bloke in the street might think he could make it in the cockshow game, but let me tell you, it's not as easy as the professionals make it look."

"Being a male stripper is the hardest job in showbiz."

But could other leading entertainment professionals hack it as top burlesque artistes? We asked Alec to use his skill and judgement, honed over four decades at the helm of Seedy Promotions Inc., to mentally audition a roster of hopeful household names to see if they have what it takes to become successful male strippers.

Audition No. 1 ...Idris Elba

ALEC'S VERDICT: "At first glance, the 46-year-old *Luther* star has everything I'm looking for when I take a new lad on my books; he's tall, good-looking and he clearly takes care of himself. He's also got legions of female fans, so he should have no trouble at all filling the back room of the Meadows Social Club on a November weeknight for a dinner lady's 60th birthday party.

What's more, working at the BBC, he'll have access to the Beeb's extensive costume department. The tired old fireman, naval officer, and New York cop outfits typically worn by male strippers would be out. Instead, Elba could strut his stuff in top quality costumes such as Captain Ross *Poldark*, Mr Darcy from *Pride and Prejudice*, or Compo from *Last of the Summer Wine*, peeling them off piece by piece to the cheers of the crowd.

He could even turn up in a Dalek, and drive the women wild by rubbing baby oil all over his twitching sink plunger before sexily lifting the lid off his outfit and seductively clambering out of it, completely Billy Bollocks.

On the downside, as an international movie star, Elba clearly has has a hectic shooting schedule. If he's in Hollywood filming an action sequence for the latest *Fast and Furious* blockbuster, it may prove difficult for him to get back across the Atlantic in time to do a Friday night hen-do at the Aircraft Social Club near Trent Bridge.

Having said that, I'd definitely take him onto my books on a trial basis if he could commit to at least three shows a week."

Alec's Full Monty Rating: 7/10

Audition No. 2 ...Jeremy Clarkson

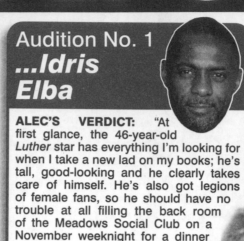

ALEC'S VERDICT: "At nearly 62, petrolhead Clarkson's been round the clock a few times, and is probably getting a bit too long in the tooth to launch a brand new career in the whip-it-out-and-shake-it-round game. And even though his high octane car shows have earned him hundreds of millions of fans around the world, every single one of them is male. Not one amongst his legions of devotees would shell out hard-earned cash to find out how many horsepower Jezza is packing under the hood.

Added to that is the old adage that men who drive big sports cars are compensating for deficiencies in the trouser department - a definite no-no for a wannabe male stripper. But even if the Ferrari-loving *Grand Tour* motormouth bucks the trend and turns out to be packing a pink stretch limo rather than a bubblecar in his Y-fronts, the ladies in the audience won't get to see it. Once Clarkson unbuckles his belt and drops his trademark jeans to the floor, his alarming paunch will plummet down like a safety curtain, covering his *Top Gear Polar Special* from view.

Also, the sight of Jezza's far-from-toned super-charged flabdomen might put the punters in the crowd off their Lambrusco. As any male stripper will tell you, if the bar takings go down, you can kiss goodbye to any chance of a repeat booking. Not only that, if the post-show sandwiches laid on by the management fail to meet his expectations, he could easily lash out, and then it'd be left to me - his agent - to sort out the mess.

All things considered, taking an old banger like Clarkson onto my books would be a plan that might very well backfire."

Alec's Full Monty Rating: 3/10

DANCING!

Audition No. 3
...Paul Dacre

ALEC'S VERDICT: "Until his recent retirement, Dacre had been editor of the *Daily Mail* for nearly three decades. Throughout that time his poisonous, fact-free tirades - on anything from immigrants and house prices to political correctness and immigrants again - demonstrated his unerring ability to drive the country's middle-aged women into a frothing, boggle-eyed frenzy. But will his skills as a male stripper manage to arouse equally powerful passions?

It's a well known fact that ladies love a silver fox, and 70-year-old Dacre certainly ticks that box; I can easily get a good mature male stripper four gigs a week, five if he's happy to do Saturday afternoons. Having said that, such a heavy workload could take its toll on Dacre's health.

Being in charge of a quality newspaper, day-in and day-out for years on end is a stressful occupation, and I would imagine that editing the *Daily Mail* would not be dissimilar. Although his paper famously boasted an excellent circulation, Dacre's own circulation is not in nearly such fine fettle. After allegedly suffering half a dozen or so heart attacks during his alleged journalistic career, Dacre would be well advised to take it easy while up on stage.

Any audience expecting a dynamic, power-packed performance from the septuagenarian ex-hack would be disappointed. Bumping and grinding, pole work, and simulated intercourse hip-thrusts would be out of the question; indeed, halfway through his routine, a puce-faced Dacre may even have to sit down to get his shoes and socks off.

But keeping his heart beating long enough to take a bow at the end of his act might not be his biggest problem. If rumours emanating from the *Daily Mail* newsroom are true, Dacre's laughably tiny "correction" is never going to be front page news. Indeed, his cock is about the size of an AA battery if cruel and unsubstantiated rumours are to be believed.

In the 'Mail' stripping game, size really does matter, and Paul Dacre is stuffed if he can only muster a feeble couple of column inches under his red-top."

Alec's Full Monty Rating: 2/10

Audition No. 4
...Billy Bragg

ALEC'S VERDICT: "A successful male stripper must be willing to work late nights and perform in front of large audiences - and Trotskyite troubadour Billy has had decades of experience doing both. The rabble-rousing *New England* fave cut his teeth playing the raucous London punk circuit in the '80s, so he should certainly be able to handle thirty pissed-up nail technicians shrieking at him to get his Leftie cock out.

That said, Bragg is famous for his outspoken political views, and the male strip show is hardly the right arena for serious governmental discourse. At my gigs, the doors are open to ladies of any political leaning - be they Labour, Tory or Lib Dem - and indeed, a few of the more boisterous female regulars at the Meadows sport extremist far-right tattoos across their knuckles and necks. If Billy were to spot these inflammatory markings whilst he was working the pole, the Stalinist singer-songwriter would no doubt stop mid-dance, and insist the DJ cut the music so he could deliver a hard-hitting anti-fascist diatribe, which would surely dampen the erotic mood no end.

What's more, as a fervent socialist, Billy could well take issue with the way finances are handled in the male striptease world. My lads are paid not so much by cash-in-hand as cash-in-thong. And at my insistence, there's not a word to the taxman. As such, it would presumably conflict with Bragg's egalitarian principles if the Leninist lyricist was prancing off stage every night in a G-string full of black-market fivers.

However, if Billy was willing to put his bleeding heart morals aside for a moment, I might well consider taking the Bard of Barking onto my books."

Alec's Full Monty Rating: 4/10

Audition No. 5
...Peter Ebdon

ALEC'S VERDICT: "Any exotic dancer that signs up to Seedy Promotions Inc. must to be limber and lithe - able to contort his naked body into mind-bending positions that will get female pulses racing. And whether he knows it or not, ex-World Snooker Champion Ebdon has been practising these sort of postures his whole career. From acrobatically cocking his leg up for a long pot, to perching coquettishly on the edge of the table for a tricky pink, the 48-year-old cue ace has unwittingly mastered the exact kind of naughty 'n' nimble poses that get my crowds going.

Employing Ebdon would also save me the thick end of fifteen quid on my costume budget, as he already possesses the requisite stripper outfit of snazzy waistcoat and dapper bow tie.

And while snooker is notorious for its chain-smoking, hard-drinking antics, Ebdon is famously a staunch vegan, which means his body will be in tip-top shape without an inch of flab on it. However, this dairy-shunning lifestyle could also pose problems. As my regular punters will tell you, the highlight of any Alec Seedy strip show is towards the end of the night, when my lads spray blobs of whipped cream over their toned six-packs and then invite the birthday girl, bride-to-be or retiree up on stage to lick them off. As a vegan, Ebdon would doubtless refuse to have any sort of animal produce spread across his naked, oiled torso. And whilst he may suggest a plant-based alternative, such as thickened soy milk or silken tofu, it would be bad for business to have a paying customer gagging and retching on stage.

In short, I could most certainly help Pete get his 'Big Break' in the male stripping game, but he'd have to re-evaluate his lifestyle choices."

Alec's Full Monty Rating: 5/10

135

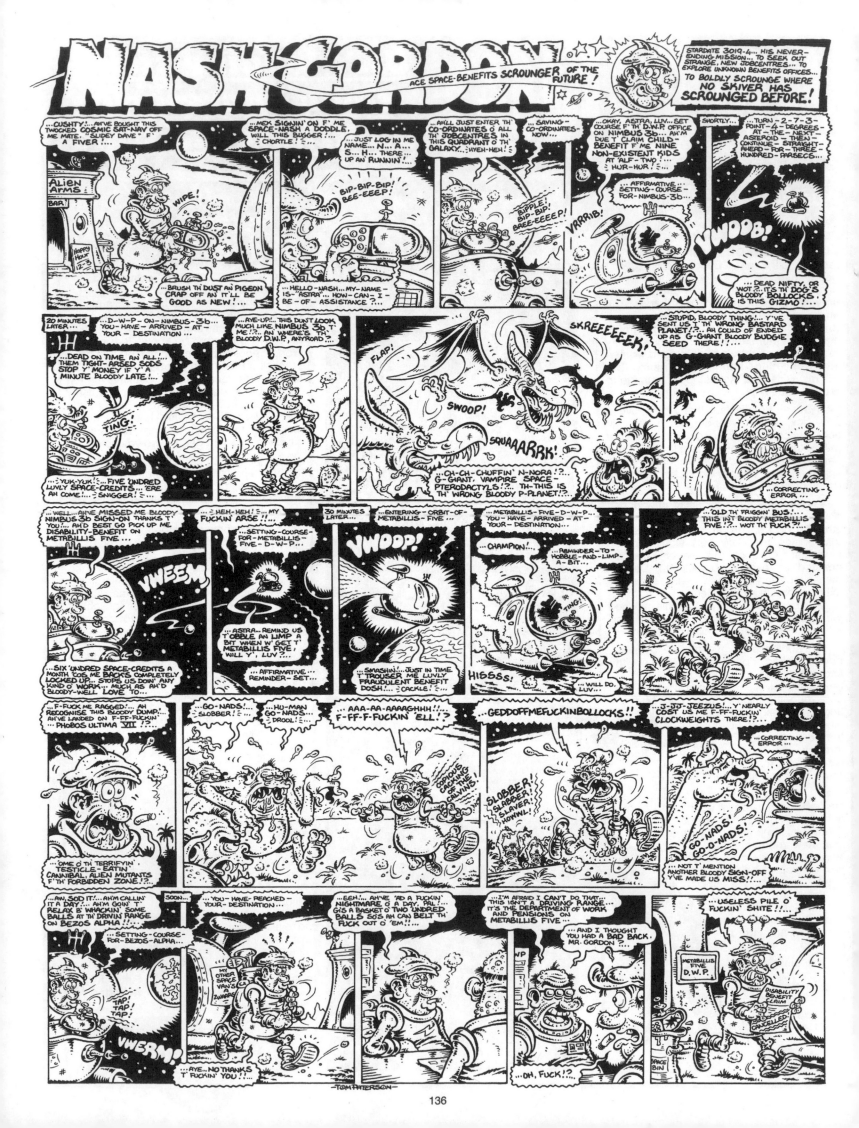

NOBBY'S PILES

Panel 1: I'M SORRY, MR GILES, BUT I'M AFRAID YOUR CLEMENT FREUDS HAVE NOW RESISTED ALL THE TREATMENTS AVAILABLE ON THE NATIONAL HEALTH SERVICE.
WHAT'S TO BE DONE, DOCTOR?

Panel 2: YOU COULD TRY NUDE SEA SWIMMING.
NUDE SEA SWIMMING..?

Panel 3: YES. THE ASTRINGENT SALTY WATER MAY WELL ACT AS A NATURAL PILE-PICKLING AGENT, AND THE COLD TEMPERATURE COULD SHRINK YOUR GIANT BUM-GRAPES RIGHT DOWN TO SHRIVELLED RAISINS.
HMM... IT'S WORTH A TRY NORBERT. COLD WATER DOES HAVE THAT EFFECT.

Panel 4: SO... THIS IS MARVELLOUS, DEAR! I CAN FEEL MY CHALFONTS ATROPHYING AND RETREATING UP MY NIPSY WITH EVERY SINGLE STROKE!
SUPER!

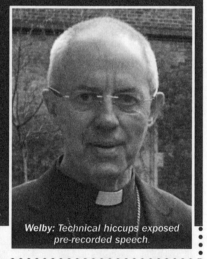

Panel 5: I SHOULD IMAGINE IT WOULD TAKE A SIGNIFICANT ANAL TRAUMA TO BRING THEM DOWN AGAIN WORSE EVEN THAN BEFORE...!
UNDOUBTEDLY. AND THAT'S NOT GOING TO HAPPEN OUT HERE IN THE MIDDLE OF THE SEA, IS IT..?

Panel 6: I SAY! LOOK AT THAT!
WHAT IS IT, DEAR?

Panel 7: I DON'T KNOW, NORBERT... IT'S GETTING CLOSER...!

Panel 8: OOH! IT'S A NARWHAL! WE'RE VERY LUCKY TO SEE ONE IN BRITISH COASTAL WATERS, NORBERT!
GAAH! ME POOR FUCKING RINGPIECE!

Just In Mime!

Archbishop Welby slammed for Synod lip sync

THE Archbishop of Canterbury **JUSTIN WELBY** has come under fire from fans and colleagues today, after it emerged that he *LIP-SYNCHED* a 45-minute speech to the General Synod.

Welby, 63, delivered his annual keynote address to the Church of England's highest governing body on Thursday morning. Initial reaction to the speech was positive, but there were one or two raised eyebrows on social media as sceptics debated whether or not the Archbishop had actually been speaking live.

Welby: Technical hiccups exposed pre-recorded speech.

The Right Reverend James Langstaff, Bishop of Rochester, took to Twitter during the lecture to say: *"Watchin GenSynod keynote rite now & I swear 2 God AB of C is MIMING! #NotCool #FacePalm #EcumenicalEmbarrassment"*

The Archbishop of York, John Sentamu, added his two penn'orth on Snapchat, claiming: *"Think Justin might WELBY lip-synching here!! ;-) #LOL #TheologicalMilliVanilli"*

skip

Video footage of Welby's address quickly went viral on YouTube yesterday afternoon. Particular attention was paid to a moment when the Archbishop's 'backing track' appeared to skip, and he was forced to mouth the phrase

THE HOTTEST ECCLESIASTICAL EXCLUSIVES APPEAR IN VIZ

"Lambeth Quadrilateral" several times in quick succession.

This morning, a spokesman for the Church of England admitted that the Anglican leader had indeed lip-synched the entire 45-minute speech.

"Dr Welby had a sore throat yesterday but he did not want to cancel his engagement and let down his fans and fellow bishops", the spokesman said. "It was subsequently decided that the Archbishop would play a

pre-recorded rehearsal of his keynote address through the Synod speakers and mime along to it as best he could."

frazzle

The spokesman added: "Dr Welby would like to apologise to anyone watching who may have felt let down by his performance. He hopes that the issue of his lip-synching does not detract from the content of the speech itself."

This is not the first time a senior religious figure has come under fire for publicly mouthing along to a pre-recorded monologue. Former Pope **BENEDICT XVI** also faced similar criticism in 2007, when it was discovered that he had mimed a three-hour Easter Sunday mass in St Peter's Square.

CORRECTION

Mr Paul Dacre

On page 135 we erroneously stated that former *Daily Mail* editor Mr Paul Dacre's penis was the same size as an AA battery. It has since been brought to our attention that Mr Dacre's penis is actually the same size as an AAA battery, even when it's on the bonk. We are happy to set the record straight and apologise unreservedly to Mr Dacre, his family and friends, and anyone who has seen his tiny little cock on the bonk.

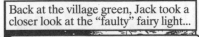

...and all the way to a big car parked in the shadows behind the vestry.

That's odd...The wire finishes in that car. I wonder what's going on...

So *that's* it!... The mystery is solved!

The next day Jack formulated his plan, and when night fell...

There, that's the extension lead disconnected. Now we just have to wait.

Woof.

It wasn't long before two shadowy figures approached from the direction of the church...

Now, PC Brown!

Hold it! You're under arrest!

Cwikey! It's the *wozzers!*

Heavens above!

What exactly's going on, Jack?

Jonathan Ross has been driving over to the village from his home in London every evening, and charging his mobile phone up using electricity from the Christmas tree fairy lights.

But... that's *ratepayers'* electricity. It comes out of the pockets of honest Dorsetvillage residents!

And that's not all, PC Brown...

...you see, the Reverend Smallpiece found out what Rossy was up to, and blackmailed him!

That's wight. He told me that he'd hand me over to the police unless I let him watch pornogwaphy on my phone while it was charging!...

...Asian Babes, Euwopean Cumbath, Mature Full Bush... you wouldn't believe some of the filth I've got on my phone that I've had to show him.

Good *God*, Aunt Meg... Just look. You can see it *going in!*

It's like Rolf Harris eating a banana!

What's going to happen to these two, PC Brown?

Well, it's Christmas Eve, Jack. We'll put them in the cells over New Year, and then decide what to do with them after Twelfth Night...

Jesus, look at the *size* of it. That's not going to happen...

Just before you put them in the cells, PC Brown...

...there's just the matter of the missing fairylight.

There!

Hoorah!

Woof!

Come on, Jack. I think that's quite enough excitement for one day...

...and there's a turkey's neck with your name on it back at the house!

Woof-woof! God bless us every one!

VIZ HOLIDAY SUN SPECIAL

IT'S a fact that, thanks to our changeable climate, we Brits simply aren't used to the sun. And in the summer months, when we jet off to hotter climes, we tend to go mad and get ourselves fried to a crisp rather than elegantly tanned. But don't despair, because the holiday experts at *Viz* are here to safely guide you through the tanning minefield. Take our advice this Summer to make sure that you come back from the Med nut brown rather than lobster pink.

WE ALL want that deep, sexy, Donald Trump-style suntan, but it's easy to overdo it and get sunburnt. Find out exactly which state you're in - tanned or burnt - by answering the questions in this simple questionnaire and totting up your score.

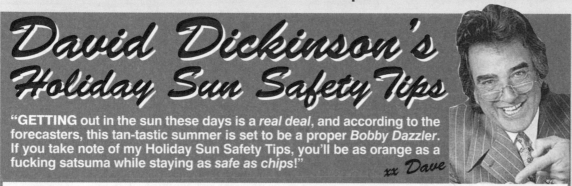

David Dickinson's Holiday Sun Safety Tips

"**GETTING** out in the sun these days is a *real deal*, and according to the forecasters, this tan-tastic summer is set to be a proper *Bobby Dazzler*. If you take note of my Holiday Sun Safety Tips, you'll be as orange as a fucking satsuma while staying as *safe as chips*!"

xx Dave

Dave's Top Tanning Tips

1 **START** gradually and allow your skin to acclimatise to the sun's heat a bit at a time. On the first day of your holiday, paint your entire body with Dulux 'One Coat' white emulsion paint. On the second day, dilute 9 parts paint with 1 part water, on the third day 8 parts paint to 2 parts water and so on. Wash the paint off at the end of each day in the shower, or if you've used an oil-based paint, shower in turps. By the end of the week, you'll be just like me – as brown as a Chippendale wardrobe!

2 **ANOTHER** good way to avoid overdoing it is to stay out of the sun between 12 and 2, when it is at its hottest. Why not spend that spare couple of hours looking round local antiques shops, which tend to be cool, dark, fusty places? You never know, you might even spot a Bobby Dazzler of a bargain while you're browsing, which you can later sell at auction. That way, your two hours avoiding the hot sun could see you trousering a cool profit!

Cheap as chips!

3 **DON'T** forget to keep safe when you're in the sea. You might feel cool when you're bobbing about in the Med, but you're still under the sun's powerful rays, and the water may have washed off your emulsion paint sunscreen without you realising. So whilst in the sea, wear something protective to keep your top half from burning – perhaps a tacky pinstripe suit jacket with wide lapels, or a colourful dress shirt with cufflinks and a white collar.

4 **IF YOU** accidentally overdo it, don't worry. Take a tip from French polishers and *restore* your tan. Gently rub after-sun lotion into your burnt skin, making small circles with a soft lint-free cloth until the deep grain of your tan begins to emerge. After a couple of hours' work your skin will come up smashing, like the hide on an antique Chesterfield!

5 **REMEMBER,** it's important to protect your eyes from the sun's rays. Get yourself a pair of good quality shades to keep the harmful UV out of your peepers. And don't forget a chain to hang them round your neck in case you need to take them off to look in a shop window at an antique vase, or a pair of Rococo figurines from the mid-to-late eighteenth century, which are in good condition but show some signs of past repair.

Letterbocks

Viz Comic, P.O. Box 841 Whitley Bay, NE26 9EQ ...uk

HENRY VIII said about Anne of Cleves "I like her not." But I disagree, certainly enough to rub one out in the museum toilets after I made an excuse to the tour guide. How about a reader poll on which of Henry VIII's six wives you'd most like to have a dirty one night stand with?

Chris P Bacon, London

NOT only is *Viz* the perfect weight to twat wasps with, but it fits perfectly in the cat litter tray as well. Keep up the good work.

Alister Jackson, Dungannon

WHY do zoos feed penguins with just fish? They must be pig sick of eating the same food every day. Come on, British zookeepers, give the little fellas a treat - a bit of steak perhaps, or a lamb stew followed by a chocolate eclair. Maybe take them out in a minibus for a curry on their birthdays. I'm sure they'd enjoy that.

Mrs Arscott, Merthyr Tydfil

MANY people have a stereotypical image of lady vicars, thinking that behind their mousey, demure image they are a load of sexual deviants who are up for anything. Well, as a lady vicar myself, I can assure you that this is not the case. And in order to prove it, if anyone wishes to put me across their knee and spank my bare bottom with a hairbrush until it turns purple, they will see that it will do nothing for me. I'm free every Sunday after evensong.

Harriet Kempton-Park, Merthyr Tydfil

vue
CUSTOMER NOTICE
This toilet is currently out of order; it has been logged and will be fully operational within the next two days.
Thank you Management

TOO much information from my local multiplex.

Barry Norman, Pinewood

HOW come you never hear of insomniacs counting sheep any more? I suppose, with calculators and what have you, the traditional ways of dropping off asleep have once again fallen by the wayside in the name of so called "progress."

Torbjorn Oaf, Edinburgh

I'VE just read that the latest security threat is the hackers' use of spy cams via your mobile phone. All I can say is, if anyone wants to watch me bent over wiping the crack of my arse after I've spent 20 minutes sat on the crapper scrolling through Facebook Marketplace, good luck to them.

Barry Onions, Saxilby

I SAW on the news about how we should all be saving bees as they pollinate our food. Yet today I saw dozens of them wasting time pollinating the weeds in my back yard. If they want our help, the least the stripy little fuckers could do is meet us half way.

Steve Lloyd, Wadebridge

I THINK the human race has enough music, films and TV programmes for the rest of history. Can you guys please pass the message on for people to stop making stuff and do something else instead? Perhaps they could breed some sort of vegetable that will power a motor vehicle, or invent a poo that doesn't need you to wipe your backside and what-have-you. Just a couple of ideas for starters.

Tim Buktu, Timbuktu

I WONDER if Brian Cox has ever had a fight in Durham's The Fighting Cocks.

Dudley Donnehugh, L' pool

✱ Are you a regular in The Fighting Cocks in Durham, and if so, have you seen the TV particle physicist/erstwhile pop star involved in a punch up? Perhaps somebody had a go at him for spilling their pint, or maybe he started on somebody for looking at his missus. Write in and let us know.

STAR LETTER

SCIENTISTS are always going on about how dinosaurs had a brain the size of a walnut. Yet these enormous reptiles died out at the end of the Cretaceous period, 66 million years ago, and walnuts didn't evolve until 20 million years later in the middle Eocene era. Honestly, I think these so-called experts are making it up half the time.

Bartram Shoetip, Devon

HAVE you noticed that women football players and pundits talk as much shite as their male counterparts do? There's equality in the game for you.

Ben, Farnham

INSTEAD of going to work, try having a nice lie-in, a late breakfast and then going out for lunch and a few drinks with friends. Afterwards you can have a lie down for an hour or so and then commence your evening as normal. You'll find its a far more enjoyable way to spend your day.

Jen Similia, Tuckton

IT recently dawned on me that anyone from Texas, Alabama or Mississippi saying "ice cream" would pronounce it so it sounded like "ass cream." I can't help wondering if any of these southern Americans visiting the UK have ever eaten Anusol, or stuck a raspberry ripple up their arse as a result of the confusion.

Kirk Flatus, Filey

WHEN I was a boy, the Visionhire man came to repossess our telly and my dad asked him if he could watch the 2.30 at Chepstow before he took it away. The man said of course, and they sat and watched the race together. It's that sort of camaraderie that went missing when the EU took over. Brexit will take us back to those good old days. And I don't care how bendy my bananas are, as long as they're good old-fashioned British bananas.

Nigel Farrago, N'berland

WHILST out walking with my girlfriend at Flatford Mills, I approached a swan to take a photo and it hissed at me. Given that swans are the property of Her Majesty the Queen, you would have thought it would have had better fucking manners.

P. Turd, Ipswich

LIKE many Christian music fans, I was dismayed when it was claimed that David Bowie was homosexual. I immediately took my collection of Bowie's records to the the Cat's Protection shop. Subsequently, however, it was revealed that he was actually bisexual, so I thought it was reasonable to ask for half of my records back. However, the staff in the shop refused to comply with my request, so I took great pleasure in running a cat over on my way home.

Stew d'Prunes, Orkney

WHY is it that on these A&E documentaries on TV you never see anyone walk in with a screwdriver stuck up their arse? Not that they'd be able to walk in, of course.

Gerry Paton, London

"SHE wore a raspberry beret," Prince famously sang. But the pint-sized erstwhile tunesmith failed to specify whether it was a beret made of raspberries, or a tiny beret small enough to fit a raspberry. Either option would have looked utterly ridiculous.

Rob Wilfort, Chesham

ROY ROGERS AND HIS HORSE, TRIGGERED

MIGHTY FINE DAY FOR A RIDE... SURE IS, PARDNER.

BETTER WATCH OUT FOR INJUNS, THOUGH...

WOAH! EXCUSE ME? WHO?! YOU KNOW - INJUNS... RED INDIANS...

THAT'S EVEN WORSE! I CAN'T BELIEVE YOU CALL THEM THAT! OH. MY. GOD!

THEY'RE KNOWN AS NATIVE AMERICANS THESE DAYS NATIVE AMERICANS!

JESUS, KEEP YOUR SADDLE ON!

YOU ARE SUCH A RACIST!

5 MINUTES OF SILENCE LATER... ERM... WOULD YOU LIKE A SUGAR LUMP? I SAID DON'T TALK TO ME!

DO NOT TALK TO ME!

I WAS appalled at the bias of the BBC news the other day, when they announced that the famous racing tipster John McCririck had died. In the interests of balance, they should have immediately had somebody on to put forward the opposite point of view and say that he was still alive.

Hampton Pilbeam, Luton

I WONDER why you never see fat whippets. All other dogs go all lardy, but not whippets.

Tommy Lambrusco, Cardiff

A very interesting observation, Mr Lambrusco. If any of our readers are vets, perhaps they could write in and tell us why you never get fat whippets. Or if you've seen a fat whippet, or perhaps own one, why not write in and tell Mr Lambrusco he's talking bollocks.

THEY say that each cigarette you smoke takes five minutes off your life. But if you would have spent those five minutes smoking anyway, it cancels itself out. So if you can make your ciggies last more than five minutes every time you smoke one, you're technically prolonging your life. I think.

Ben Nunn, Caterham

WHY do tennis players lug a massive bag of stuff to the pitch with them? Surely all they need is a spare bat and a bottle of barley water. So why do they turn up on court looking as though they're ready for a fortnight in Skegness?

The Owl, Northfields

THEY say that global warming means the Arctic's days are numbered, but so what? I mean, who wants to go paddling in a freezing cold sea anyway? I went to the seaside recently in Wales and the ocean was really warm and nice on my toes. And I had some chips. You wouldn't get that at the North Pole.

Richard Devereux, Hereford

MY milkman failed to deliver my milk on Monday and Tuesday last week. On Wednesday, I discovered he had died. Strange, but I did not think being a milkman was a particularly dangerous occupation to be honest.

Terry Farricker, Blackpool

IN reply to to Hector Crampons (*Letterbocks page 121*). Nobody was terrified of waking the Kraken in Greek mythology. The Kraken is a legendary giant monster in Scandinavian mythology, that preys on unsuspecting sailors; very much like your mother, who is both of enormous size and can often be found hanging around the back of Iceland, swallowing semen.

Trim McKenna, Surbiton

Oh, dear, he's at it again. A perfectly good letter pointing out a correction in the comic is spoiled by Mr McKenna's infantile, and rather weak, insults aimed at the Viz staff's mother, much like he did on page 55. We are vehemently opposed to censorship, but see no other alternative than to ban Mr McKenna from the pages of Viz. And his mum, who offered to do anal with all the Viz staff last night in return for a packet of 10 Woodbines.

THE person on the sun lounger in front of me in Bulgaria has an unfeasibly huge penis.

Geoff Greensmith, Chod Bin Under Lyme

VEGANS tell us that cows are one of the biggest threats to the well-being of our planet. But if this is true, surely it's a good thing that I try to eat as many of them as I can.

Dan, Deal

WHY do charity appeals always end with the line "every penny helps"? Of course it doesn't! What the fuck can you buy with a penny? Even Black Jacks and Fruit Salad chews are about ten pence each these days.

Barnaby Fluglehorn, Kent

IF they made motorbikes with 4 wheels instead of 2, they wouldn't wobble so much and there might be fewer accidents. You could also put proper chairs in between the wheels for a far more comfortable ride. It's not rocket science.

Jack N'decker, Hasp

PEOPLE say 'Don't shit on your own doorstep.' But after 11 pints and a rancid kebab last night, I was too pissed to find my door keys and frankly, I'd like to know what the alternative was.

Barry Arse, Swansea

"YOU can't hurry love," sang Phil Collins. I can only assume that he's never hurriedly cracked one out in the bathroom while his lass is desperate and waiting outside like I just have.

Terence Trent d'Arby, N Shields

WHY do birds of prey always eat their dinner in the middle of the road? Surely it would be a lot safer up a tree or in a bush or something like that.

Grant B Warner, NZ

DOES anyone know what happens at the end of a porn film? Do they have a cuddle or something?

Ross Kennett, Rochester

IF there are any birds of prey reading this, there's an injured seagull in my back garden which would make an ideal snack.

Jonny Quail, Birkenhead

IF music be the food of love, how come my wife lays on the sofa listening to her iPod all day and I still don't get a shag?

Kirk Flatus, Filey

IN the late 70s my mother was on her knees digging in the garden when she lost her wedding ring. Forty years later, my brother was digging in the exact same part of the garden when he dropped to his knees and sharted in his shorts and all down the back of his legs. Coincidence? Perhaps, perhaps not.

Chris Owen, Maidstone

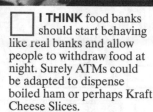

I'VE just noticed that everyone in opera is dead good at singing. Yet when I hear ordinary people on the bus singing, they're usually shit. Come on opera producers, let's have a bit of social realism in your performances and add in a few people who can't hold a tune.

D Cooper, Malta

I THINK food banks should start behaving like real banks and allow people to withdraw food at night. Surely ATMs could be adapted to dispense boiled ham or perhaps Kraft Cheese Slices.

Barnabus Doolittle, Cromer

I CAN'T help but think that guide dogs are only using a fraction of their ability. Couldn't we teach them to make a nice lasagne or boil an egg as well?

Andy, Inverness

"YOU should never smile at a crocodile" the old song warns. Well I smiled at one in the Welsh Mountain Zoo in Colwyn Bay and absolutely nothing happened. Once again it's health and safety gone mad.

Mark, L'pool

DJ '19

...AND THE SALAD FOR YOU, MADAM.

LOVELY, THANK YOU!

OH! MY EARRING HAS SNAPPED OFF!

IT'S FALLEN INTO MY SALAD!

I CAN'T SEE IT... WHAT DOES IT LOOK LIKE?

IT'S A TINY LITTLE SILVER EGG... THESE EARRINGS BELONGED TO MY MOTHER!

WHAT IS THE PROBLEM?

A TINY LITTLE SILVER EGG... IT'S FALLEN INTO THE LADY'S SALAD...

>SNIFF< OH DEAR! PLEASE DON'T LET ME HAVE LOST IT!

CHRIST ALMIGHTY!

YES, I THINK EVERYONE HAS GOT THE MESSAGE NOW, THANK YOU. YOU'RE A "VEGAN." WELL DONE YOU!

WE'RE ALL DEEPLY IMPRESSED BY YOUR ETHICAL LIFESTYLE CHOICE.

SO YOU CAN STOP PUTTING ON THIS RIDICULOUS DISPLAY OF AMATEUR DRAMATICS.

OH BOO HOO, THERE'S A TINY BIT OF EGG IN YOUR SALAD!

ANYONE WOULD THINK YOU'D JUST BEEN OFFERED A FRESHLY SLAUGHTERED HORSE!

ABSOLUTELY LUDICROUS PERFORMANCE!

I BET YOU EAT SAUSAGES WHEN NOBODY'S LOOKING.

THE BACONS

EEK!

BIFFA! COME QUICK! THERE'S A BAT IN THE SITTING ROOM!

DIVVEN'T WORRY, MUTHA... I'LL GERRIT!

NOW, FATHA!

144

RICHARD OSMAN
HE'S POSH, HE'S BIG AND HE LOVES A QUIZ!

CRIPES! I HAVEN'T INVENTED ANY NEW QUIZSHOW FORMATS SINCE TUESDAY... HMMM... NEED IDEAS... HMMM... HOW ABOUT A GAMESHOW ABOUT...

DRIVING A CAR! RIGHT! CUE MUSIC... OPENING CREDITS AND I GUESS IT COULD START WITH...

SCREEECH! THUNK!!
...AN ACCIDENT! SMASHING IDEA! QUITE LITERALLY. HO HO.

HMMM... A CAR ACCIDENT GAME SHOW! TOP GEAR MEETS 3-2-1! INTERESTING...

...BUT WHAT COULD WE CALL IT?
JESUS, I THINK HE'S DYING!!
NO, NO, NO. THAT'S A BIT, WELL... CHANNEL 5, DON'T YOU THINK?

COME ON, MAN, DO SOMETHING! THIS IS LIFE OR DEATH!
LIFE OR DEATH!! GREAT TITLE! BRILLIANT!! WHAT HAPPENS NEXT?

GET SOMEBODY TO CALL A BLOODY AMBULANCE, MAN!
RIGHT, RIGHT...A TASK ROUND! LIKE CRYSTAL MAZE... GOOD THINKING.

OH, FOR FUCKS- LOOK, I'LL DO IT THEN.
RIGHT, SO HERE WE CAN LAY A BED OF TENSE MUSIC... YOU KNOW... DUH-DUM! LIKE A HEARTBEAT THING... DUH-DUM!

RIGHT, WELL THE AMBULANCE WILL BE HERE IN A FEW MINUTES!!
NO PROBLEM. WE FIX IT IN THE EDIT. SEND OUT THE WARM-UP GUY, KEEP THE CROWD HAPPY, ETC, ETC...

RIGHT, SO WHAT HAPPENS NEXT?
WE'RE TAKING HIM TO THE HOSPITAL.
HMMM...WE'LL NEED A SET CHANGE. COULD BE STRETCHING THE BUDGET.

AND WHO ARE YOU?
CREATOR/EXECUTIVE PRODUCER...
NO, I MEAN... WE NEED TO PHONE HIS FAMILY OR FRIENDS.
PHONE A FRIEND? REALLY?! A BIT PASSÉ, DON'T YOU THINK?

THIS MAN IS IN A CRITICAL CONDITION! WE HAVE TO INFORM THE NEXT OF KIN AND GET THEM TO THE HOSPITAL RIGHT AWAY!
LIVE ON AIR?! BRILLIANT! THEN WHAT?!

ERRMM.. WELL... A BLOOD TRANSFUSION OR MAYBE EVEN AN ORGAN TRANSPLANT...
WOWSERS! DRAMATIC TENSION! YOU'RE A NATURAL AT THIS! BUT WE STILL NEED A QUESTIONS ROUND.

AT THE HOSPITAL...
MR & MRS PLYWOOD, WE'LL NEED TO KNOW YOUR SON'S BLOOD TYPE... COULD IT BE O? A? OR B?!!
MULTIPLE CHOICE! VERY CHRIS TARRANT! NOW WE ONLY NEED ONE MORE ROUND. A FINALE. SOME KIND OF DILEMMA MAYBE...

SEVERAL HOURS LATER
MR AND MRS PLYWOOD? I'M THE HEAD SURGEON IN YOUR SON'S CASE.
I'M AFRAID IT'S LOOKING RATHER GRAVE. HE'S SLIPPED INTO A COMA.

IN MY MEDICAL OPINION, IT'S COMPLETELY IRREVERSIBLE. I WOULD SUGGEST TURNING OFF THE LIFE SUPPORT MACHINE...
...BUT THAT HAS TO BE YOUR DECISION.

BRILLIANT! PERFECT!! ZOE, CAN YOU SEE IF THE RIGHTS TO THE BOARD GAME "OPERATION" ARE AVAILABLE? AND GET JIMMY CARR'S AGENT ON THE PHONE...
SOMEONE GET THIS IDIOT OUT OF HERE!!!

AT THE FUNERAL...
I NOW CALL ON MR AND MRS PLYWOOD TO STEP UP TO SAY THEIR FINAL FAREWELLS, AS THEIR BELOVED SON IS LAID TO REST...

...IN ONE OF THESE TWO COFFINS! AND IN THE OTHER COFFIN IS...
1
2
FIFTY THOUSAND POUNDS !!

JOBS FOR THE BOTS

THE robots are coming... And they're after YOUR job! That's the spine-chilling message from the World Economic Forum, which recently predicted that by 2030, HALF of all workplace tasks in factories, offices and shops will be carried out by machines.

It sounds like something from science fiction. But take a quick look around your local high street and you'll see that it's increasingly becoming science FACT. From automated checkout systems to package-delivering drones, androids have already begun to edge their way menacingly into the human workplace. And now experts are forecasting that these conniving cyborgs will complete the job within a decade, leaving billions of us *Homo sapienses* on the breadline.

But are the planet's employers REALLY willing to hand over our beloved green and pleasant jobs to a bunch of cold, emotionless automatons? And if they are, just how safe would a world staffed by robots actually be?

To find out, we sent award-winning *Viz* reporter **MAHATMA MACAROON** undercover in a variety of disguises to expose the terrifying truth about the forthcoming automaton takeover.

And what he discovered is sure to SHOCK every gainfully employed reader to their very human core...

I need your clothes, your boots and your job! Posing as The Terminator, Mahatma takes on burger flipping in a lay-by.

HUMAN JOB DESCRIPTION
CLEANER

*“ **Ever since our Neanderthal ancestors first dusted their caves with a woolly mammoth tail, cleaning has gone hand in hand with human civilisation. But with their powerful mechanised limbs, the average robot can scrub a toilet or unblock a sink up to ten times as fast as a sentient being. So what hope will the sluggish human race have when forced to compete against these superior mechanoids for ablution-based employment?***

On a card in the local newsagent window, I spot an advert for a part-time job. The owner of a nearby scrapyard is looking for a cleaner to do the lavatories in the portacabin, 3 hours a week at £6 an hour... cash in hand! £18 is a precious sum to any food-and-shelter-requiring human, but it's meaningless metal and paper to a cold, clinical android who wants for nothing.

Disguising myself as the renegade robot Roy Batty from the 1982 film *Blade Runner*, complete with bleached blonde wig and an ankle-length trenchcoat, I arrive at the scrapyard for my interview. A rival candidate has also spotted the card and is already waiting patiently inside the portacabin. I engage her in conversation and learn that she is a single mother, badly in need of this wage to help put food on the table for her five hungry children.

shuttle

The scrapyard manager calls me into his office where I explain that I am a Nexus-6 replicant, model number N6MAA10816, and I have hijacked an off-world shuttle in order to seek gainful employment in this town. The man doesn't seem in the least bit surprised, muttering that he gets "all sorts" in here.

He asks me what experience I have, and I tell him that I have seen things he wouldn't believe – attack ships on fire off the shoulder of Orion and C-beams glittering in the dark near the Tannhäuser Gate. I add that all these moments are now lost, like tears in rain.

invaders

My would-be employer appears confused and irritated, but just as he is beckoning the next candidate in, I hit him with the dealbreaker: I will happily eschew the six humanoid 'pounds' he is offering per hour, and instead work for just one can of WD40 per month.

His eyes light up and he offers his sump oil-covered hand for me to shake. The job is mine.

As I begin my day's toil scrubbing skidmarks in the toilet, I watch my rival jobseeker trudge disconsolately across the scrapyard, back to her hungry human family.

I cannot help but think that she is the first of many casualties in the robo-revolution. ”

HUMAN JOB DESCRIPTION
CHEF

*“ **A quick glance at your food processor, blender or George Forman grill will tell you just how far the machines have already wormed their pitiless way into our kitchens, and I wonder how long will it be before Homo sapienses are not required for any stage of food preparation? I decide to find out...***

On the way home from my new cleaning job, I notice a sign at a roadside burger van that reads: HELP WANTED. I return an hour later, bare-chested in a leather jacket and dark glasses, posing as The Terminator, from the 1984 film *The Terminator*.

Adopting a thick Austrian accent, I tell the van's proprietor that I am a T-800 cyborg assassin from the year 2029 and I will need his clothes, his boots and his motorcycle. He laughs nervously. Then I indicate the sign and ask if I can apply for the job.

jam

He seems doubtful when I tell him I have no experience of either short order cooking or serving customers. But, surprise, surprise, he starts grinning like a Cheshire Cat when I explain that, as a T-800, I am able to work 24 hours a day, seven days a week. I add that I cannot be bargained with, I cannot be reasoned with, I will not feel pity, or remorse, or fear. And I absolutely will not stop, ever, until all the customers have been served. What's more, I will do it for nothing. I tell him that the only respite I require is to be turned off and then on again once every couple of months.

switchblade

After a cursory run through of the van's cooking area and a quick demonstration of how to cook a burger from frozen, my new boss departs cheerfully to a nearby pub, leaving me – a robot – in sole charge. *But in his eagerness to cut costs by hiring an insentient android, my employer has unwittingly put his entire business at risk.*

A kitchen is a highly dangerous environment, and while human beings, with their heightened sense of smell and fear, can detect and quash peril in an instant, a heartless, emotionless machine simply isn't equipped to handle hazardous situations alone.

Glade Runner: Macaroon's replicant cleaner sampled sweet smell of success at scrapyard.

With this in mind, I douse the grill with six litres of chip oil and fling a match onto it. Smoke instantly fills the van, and I feign a system malfunction, blinking manically and shouting 'Does-not-compute' over and over again in a staccato voice.

I finally stumble outside to see that the whole vehicle is now engulfed in raging orange flames. My employer comes dashing back out of the pub, screaming four-letter abuse at me as he watches his hard-earned livelihood go up in smoke.

But I have little sympathy with him. Sorry, pal, that's what happens when you hire a bot to do a man's job. "

HUMAN JOB DESCRIPTION
DELIVERY MAN

" *Companies such as Deliveroo, Uber and AirBNB have revitalised the job market in the past few years, allowing people to use their bikes, cars and even homes as a way to earn extra cash. But what will happen when the cold, dead-eyed androids inevitably begin to edge their way into this sharing economy?*

Retrieving my old mountain bike from the shed, I download the Deliveroo app and sign up as a rider. Within minutes, my first order comes through: a large pepperoni pizza, garlic bread and a can of Lilt. Donning a fancy dress shop costume, I disguise myself as the neurotic golden android C-3PO from the *Star Wars* films. I straddle my vehicle and make my way to the nearby fast food restaurant to pick up the order.

assignment

The woman behind the counter barely looks up from her phone as she hands me the delivery bag – she clearly has no qualms *whatsoever* about giving this valuable assignment to a dispassionate machine when there are dozens of humanoid riders waiting for work outside.

I wonder if she will be quite so laid-back when the robots arrive to take her own job?

I strap on the large cuboid rucksack filled with steaming hot food and begin the one-and-a-half mile cycle to my delivery destination. However, my stiff plastic legs are clearly not made for pedalling, and I can barely see a thing through the eyeholes of my golden mask.

I hurtle blindly across a busy crossing, crashing straight into the front gate of my delivery address and land painfully on my pizza-filled backpack. My customer opens the door to see what all the racket is about, and I adopt a plummy, vaguely camp accent. "Oh dear, Master Luke, I'm afraid there's been a bit of an accident," I tell him, walking away taking short, quick steps.

He surveys the remains of his dinner, which is now splattered across his driveway and furiously demands a refund

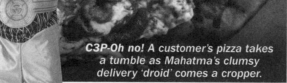

C3P-Oh no! A customer's pizza takes a tumble as Mahatma's clumsy delivery 'droid' comes a cropper.

whilst calling me every name under the sun – and a few more to boot.

Get used to it, mate – this is the kind of hapless service we'll ALL be receiving once the robo-revolution is in full swing. "

HUMAN JOB DESCRIPTION
BANKER

" *One of the great myths about the impending robotic takeover is that it will only swallow up the human race's most boring or badly paid jobs. High-earners are told time and again that they need not worry about mechanoids filling their shiny designer shoes, as only humans are equipped to perform the top jobs. But is that REALLY the case? To find out, I decide to apply for one of the most difficult, prestigious and lavishly rewarded jobs in the Western world: an investment banker.*

I arrive at Goldman Sachs International in London disguised as the 1980s chess computer Deep Blue. My costume, made from an old Ikea box painted black with an IBM logo stencilled in the top corner, is large and unwieldy. After getting stuck for a few turns in the revolving door, I waddle up to the sharp-suited man at the front desk.

Adopting a sort of Stephen Hawkings voice I inform him that I am a highly advanced superbot with unparalleled artificial intelligence, capable of evaluating more than 200 million stock market positions per second. I then enquire if he would like me to replace all of his staff.

The man stands, presumably about usher me through the golden double-doors into a top-floor office and six-figure income – all at the expense of the poor humans who'll be given the heave-ho. However, before I can be guided to my brand new desk, a security guard approaches and lifts my cardboard disguise right off me.

branch

When it is revealed that I am actually a *human being* rather than a super-intelligent chess computer, the hypothetical job offer is instantly withdrawn and I am immediately strong-armed back towards the door and hurled violently out onto the street.

Surprise! Surprise! Apparently, when it comes to even the highest-earning jobs, only real robots need apply. "

HUMAN JOB DESCRIPTION
PORN ACTOR

" *We all dream of owning our very own sex robot. But would human beings really be willing to pay good money to watch an insentient android make love? And if so, what implications would that have for the millions of hard-working grumble men and women currently employed in the international bongo industry?*

One night in the pub I overhear mention of a notorious dogging hotspot in a layby just a few miles up the road and I decide to investigate. I go straight home and change into the *RoboCop* 'cosplay' outfit I bought off eBay a few days earlier. Once fully disguised, I head straight to the location.

Twenty seconds to come-ply: in the guise of futuristic Detroit law-enforcement cyborg, Robocop (bottom of page), Mahatma makes money making out at local layby.

I arrive just after 1am to find that the sickening action is already in full swing. A crowd of mackintosh-clad perverts are rummaging frantically in their pockets whilst watching an obese couple copulate loudly on the tailgate of a Seat Alhambra. However, when the onlookers spot me, the public fornication is quickly forgotten as all heads turn my way.

brew

I inform the depraved gaggle that I am an enhanced cyborg law enforcer from a dystopian future Detroit, and I have been sent back through time to spread sexual gratification among the women of the past.

The burly female exhibitionist giggles and shoves her current partner out of the way. "Oh, aye?" she rasps playfully. "Come on then, *RoboCock*, show us what you've got."

In order to maintain my cover, I am forced to have full penetrative intercourse with the woman whilst the assembled crowd masturbates enthusiastically around us. Once everyone present has climaxed, my sexual partner and I are showered with crumpled five and ten pound notes. One of the punters even mutters as he zips his trousers up that ours was "the best show he's seen in years" and I should "definitely come back next week."

Talk about the Rise of the Machines! ~Clearly, when it comes to having sex in public for money, human beings are no longer up to the job. "

NEXT WEEK: *Posing as Gort from* **The Day The Earth Stood Still,** *Macaroon gets arrested for fraud, arson, vandalism and indecent exposure, in order to investigate how the robo-revolution will play out inside Britain's prison system.*

IBM   RS6000 SP

Checkmate: Macaroon's cheeky chess computer disguise (Deep Blue - right) was rumbled by receptionist at Goldman Sachs.

TRICK or TREATMENT!

"What you dress up as for Halloween says A LOT about why you can't satisfy your wife sexually," says Dr Raj Persaud

HALLOWEEN is here again, and from Land's End to John O'Groats, we're all set to don our spookiest outfits and give our friends and family a good old fright. But becoming a spooky character for the evening is more than just a bit of fun. Because did you know that the kind of monster YOU dress up as on October 31st speaks volumes about the reason you're unable to bring your wife to orgasm?

"It honestly does," says disgraced and then undisgraced TV shrink **DR RAJ PERSAUD**. "If you're a flop between the sheets, one glance at your choice of scary costume on All Hallows' Eve will instantly reveal why."

Here, Dr Raj assesses this year's four most common Halloween outfits and lays bare the humiliating and shameful sexual inadequacy that each one reveals.

FRANKENSTEIN

Dr Raj says: "With his prominent neck bolts, livid forehead scar and ill-fitting suit, Frankenstein has long been a hugely popular choice of Halloween costume. In Mary Shelley's seminal novel of 1818, the original Frankenstein is cobbled together out of all different parts of rotting corpses, which means he has no human blood pumping through his veins. And unfortunately the same can be said for the manhoods of the people who dress up like him. Every Trick-or-Treating Frankenstein you spot this year will find it impossible to achieve full penile rigidity, leaving countless thousands of unfulfilled Brides of Frankenstein frustratedly reaching for the nearest sex toy."

Celebrity Frankensteins:
Giles Coren, Sting, Rod Liddle

WEREWOLF

Dr Raj says: "These ferocious beasts look just like regular guys… until the clouds part and they catch a glimpse of the full moon. And as soon as that happens, they transform instantly into screeching, dribbling, wild animals. Put simply, werewolves are unable to control themselves - and regrettably the same is true for the cocks of their Halloween impersonators. It's widely accepted that every man who dresses up as a werewolf on October 31st almost certainly suffers from the crippling condition of premature ejaculation. Whenever these hirsute two-push Charlies spy the 'full moon' of their wife's naked buttocks, they begin howling, sweating and foaming at mouth, before shamefully plastering their Y-fronts a few seconds later."

Celebrity Werewolves:
Jon Humphrys, Will Self, George Lamb

GHOST

Dr Raj says: "This iconic Halloween look can be achieved quite simply with a pair of scissors and an ordinary bedsheet. In reality, though, we all know that ghosts are completely see through, and tragically, the same is true of the fellas who don a ghost outfit for Halloween. Because, whenever they are having penetrative sex, their wives are looking right through them and thinking of another man. It's time to accept it: he no longer turns her on, and her constant failure to climax is down to the simple fact that she's dreaming of someone else. In fact, dressing up as a ghost is the most fun under a bedsheet these fellas are ever going to have."

Celebrity Ghosts:
Mark Zuckerberg, Kanye West, HRH Prince Edward

DONALD TRUMP

Dr Raj says: "A nice change from the tried-and-tested monsters of yore, dressing up as the orange-skinned 45th POTUS has been a popular practice ever since November 2016. All you need is a ridiculously long tie, a jingoistic baseball cap, some white candyfloss and six bottles of bright orange fake tan. However, the downside to this simple and effective costume is that The Donald himself was famously described by porn star Stormy Daniels as being hung 'like a mushroom'. And lamentably, the people who choose to imitate Trump on Halloween share the very same shameful affliction. As such, if you see someone done up like the 45th POTUS on October 31st, you can be 100% certain that his sexually frustrated spouse spends most of her life forwarding him spam emails about penis enlargement pills."

Celebrity Donald Trumps:
Nigel Farage, Sir Geoffrey Cox, Donald Trump

NEXT ISSUE: *STOCKING KILLERS! Dr Raj explains how the gifts YOU put in your wife's Christmas stocking speak volumes about why she's planning to have you assassinated.*

MEDDLESOME RATBAG

IN THE PARK —
TED'S BBQ HOT DOGS £1·50

LET'S HAVE OUR PICNIC HERE DADDY!
OKAY, TRISH!
!!
GASP!

DISGUSTING! PEOPLE LIKE THAT SHOULDN'T BE ALLOWED TO LOOK AFTER A SMALL CHILD!
IT'S AGAINST NATURE!

WHAT DO THEIR SORT KNOW ABOUT TAKING CARE OF CHILDREN?
MAM, LOOK! SAUSAGES!
TED'S BBQ HOT DOGS £1·50
I SHUDDER TO THINK WHAT SCENES OF DEPRAVITY THAT POOR LITTLE GIRL HAS WITNESSED!

I'M NOT PREJUDICED, BUT A HOUSE FULL OF GAY "GOINGS-ON" IS NO PLACE TO BRING UP INNOCENT TOTS!
TOPPLE!
OOH! GOT SAUSAGES!

SPEAKING AS A MOTHER, I'M NOT GOING TO TURN A BLIND EYE WHEN A CHILD'S WELFARE IS AT STAKE...
BLIP BLIP BLIP BLIP
OH MY GOD!
PRETTY FIRE!

PSSSHHHT!
HISSSSSS
WHEE!
HELLO? SOCIAL SERVICES? I WISH TO REPORT A YOUNG GIRL POTENTIALLY AT RISK...

AND SORRY TO DISTURB YOUR PICNIC, BUT WE'VE RECEIVED AN ANONYMOUS PHONE CALL...
SOCIAL SERVICE
FUNNY! DO IT AGAIN!

999-EMERGENCY BOMB SQUAD!

EBS IN THE heart of the city, construction workers make a heart-stopping discovery - A relic from WWII in the shape of an unexploded nazi bomb. It's time to call...

At Emergency Bomb Squad HQ, Colonel Jed Quicksilver takes the urgent call...

...Right. Get everybody clear. We'll be there in three minutes.

It's a *Code Red*, everyone. UXB in the High Street!

WOO! WOO! WOO!

EMERGENCY BOMB SQUAD HEADQUARTERS

EMERGENCY BOMB SQUAD

Three minutes later...

SCREECH!

Okay, Quinn, secure the perimeter. Dupree, you set up the blast containment barrier...

Fargo... You get a mark on the detonator type! Let's find out what we're dealing with.

Roger that, Colonel

Suddenly...

Oh my God!

What is it, sir?

I've trod in some dog shite.

Oh fuck. It's one of them orange, blancmangey ones.

Just give it a wipe on some grass, sir.

There isn't any grass. We're in the middle of the street...

...oh, *bollocks!*

Oh, that fucking stinks.

Just give your boot a swish round in that puddle, Colonel. That'll clean it.

I mean, who just lets their dog shit in the fucking street and leaves it? What is it with these people?

Aw, it's up the fucking sides, look.

Why don't you just scrape it on the ground, sir?

No, that'll just spread it all around. Has anyone got a stick?

Here, sir.

Fucking selfish bastards, honestly.

How's that?

No, it's still all in the tread sir.

Give it another go in the water.

Fuck's sake!

No, it's still there, sir... I think you'll have to poke it out with something like a lolly stick.

Anyone got a lolly stick?

I've got some matches, Colonel. Would a match do?

Better than nothing, I suppose.

You've missed a bit, sir, on the heel...

...Just there, look, sir.

It's not the dogs, it's the fucking owners. Honestly, if I caught them, I'd rub their fucking noses in it.

There, that'll have to do. I'll get some bleach on them when we get back to HQ.

Right, squad. Let's get this bomb made safe!

Action stations, everyone. Fargo, do we have a mark on that detonator yet..?

Oh, for fuck's sake...*FUCK!*

Fucking hell...

It's started ticking!

Next Week in 999 Emergency Bomb Squad: *As the detonator begins its deadly countdown to disaster, Colonel Quicksilver sends the squad in search of a chemist to get some wet-wipes and a roll of kitchen paper.*

GILBERT RATCHET

LOOK AT YOU TWO STUFFING YOUR FACES WITH SNACKS IN FRONT OF THE TELLY!

WHAT AN UNHEALTHY PAIR OF LUMPS!

IT'S TIME YOU GOT YOURSELVES IN SHAPE BEFORE YOU BOTH DROP DEAD OF HEART ATTACKS!

SNATCH!

HEY!

DON'T WORRY DAD!

I'LL INVENT SOMETHING WHICH WILL ALLEVIATE MUM'S CONCERNS ABOUT OUR UNHEALTHY LIFESTYLE!

I'VE CREATED THIS "FICTITIOUS-GREAT-UNCLE-O-MATIC" WHO EATS NOTHING BUT CRISPS, SMOKES 90 FAGS A DAY, AND YET LIVES TO THE RIPE OLD AGE OF 120!

PUFF! PUFF!

MUNCH! CRUNCH!

YOU SEE MUM?

MY FICTITIOUS GREAT-UNCLE-O-MATIC DOESN'T BOTHER WITH KEEPING FIT AND IT HASN'T DONE HIM ANY HARM!

UH OH!

HE HAS CARELESSLY FLICKED HIS FAG END INTO THOSE HIGHLY FLAMMABLE RED-HOT-CHILLI-AND-JALAPENO CRISPS!

BOOM!

WELL THAT WASN'T PARTICULARLY REASSURING, GILBERT!

GET YOURSELVES OFF TO THE GYM AND START KEEPING FIT AT ONCE!

SIGH! WE'D BETTER GO IN AND GET THIS OVER WITH, GILBERT!

HANG ON DAD - I'VE HAD ANOTHER IDEA!

I'VE INVENTED THIS ROBOT FIFTH-FORM-BULLY-O-MATIC WHO WILL GRAB OUR GYM BAGS OFF US AND THROW THEM ON THE BICYCLE SHED ROOF!

GREAT! WE WON'T BE ABLE TO JOIN THE GYM IF WE'VE GOT NO P.E. KIT!

OOPS! I'VE MISJUDGED THE TRAJECTORY OF MY FIFTH-FORM-BULLY-O-MATIC'S THROW!

FLING!

HE'S CHUCKED OUR BAGS INTO THE ROAD INSTEAD!

LOOK OUT FOR THOSE BAGS!

SCREECH!

WELL THAT WAS A STROKE OF LUCK!

YOU CAN GO INSIDE AND GET CHANGED INTO THIS BRAND-NEW GYM KIT!

AND SO

GASP! PHEW!

THE WORST THING ABOUT THIS IS HAVING TO LOOK AT MY FAT, SWEATY BODY IN THAT BIG MIRROR!

NO WORRIES, DAD!

I'LL USE THESE CLAMPS TO BEND THE GLASS AND TURN IT INTO A DISTORTING MIRROR!

CREAK! GROAN!

THAT'S BETTER, GILBERT - I'M LOOKING WELL FIT, NOW!

KER-AACK!

YOW! THE GLASS HAS SHATTERED UNDER THE PRESSURE OF THOSE CLAMPS!

BAH! I'VE BEEN WORKING OUT IN THIS GYM FOR TWENTY MINUTES AND I STILL HAVEN'T GOT RID OF MY BIG POT BELLY!

WE MILLIONAIRES ARE VERY IMPATIENT ABOUT SUCH THINGS.

SLICE!

PLOP!

THANK YOU! YOUR "MASSIVE FLYING SHARD OF GLASS" REGIME HAS GIVEN ME THE FLAT STOMACH I SO DESIRED!

HERE'S £500!

AND NOW ME AND DAD CAN AFFORD THE "EXCLUSIVE VIP" GYM MEMBERSHIP!

THAT MEANS WE GET TO LIE AROUND EATING SNACKS WHILE OUR BUTLERS TOUCH OUR TOES AND RUN ON THE SPOT FOR US! CHOMP!

YOU ARE NIGEL FARAGE THE REF

Test your Xenophobic Football Knowlege with the Brexit Party Leader

1 You have awarded a direct free kick to a defending team just outside their 18-yard box, and the kick-taker taps the ball back to his keeper. However, the keeper is in the back of his goal changing his gloves, and doesn't see the ball until it has crossed the goal line into the back of his net. What do you do?

RAPSCALLION

2 A player takes a shot on goal which hits the arm of a defender in the penalty area. You hear the appeals for handball, but you didn't see the incident as you were on the touchline having a conspiratorial meeting with shady, right wing cunt Steve Bannon when the shot was taken. What do you do?

3 After crashing your light aircraft onto the pitch, you stumble out of the wreckage, dazed and bleeding heavily. You notice that an attacking player has been brought down by a defender off the ball outside the 18-yard box. What do you do?

1. LEAVE the stadium and go to the nearest pub, where you pose, holding up a glass of bitter for press photographers whilst grinning like something out of a Dr Seuss book. Then you return to the stadium and insist that the kick be taken again, as a team cannot disadvantage itself directly from a free kick.

2. THE first rule for a referee is that you cannot blow the whistle for what you didn't see, no matter how loud the appeal. You must simply allow play to continue.

3. YOU award a free kick to the attacker as he has been fouled and show the defender a yellow card. You do not award a red card, since the attacker did not have the ball and was therefore not denied a goal-scoring opportunity.

ANNIVERSARY SURPRISE FOR LYN

Fish course gives up 50-year-old secret

Fish finger! The slap-up supper (below) and Lyn's ring in situ (right).

WHEN Lyn and Ken Sampson honeymooned in the Lake District in May 1969, the couple were on top of the world. But on the second night of their visit, disaster struck during a meal on their hotel's waterside terrace, when 28-year-old Lyn's wedding ring slipped from her finger and into the lake.

The ring had cost a week's wages for Ken, an apprentice drayman, and his heartbroken bride thought she had seen the last of it.

The pair returned home to Chorley, and life returned to normal with the couple raising a family of three children in the forthcoming decades. Over the years, Lyn steadfastly refused to buy a new wedding ring, despite her husband's repeated offers.

But the retired seamstress, now 69, got the surprise of her life when the couple celebrated their golden wedding anniversary last week with a return trip to the same hotel in the Lakes where they had honeymooned half a century earlier, taking lunch on the very same waterside terrace.

"It was lovely to be back at the hotel after all these years," Lyn told the *Keswick Prolapse and Argos*. "I ordered the fish and chips with mushy peas and bread and butter.

When it arrived, I cut into the

EXCLUSIVE!

fish and I could see something glistening inside."

And a gobsmacked Lyn could not believe her eyes when she looked a bit closer. She told the paper: "It was my wedding ring, right there inside my fish."

fish

"I was speechless with surprise and delight. It must have lain on the bottom of the lake for fifty years before being swallowed by the fish which ended up on my plate as my anniversary lunch," she said. "It was a million-to-one chance!"

Both Lyn and Ken were lost for words. But the day's surprises were not over yet.

"When I looked closely, I saw that the ring was in the hand of a tiny version of me, sitting on the terrace restaurant eating fish and chips with a tiny version of Ken across the table from me, all inside the fish," she said.

The Chorley pensioner then watched in amazement as her minuscule doppelganger dropped the ring into what appeared to be a tiny Lake Windermere, also inside the fish.

ladies'

"At that moment, the little version of me looked up, saw me and screamed," she told the paper. "I started screaming too. I couldn't help it."

"The next moment, the sky seemed to split open and an enormous fish knife came scything down over our table, nearly knocking Ken off his chair," she said.

She continued: "Then two hands prised the clouds apart above us, and

an enormous version of me peered down. I looked up at it and screamed. And the enormous me screamed back. The tiny me in the fish was still screaming from before."

stiff little

Eventually, all three versions of Lyn calmed down after various-sized waiters brought them each a glass of water and a paper bag to breathe in. Once they had gathered their wits together, the three Lyns got chatting.

"Me and Ken ended up having lunch with the tiny and enormous versions of ourselves," she said. "Despite our size differences, we all got along famously. We've all been married fifty years but the tiny us said that it had felt like half an hour and the enormous ones said it had felt more like four hundred years."

And like all good tales, this one has a happy ending. "I got my ring back and met two wonderful new friends," said Lyn.

"And we got on so well that we're all coming back to the hotel together for our fifty-first wedding anniversary next year," she said.

March 2019 £3.75

School Run Mum

Incorporating PRACTICAL MATERNAL PARKING

IN THIS ISSUE
ABREAST IS BEST
We block an ordinary pavement with THREE Range Rover Evoques!

SRM 1 SRM 2 SRM 3

KEEP ON RUNNING
Why you should NEVER switch off your 4 litre diesel engine when sitting in traffic in case it never starts again

OPEN DOOR POLICY
Make sure your precious darlings never have to walk more than 6 foot to the fucking school gates

20 30 40 50 60 70 80

50 60 710 810 90 200 10 20

WIN!
4 NEW 20" ALLOY WHEELS
EVERY WEEK for 12 MONTHS!

School

No stopping
Mon-Fri
8 am-9 30 am
2.45 pm-4.30 pm
on school entrance
markings

Welcome to
Rookery Nook
Primary School

STOP

SLOW DOWN

LJY

IGNORE THE SIGNS
Why the rules don't apply to you if you leave the hazards on in your brand new XC90!

TRUE LIFE DRAMA
"I'll only be five minutes!"
A doting mother's plea as she blocks a resident's drive for half an hour, twice a day for seven fucking years

ON SALE NOW!

IN days gone by, a grand parade down the main street told everyone when the circus was in town. These days, they may just park up in a field and paste their posters in bus shelters and the windows of disused shops, but there's one thing that hasn't changed: *The circus is still the Greatest Show on Earth!*

You can take your big budget Hollywood movies and Sky box sets and stick them where the sun don't shine (ie, up your arse), because NOTHING beats the traditional, nail-biting excitement of a real-life Big Top circus.

When the circus comes to town, get ready to make your way to the nearest brownfield site that hasn't yet been ear-marked for a big Persimmon housing estate, where an evening of edge-of-your-seat excitement, death-defying spills and madcap laughs awaits for everyone of all ages, from 4 to 40.

But these thrills don't come easy. Every specialist act that parades across the sawdust for your delight is the product of many years of hard work and sweat. With performers hailing from the four corners of the world performing feats they have honed over countless hours of practice, it's no wonder it costs £4.50 to get in.

So let's take a front row seat on a splinter-ridden plank to discover just Who is Which and What is Whom in ...

THE GREATEST SHOW ON EARTH!

WILD ANIMALS...

IN THE past, visitors to the circus were treated to performing lions, tigers, bears, elephants and zebras cavorting around the ring for their entertainment. And these exotic animals are still to be seen to this day, although only on the circus's posters and flyers. Once the show starts, the ringmaster goes into a well-practised spiel about how all the animals are ill and at the vets, or that local council public safety by-laws prevent them from being used, before informing the disappointed crowd that no refunds are available.

And the demise of the circus wild animal is down squarely to Animal Rights protesters. Contrary to what do-gooders would have you believe, circus animals of the past enjoyed a glamorous showbiz lifestyle that would have been the envy of their jungle-bound cousins. While the lions of the African plain were forced to hunt their own food in the blistering sun, their showbiz cousins lived the life of Riley, travelling the length and breadth of the UK in the five-star comfort of a converted horsebox or abattoir truck, feasting on the finest condemned offal that the ringmaster could blag off a local butcher in return for four tickets to a slow-selling Sunday afternoon show.

This circus is lucky to retain one exotic performing animal, a 25-year-old man-eating tiger. Zoltan was originally born in a zoo in Kazakhstan, and was sold to a circus in Hungary by official receivers when the zoo went bust. After his original circus owners were banned from keeping animals for ten years, he was sold to a Rumanian magician and then passed through a number of hands before finally ending up in his present home, when he was swapped with another circus for a diesel generator.

THE RINGMASTER...

EVERYONE knows the ringmaster. He cuts quite a dash as he strides into the sawdust ring in his shiny black boots, white jodhpurs, top hat and scarlet hunting tailcoat. It is his job to introduce the various acts, whipping the sparse crowd dotted around the Big Top each night into a frenzy of half-hearted enthusiasm.

Away from the sawdust ring, the ringmaster's life could not be less glamorous, as he battles to fend off creditors, alimony demands from former wives and fines from local authorities for the fly-tipping of wet sawdust and tiger shit.

THE JUGGLERS...

TO MAKE their arse-numbing display slightly less un-entertaining than it is, jugglers are constantly looking for new, exciting, and more dangerous objects to throw about and catch. Razor-sharp knives, sickles and chainsaws have all been pressed into service by jugglers in the hope of lending an air of death-defying danger to their act.

These jugglers, however, have opted to use one-foot diameter plastic rings in their show. This gives crowd members a chance to go out and have a piss round the back of the tent before the trapeze artistes come on, safe in the knowledge that they're only missing the sort of drab spectacle they could see any busker doing outside Marks & Spencers on a Saturday afternoon.

THE TRAPEZE ARTISTS...

"OH HE flies through the air with the greatest of ease, that daring young man on the flying trapeze," or so the old song says. This performer, however, is 62, and his wife is even older. Together with the couple's middle-aged son, the family troupe perform as 'The Flying Mexican Zapatos', despite hailing from Glossop and their surname being Collins.

The threesome - who prior to a series of accidents, defections to other circuses and members leaving to do proper jobs, began in the late 1960s as a fifteen-strong family troupe - have now been performing the same death-defying act for more than half a century. Over their thousands of performances, they have only ever lost their grip and plummeted into the crowd or the sawdust below a few dozen times.

Like the troupers that they are, after each one of these falls, the Flying Zapatos abide by the old showbiz maxim "the show must go on." And after taking a few months off in traction to get their breath back and have metal plates screwed into their bones, they get straight back up the ladder to take their place up in the air about twenty feet above the crowd.

THE CLOWNS...

EVERYONE loves the clowns, except grown-ups, small children, teenagers, and anyone suffering from coulrophobia, which is the fear of clowns. Their madcap antics in the ring always leave everyone, except the people listed above, in fits of helpless laughter.

When they drive on in their hilarious knockabout clown car, a backfiring slapstick vehicle made from gaily painted plywood on a Hillman Imp chassis, you know that everyone is in for a side-splitting five minutes of slapstick fun. Except the people listed previously. Each troupe has one clown who is even less funny than the others. With their conical, white, pom-pom hats, blank faces

EST SHOW ON EARTH

and spangly costumes, these so-called white-faced clowns don't go for laughs, opting merely to play *When the Saints Go Marching In* on the rumpet instead.

It's a little known fact that every clown's make-up is traditionally ecorded on a painted egg that is kept at a special registry in Wookey Hole, Somerset. Each unique, painted egg is absolutely identical to all the others, with a red nose, wide, sausage-shaped mouth, Groucho Marx eyebrows and tufty orange hair.

THE BAND...

ASK anyone to describe the sound of the circus and they'll tell you it's the rousing racket of a big brass band, complete with drums and cymbals. Throughout history, stars of the big top have all traditionally performed their acts to the accompaniment of such a stirring ensemble sitting at the side of the ring, arrayed in all their glittering, epauletted finery, blowing away for all they are worth.

These days, however, the job of the band is performed by one man sitting in front of a pre-programmable Casio LK 136AD keyboard (Argos ordering code 760/0153). Even cheaper, and no-less stirring for the audience, the circus owner could invest in a copy of Sounds of the Circus by the Merle Evans Circus Band (Jasmine Records B00FEFCLVC) and stick it on a CD player until the Performing Rights Society catch up with him.

CAN YOU SPOT...

• A trapeze artist who has fallen and broken his spine in three places, being picked up and dragged out of the ring by two clowns...

• A man from Matlock dressed as a Red Indian, whipping a cigarette out of his wife's mouth in the traditional Cherokee manner, whilst blindfolded...

• A dad in the audience staring at a tightrope walker, trying to work out whether she's wearing a flesh-coloured body stocking, or whether her cossie is really going up her crack...

• A dad in the audience gazing longingly at a contortionist whilst running few a series of highly-charged X-rated scenes in his head...

• A dad in the audience watching a woman ride round the ring whilst standing on the back of a white horse, mentally weighing up the chances of one of her tits popping out...

• A jolly clown having fun with a toddler, instilling in him a bed-wetting nightmare that will recur at least once a week until he is in his mid-fifties...

• A trick cyclist from Mexico who looks remarkably similar to the man with a Leeds accent who sold you popcorn from a barrow outside ten minutes ago...

• A man and wife Spanish acrobat team, who look like they could be the twin brother and sister of the Italian couple who did the act with a dog in a skirt pushing another dog in a pram...

• A man who has driven twelve hours through the night after taking the tent down after the previous show, who has fallen asleep while tightening up the bolts on the seating...

• A man exiting the barrel of a cannon at about 15mph, approximately two seconds after a dramatic flash and a bang, which failed to cover up the sound of a big spring...

WE TIME MOTIONS

You wanted to see me?

Yes. Step in. Close the door.

We need to talk about the money you are *thieving* from the company.

What?! No, I ain't!

I see. So what do you call agreeing to sell a quantity of something at a fixed price –

– then wilfully, *repeatedly* delivering short measure?

Eh?

Time, man! According to these figures you have already *pilfered* 27 minutes – almost four pounds wages – just this past month!

How?

We pay you to pick orders, not to stand around holding your penis willy-nilly.

I don't.

You were seen. Twice today, urinals 2 and 7.

Three minutes, 48 seconds.

Everyone needs the odd pee.

Hence the generous ten minute break per four hours worked.

They don't always overlap.

So dip your hands in the till, is that it?

Well your little *zero hours piss bonanza* is over.

Carry this at all times, empty at breaks or the end of your shift.

Next day

You wanted-

Today you *stole* a full 50 seconds opening and closing your *relief vessel.*

Fortunately we have identified a cost-effective solution.

Bottles to be taped in situ *before* your shift begins.

Next day

You-

If you think you're paid to sit around expelling faecal matter, think again!

It was an hour to my break, I could hardly walk with it!

How sad, *for us*, five minutes down.

Fortunately...

Lightweight, elasticated leg for leak-free unrestricted work.

Next day

Uh-oh.

GNN!

What's going on? Why've you stopped moving?

I – nobody can go *and* work at the same time!

That being so, explain how I just defecated –

– *while* cancelling all your shifts until further notice.

EIGHT! IT'S ME FUCKIN' BIRTHDEH!
EH?!... AYE, A KNOW...
YER F-FFUCKIN' PRESENT'S NEVEH CUM, Y'SEE, AN' A'VE GOT YER A BIG F-FFUCKIN' CAKE... BUT A LEFT IT ON F-FFUCKIN' BUS... AN' YER CARD'S GOT LOST IN F-FFUCKIN' POST... AN' ER.. ERM..
...ER..
THAT DUN'T MATTEH EIGHT... YOO'VE FORGOT ME FUCKIN' BIRTHDEH EVEREH SINGLE YEAR IN THIRTEH-NINE YEAR OF FUCKIN' MARRIAGE!
A DIDN'T F-FFUCKIN' F-FFERGET IT... A JUST DIDN'T F-FFUCKIN' REMEMBEH IT...
ANYWEH... A'M FIFTEH-FIVE... AN' YER KNAW WOT THAT MEANS..?!
ERM... AYE..?
A CAN FINALLEH DRAW DOWN ME PRIVATE PENSION FUND, EIGHT!
P-PPRIVATE F-FFUCKIN' PENSION?... I DIDN'T KNOW YOO 'AD A F-FF FFUCKIN' PENSION..!
OH AYE. A'VE 'AD IT SINCE WE WOS MARRIED, EIGHT..! A'VE BIN PUTTIN' AWAY ONE FORTEH-NINE EVEREH SINGLE WEEK!
'AVE YER..?
YOO SHOULD KNOW, EIGHT...! IT'S YOO WOT'S BIN TAKIN' MUNNEH AN' PAYIN' ME CONTRIBUTIONS IN AT BANK EVEREH WEDNESDEH AALL THESE YEARS!
OH AYE...
...F-FFUCKIN' DEFNINITLEH... A'VE BIN TEKKIN' AALL THEM ONE FORTEH-NINES AN A'VE BIN PAYIN' 'EM IN...
OH YES...
AT F-FFUCKIN' BANK...
THERE SHOULD BE FOUR THOUSAND POUND IN ME FUCKIN' PENSION POT. A'M OFF T'TH' BANK TEH DRAW DOWN 'OLE FUCKIN' LOT ON IT AN' BUY MESEN A MINK COAT AN' A BIG BORREL OF PRECIOUS LOVE BY KATIE PRICE..!
HALF AN HOUR LATER...
SORY LUV
hAPY BerTHdAY
PS i hav gon to China

TITANIC SINKS AGAIN

Lightning strikes twice for unlucky cruise ship

OCEANOGRAPHERS have discovered that doomed luxury White Star liner RMS Titanic has sunk... *a second time!*

The famous passenger liner first sank in 1912 whilst on her maiden voyage to New York, killing over 1,500 on board. And it was thought that Titanic's final resting place had been discovered in 1985 after a US military mission off the coast of Newfoundland identified the hull 12,500 feet below the surface.

But boffins exploring the sea bed in the area of the wreck yesterday discovered that a chasm had opened up in the ocean floor and the wreck had fallen down that as well.

tectonic

"It seems that a tectonic disturbance many miles below the sea bed caused an abyss to open up directly beneath the main section of the hull," said Tibor Szakacs, Professor of Oceanography at the University of Buenos Aires.

"Our sonar tells us that the ship is now resting at the bottom of a trench 12,502 feet lower than its original position," he told reporters.

"In fact, it's sunk two-foot further than it did first time round," he said.

"I don't know what to say," said Alan Bjorgdottir, President of the Titanic Memorial Society. "The first sinking was a truly awful. But for it to sink a second time is just beyond tragic."

isotonic

'When Titanic sank in 1912, over fifteen hundred people perished in the icy waters of the Atlantic. Thank goodness there was no loss of life this time," he added.

gin & tonic

Meanwhile rumours have begun to circulate that the event could form the basis for a sequel to 1998's wildly successful *Titanic* film.

"It's certainly a possibility," said the movie's director James Cameron. "I mean, the first one did so well and the thing has sunk again. Perhaps Kate Winslet could play a diver or something. And Leonardo DiCaprio could play another one. I don't know."

Meanwhile Elon Musk is rumoured to be in the process of planning a project which will see the wreck raised back to its original position on the sea floor.

rum and raisin

It is thought that the project, codenamed 'Raise The Titanic (back to where it was)' will see the Tesla billionaire marshalling his vast wealth to hire the world's foremost oceanographers, deep sea divers and marine engineers to bring the wreck back up to its previous 12,500 feet-deep resting place, before accusing them all of being paedophiles on Twitter.

Tragic: Titanic and Musk (inset).

Brian or Brian - *Which Cox is the Best?*

BRIAN COX v BRIAN COX

NAME
ROUND 1

THE dreamboat physicist was christened Brian Edward Cox in 1968, when the UK's most popular boy's name was Michael, followed by David and John in second and third positions. In fact, the Prof's name - Brian - languishes in a lowly tenth position in that year's chart, with a paltry 29,938 of the TV boffin's namesakes born that year. However, in a strange twist of fate, Cox is well known for his science-fact-packed *brain* - which is an exact anagram of Brian - an eerie coincidence that earns him some extra points in his opening salvo in the Battle of the Brians.

9

5

NAME

ALTHOUGH he has portrayed countless characters with a variety of weird and wonderful names throughout his long and varied stage, television and movie career, the Emmy Award-winning actor was born plain Brian Denis Cox back in 1946, when the most popular boy's name in Britain was Brian. What's more, growing up in Dundee, Cox was often referred to by locals as a *bairn* - a Scottish slang word meaning child that is, unbelievably, a perfect anagram of his Christian name - so it's a solid opening round for the veteran RSC skull-waver.

DR WHO APPEARANCES
ROUND 2

LIKE many scientists, Cox was a big fan of sci-fi drama *Dr Who* when he was growing up, so it was no surprise in 2012 when he jumped at the chance to make an uncredited cameo appearance in the episode *Power of Three*, which featured Matt Smith as the eponymous Timelord. 7.7 million viewers tuned in to catch the Manchester University Professor of Physics's somewhat wooden and unconvincing portrayal of himself in the show. Had his fellow cameo star in the same episode - *The Apprentice*'s Sir Alan Sugar - not turned in an even more execrable and wooden performance, the Prof's score would arguably have been much lower.

6

0

DR WHO APPEARANCES

IN THE episode broadcast on Christmas Day 2009, actor Brian played the character Elder Ood, memorable due to his grotesque nose tentacles and external fore-brain. However, although over 12,000,000 viewers tuned in to watch the show, not one of them actually saw Cox on screen! That's because a much more poorly paid actor - Ruari Mears - was drafted in to sweat it out under the studio lights in a boilingly-hot rubber mask, whilst Emmy Award-winning Brian phoned his performance in from the air-conditioned comfort of a nearby recording studio.

SAYING "FUCK" ON TV
ROUND 3

CLEAN-cut science presenter Brian is a family favourite whose fascinating shows about the workings of the Universe appeal to all the family. Dropping the F-bomb - for example describing Jupiter as "the biggest fucking planet in the Solar System", the Sun as "our nearest fucking star", or a teaspoonful of matter in a black hole as "weighing more than the fucking Moon" - would be career suicide. The mild-mannered science presenter clearly reserves his F-bomb outbursts and 4-letter tirades for after the director shouts "Cut!", and as a result scores "Eff all" in this foul-mouthed round.

0

10

SAYING "FUCK" ON TV

IN THE hit HBO series *Succession*, Cox stars as aggressive, self-made billionaire Logan Roy, whose 4-letter catchphrase is "No. Now fuck off." This no-nonsense, X-rated rejoinder is repeated at least 30 times per episode, and after 2 series of 10 instalments each, that means Brian has dropped his F-bomb catchphrase at least 600 times, turning the air blue in every home with a Sky dish since the show premiered on June 13th 2018. It's top fucking marks for the potty-mouthed thesp in this round.

CANNIBALISM
ROUND 4

 WITHIN a few minutes' walking distance of his office in the Physics department of Manchester University, Brian can find a variety of sandwich shops, takeaways, bistros and restaurants. Similarly, when he is working at the CERN particle accelerator facility in Geneva, Switzerland, his office is just a short stroll from a well-stocked staff canteen which is open 24 hours, offering hot and cold food, drinks and snacks. As a consequence, we can be reasonably confident - almost beyond reasonable doubt - that Professor Brian has never been forced by gnawing hunger to resort to consuming human flesh.

4

7

CANNIBALISM

WHILST flying to attend the 2000 Golden Globe Awards in Hollywood, Cox's charter plane developed engine trouble and went down in the Andes. He was the only survivor, and was found 5 months later, claiming to have survived by eating reindeer moss, twigs and snow. Although Cox denied butchering and eating the mangled corpses of his fellow passengers whilst awaiting rescue, critics noted that he had put on 5 stones since the crash, a weight gain that would have been impossible if he had indeed, as he claimed, been subsisting on sparse and scrubby high altitude vegetation. With this disturbing anthropophagistic question mark hanging over him, it's a high scoring round for the *Frasier* bit-part fave.

ACADEMIC HONOURS
ROUND 5

AFTER the failure of his one-hit-wonder pop career in D:Ream, synth-stabber Brian decided to try his luck in the world of science. Then, in the words of his hit, things can only got better, as he quickly tucked academic honours including a BSc., a doctorate and a professorship under his mortarboard. As the author or co-author (mainly co-author) of over 950 peer-reviewed scientific papers, it's a first class degree of academic success for the one-hit-wonder-cum-egghead.

10

7

ACADEMIC HONOURS

AFTER leaving school to join his local rep theatre at the age of 15, actor Brian got his education at the University of Life, followed by three years at the hard-bitten London Academy of Music and Dramatic Art. But although he never went to a fancy-nancy university, Cox's academic honours - including an honorary doctorate from something called 'Napier University' in Edinburgh and the Rectorship of the University of Dundee - easily rival those of his scientist namesake.

• • • • • • HOW DID THEY DO? • • • • • •

29

Professor Brian famously got a shit D in his Maths A-level, but even he could do the sums to reveal that he's got a very respectable score of 29 points in this titanic Christmas issue Cox Fight.

• • • • • • HOW DID THEY DO? • • • • • •

Presumably to pay his bills, back in 2005 Brian appeared in the little-known pot-boiler *Match Point*, and in this epic battle to the death, he's got 29 match points to pit against his Mancunian boffin nemesis.

29

---

*Would You Believe It? It's a **DEAD HEAT!** There's not an atom's width to separate these two Coxxes. In fact, the only way to separate them is to look at their **Star in a Reasonably Priced Car** times from when they both appeared on **Top Gear**. And we can reveal that back in 2016, Professor Brian drove a Mini Rallycross car round the track in **1 minute 53.9 seconds**, whilst 13 years earlier his actor namesake clocked up a time of **2 minutes 1.0 seconds** over a different course in a different car… a full 6.1 seconds slower. As a result, Physicist Brian - who also wrote the introduction to our latest Profanisaurus - War and Piss - victoriously takes the chequered flag and is crowned "Cox of the Walk"!*

HOLY CRUMBS!

Vatican tie-in with cheese cracker multi-national

A PAPAL edict could see the much-loved cracker *MINI CHEDDARS* being used in the holy communion service as early as next year. The move is seen as part of Pope Francis's programme of updating the Roman Catholic Church's canonical law to make it 'fit for purpose' for the 21st century.

The move follows the extraordinary summit of bishops convened in the Vatican earlier this year, where the 82-year-old Christ's representative on earth decided to 'open the doors' of the church to appeal to new members of the flock and expand its estimated 1.3 billion client base.

An historic worldwide Eucharist deal is believed to have been secured with Mini Cheddars after parent company Jacobs beat off stiff competition from a lucrative rival bid by Dairy Lea Lunchables.

heavy

"It was a close run thing, but in the end the Holy See decided to go with Mini Cheddars," said Vatican spokesman Fr Antonioli Fiorino. "The Lunchables were good, but we thought they were a little too heavy and unwieldy to do the job," he added.

"More importantly, the Lunchables took a second or two longer than Mini Cheddars to transubstantiate when we rang the bell," he continued. "That may not sound like much, but

when you have 300 plus in the congregation, all wanting to take communion, it soon adds up."

scrap

Other biscuits were rejected early in the bidding process, with Ritz crackers being deemed too salty and Carrs water biscuits described by many bishops as simply "too bland." Other biscuits were omitted for their shape, the Papal accord having decreed that the new wafer should follow the form of the original circular wafer as closely as possible.

The chief spokesman for the Vatican Secretariat for Sacramental Snacks, Monsignor Umberto Castilliano told a press conference in Rome that the move would 'strengthen the Catholic Church's brand' by enhancing the Eucharist with a slight twist on the sacramental bread that represents the body of Christ.

"We must make sure the Church is strong enough to survive all the challenges presented by the modern world," he said. "A reboot like this is sometimes necessary. We have long accepted variations on the blood of Christ with non-alcoholic versions of sacramental wine, such as Shloer and Um Bongo being in use for many years now."

precious

However, the scale and reach of the Catholic Church means that universal decrees issued from the Vatican are notoriously difficult to implement because of the differing cultures and

Crackers: Mini Cheddars get papal thumbs up, but it's excommunication for other snacks

ecclesiastical traditionalists across the Roman Catholic diaspora have expressed their displeasure at the move.

"Many people in South America don't like cheese. What's wrong with a pitta chip or rice cake?" said Father Enrique Inglesia, Bishop of Lima. "A cheese-based savoury biscuit is not a suitable update for something as sacrosanct as communion bread," he continued.

"And apart from that, they taste fucking horrible," he added.

SHITTER

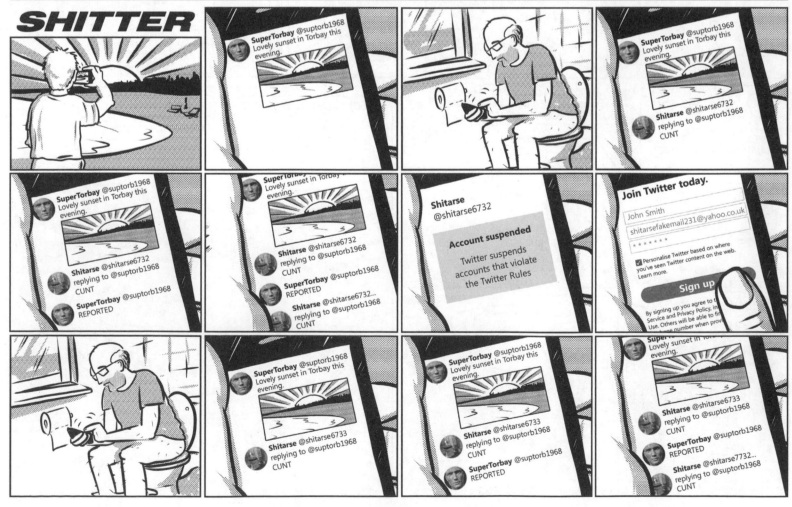

Next Week: Ben and Fanny leap into action when aliens from Jupiter land on the moors looking for humans to lay their eggs in.

LetterbOcks

Viz Comic, P.O. Box 841 Whitley Bay, NE26 9EQ : letters@viz.co.uk

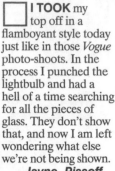

I'VE just read that 20 Prime Ministers went to Eton School. My kids go to a real rough as fuck comp, and I doubt anyone going there is ever going to see the inside of 10 Downing Street. They must have fantastic teachers at Eton. Does anyone know where it is, just in case we're in the catchment area and I could move my kids over? They'd have to do free dinners for them though, because I'm on benefits.

Ed Scrabbley, Driffield

WHILE we were out the other day, somebody drove down our road and ran into the neighbour's gatepost. The impact knocked the stonework off the top which fell onto our wall and knocked it over. Nobody saw the incident and the culprit didn't stop, so it looks like he or she got away with it scot free. However, I am confident that they will be judged harshly on their death and pay for it in the afterlife, perhaps by being boiled for eternity in a lake of sulphur or something.

Maureen Mild, Hexham

PEOPLE always seem to be moaning on this letters page about there being one law for them and another one for us. Well, that's one law each. Sounds fair enough to me.

Tim Horrocks, Manchester

I WENT on holiday to the Netherlands the other week, and when I watched YouTube on my laptop, all the adverts between the videos were in Dutch. You'd think with all their algorithms they'd know that I've never spoken Dutch in my life and wouldn't suddenly just start because I go cycling there for a few days.

Torquil Roll, Luton

BRIAN Cox says that the universe is constantly expanding. So there must have been a time when you could have literally stepped off the Earth straight onto the Moon. It would have saved NASA a lot of faffing about.

Buzz Lightbulb, Florida,

I KNOW Mike Tyson bit Evander Holyfield's ear in 1997, but apart from that you don't really see much cheating in boxing any more. I think it added an extra element of excitement to the proceedings. Come on, boxers, let's get back to those halcyon days when you used to sneak the odd horseshoe into your glove

Barnaby Rudgeford, Hull

IF Chumbawamba got knocked down today, they probably wouldn't get up again. They'd more likely than not be straight on the phone to Injuryclaimsdirectlawyers4u, making out they've got whiplash. What's the world coming to?

TC Rusling, Cottingham

ON a recent documentary, David Attenborough said that a blue whale can weigh more than twenty elephants. Well, that's all well and good, but I've never picked an elephant up so I can't begin to imagine what one of them weighs, let alone twenty. If he wants to appeal to 'the people' he should tell us what the weight of a blue whales is in cats or toasters which everyone can quantify.

Damo, Sunny Guernsey

I'VE just caught the bus from Winchester to Havant and it had audio stop announcements. Imagine my surprise when I heard "Next stop, Jane Austen's house." I've never heard a bus announce "Next stop, Andrew Duggan's house." I have to walk half a mile in all weathers.

Andrew Duggan, Winchester

NOW the kids are on holiday, it's so much easier to get my Transit around town. If this government is so keen to reduce traffic congestion, why don't they simply ban schools? Come on, Boris mate. It's up here for thinking, your bit downstairs is for shagging.

Dave Scratter, Romford

IN my youth, I'm sure I remember a television show in which a bald Chinaman wandered around America, fighting people, having previously picked up a hot barbecue and having had spears thrown at him by a man with ping pong balls for eyes. However, as an extremely heavy drinker, I may be wrong.

Ben Wa-Balls, Orkney

I TOOK my top off in a flamboyant style today just like in those *Vogue* photo-shoots. In the process I punched the lightbulb and had a hell of a time searching for all the pieces of glass. They don't show that, and now I am left wondering what else we're not being shown.

Jayne, Pissoff

WOULD someone please invent a stronger epithet than 'cunt' because my wife wants her mother to visit next month and I need to present my counter argument.

Mike Synnott, Greystones

ON our way home from school, me and a few mates would often take a detour down a back alley and fill one of those old glass milk bottles with our collective piss. Putting 5p each into a pool, we'd retreat to about 20 paces and then hurl stones at the bottle until one of us smashed it, leaving broken glass and piss all over. The marksman who threw the successful stone would pocket the winnings, usually no more than five bob. How innocent the days of childhood were back then and how ingenious we were in making our own harmless fun. So unlike today's spoilt brats with their mobile phones, social media and ipads.

R. Spand, Luton,

WHY is it that women's bikes have no crossbar but men's bikes do? If a man had an accident, a crossbar would do his bollocks an awful lot of damage. Whereas, as a man, I would imagine a woman might enjoy her vagina sliding over the bar. Come on, bicycle manufacturers, be more gender aware in your crossbar design.

Jimmy Murphy, Clonmel

MY dad used to say that 'a shroud has no pockets.' Frankly, I don't see why not. It might be nice for the deceased's hands to casually rest in some pockets by their sides rather than crossed over their front like Dracula. Perhaps it's time for the next celebrity death to start a new fashion trend and reinvigorate the stagnant shroud business in the process.

Ivor Very Biggunn, email

LADIES. When taking a wee in the sea on holiday, introduce an element of doubt in all the other people on the beach's minds as to what you're doing by not just wading in to your labia and looking pensively out to sea for thirty seconds before going back to your spot on the beach.

Brucie Bonus, St. Leonards

MAKE people think you're an Amazon delivery driver by knocking aggressively at the door 8 seconds after ringing the bell.

Matthew Sparks, email

IT came as no surprise to me that the queen's favourite biscuit is Rich Tea. But perhaps it would make her seem more in touch with her subjects if she preferred a more working-class biscuit, such as Jammy Dodgers. On second thoughts, however, let's not forget what happened to Marie Antoinette when she got embroiled in the whole pastry and confectionery debacle.

Toby Crumpledick, Cheam

PUTTING icing on a hot dog roll does not make it a pudding. Come on cake makers, pull your 'finger' out!

Patty, Surrey

I'VE just been to South Wales and I noticed that an ambulance is called an 'ambiwlans', a school is a 'ysgol' and a castle is a 'castell.' And I thought Welsh was supposed to be some complicated mystical heritage language. If you ask me it looks like a piece of piss.

Adrian Newth, Stratford

WHAT'S so essential about essential oils, exactly? I've been getting by just fine without them for years, and I'm forty-eight. Essential, my arse!

R Wilson, Swansea

TICKLE ME EMO

TICKLE! TICKLE! TICKLE! TICKLE! TICKLE! TICKLE!

WHY AREN'T YOU LAUGHING?

BECAUSE LIFE FUCKS US ALL.

MAKE an 'arse kazoo' by wrapping a comb in a piece of toilet paper and placing it between your cheeks. Adjust the clench of your buttocks as you pass wind in order to play different notes. A little practice works wonders and soon you'll be impressing colleagues, friends, family and neighbours.

Phil Kitching, Isle of Jura

QUIZ-SHOW hosts. When it's clear that your contestants haven't got a fucking clue what the answer is, try repeating the question several times slowly in a soft voice as the seconds tick down. The answer is bound to come to them.

Hadrian Wall, email

LADIES. Leave your feminine hygiene products in a prominent position when they're in use so that your husband knows when to keep his fucking mouth shut.

Tammy Huff, Blobstropolis

SAVE yourself the expense of going to the zoo by staring at your garden and wondering where the animals are.

Darren Hobden, Horsham

SCI-FI fans. Feel like you're in a dark, other-worldy dimension by popping into any branch of Hollister.

Neil S, Rainhill

TIPs
toptips@viz.co.uk

WHILST relieving myself in the fountains at Trafalgar Square recently, I noticed that all the pigeons wander about nodding their heads constantly backwards and forwards. It looked like tremendous fun. We humans however are obliged to walk with our necks all stiff and erect with heads held high. It doesn't seem fair.

Simon Spermwhale, Swinford

IN order to ease tensions between North and South Korea, why don't they just use the demilitarised zone and invent a country called 'Middle Korea?' They could act like a mate who stops two blokes fighting during a night out. The same could be said for Northern Ireland and the Republic. My mate Dave would be able to sort out the borders as he went to college and did Geography.

Keith Queef, Llandwrog

I THOUGHT it was only supposed to be intelligent, well-educated people who get to fly planes? I recently flew long haul to Asia, and the pilot made his announcements in about five languages, but in English he pronounced 'Flight' as 'Fleet.' I've got a full, counter-balance forklift truck licence and I can say it stood on my head. God help us, I say.

Barry Boils, Tooting

IS it me, or is Dracula a right messy bastard? His house is covered in cobwebs and dust. For a fella who is supposedly from aristocratic stock and owns his own castle, surely he can afford to get a cleaner in for a few hours a week? They can even come in during the day when he's having a kip.

Fluff Freeman, Halebarns

I DON'T know why people keep going on about how great the police are. I've watched loads of those TV programmes where they follow them around in their cars or helicopters and if anything, they just go around looking for trouble.

Mr Baboon, Foetz

HAY fever sufferers are literally choking on flower-spunk. No wonder it makes your fucking eyes water.

PJ, Islington

I'M looking forward to the year 2035 because at that point, Elvis would have been 100, and it's highly unlikely he'd still be alive regardless, thus ending the conspiracy theory bollocks we've had to put up with since 1977.

E Furse, email

MY student son had a £150 deposit retained by his landlord when he vacated the property due to their being dust on top of a single plug socket. I reckon it would have been the work of five seconds to wipe it down, meaning that the cleaner at the property must be making something in the region of £5 million pounds per week. And they say that premiership footballers are being overpaid.

Bert Crumbhorn, Bury

WHY do they send the police, fire brigade, ambulances, and negotiators every time some daft twat threatens to jump off a roof or a bridge? They should try enticing them down with a saucer of milk first. It works every time with our cat, the dopey little bastard.

Bobby Bowels, email

I LIVE in Yorkshire, and my local bus is the number 66. Imagine my surprise at seeing the number 66 in London this weekend. No wonder they take so long to turn up.

David Craik, Hull

THEY say a good tip for losing weight is to use a smaller plate when eating. How on earth am I going to fit 4 sausages, 4 bacon, 3 eggs, 3 hash browns, 4 slices of toast, black pudding, beans and tomato on without spilling any?

Big John, Sheffield

FOR some reason that song about the mouse with clogs on in the windmill has got stuck in my head, and I've been thinking about it for a while now, and I reckon it's bollocks. Never happened.

Joe Williams, Leeds

New Scientits
Your Questions from the World of Science & Knockers

Waste not want not

WE ARE always being told that plastic micro-particles are getting into the food chain via the fish we eat. Most worrying though must be the question of what happens to all the plastic tits of the likes of Pamela Anderson and Jordan when they die?

R Molehusband, Surbiton

ANSWER: Silicone Gel implants were first introduced in 1961 for reconstructive purposes, and over the years the phenomenon of upping the cup size for purely cosmetic reasons has become mainstream. Though plastic tits are often now simply a saline gel, they do explode during cremation. A shower of molten tit juice is the last thing weeping mourners expect, so generally the false knockers are removed shortly before burial and recycled

Albert E, M.C. Square

Event horizon

GENERAL relativity predicts that the gravitational pull of a black hole is so immense that no light can escape. If I was in a spaceship travelling at or near the speed of light, would this affect reading *Escort Readers' Wives Over 50s Special*, and if so, how?

George Galileo, Hants

ANSWER: A common error here is that an event horizon is fixed in space. In fact, it is the relative position and speed of the observer that dictates where the black hole appears to be, if at all. However, we can postulate that as the onanist nears the point in spacetime where a black hole appears to be, quantum gravitational lensing effects will be noticeable and therefore both the tits of the amateur-and-willing models and the throbbing member of the observer, will appear to stretch out to infinity.

Max P, Germany

Rise of the robots

HOW close are we to a truly sentient robot? And will they come with interchangeable knockers?

Arthur C Clark, Sri Lanka

ANSWER: The issue of sentience is not cut-and-dried. For example, the complex Sophia is a social-centric robot which utilises data processing, facial recognition and AI to hold a conversation on an apparently equal level with humans. However, as Sophia is pre-programmed, she is essentially an upgraded version of any search engine chatbot. Research continues into issues of robot knockers, specifically the areas of balance, nipple-bitability and phwoarness. But it may be a while before your correspondent gets his hands on a set of chebs that are even close to passing the Turing Tit Test.

I Asimov, California.

NEXT WEEK'S QUERIES
PLEASE WRITE TO THE EDITOR WITH YOUR ANSWERS.

Ray B asks: There is much talk of a manned mission to Mars. As surface gravity is only about 40 per cent that of the Earth, what measures has NASA put in place to stop the women astronauts' hooters floating all around and getting in everyone's faces?

Elliot Phonehome asks: A million people have signed-up to storm Area 51, the notorious military compound in Nevada on 20th Sept. 2022. If aliens are found there, how many tits will they have?

C Smallpiece asks: If a Neanderthal woman is found in permafrost, what are the ethics of cloning a living specimen of this long-dead Hominid, and what bra size would she need?

CACK... TO THE FUTURE

A VIZ SCIENCE EXPOOSIVE!

THE SCIENTIFIC world today reacted with shock at proof that time travel is real, as a visitor from the future manifested in a London street, then promptly went on to shit himself.

Where we're going we might drop loads: Whitehall time-traveller might have benefitted from a custom De-loo-rian like the one above.

Pedestrians in London's Whitehall reported a loud bang and a flash of light, as a man in futuristic silver clothes appeared out of thin air. The incident was caught on camera by a BBC crew filming an interview with a government minister, and broadcast live on the lunchtime news.

"It was like something out of a science fiction film," said souvenir vendor Des Minnock. "This geezer just appeared out of nowhere. He looked really surprised, as if he hadn't expected his experiment to work."

"As a crowd gathered round him, he pulled something out of his coat – it was a newspaper. He held it up and said this was proof that he had come from the future."

Minnock said he was unable to see all the newspaper's front page but could make out the date at the top – 25th May 2503 – and part of a headline which read *'HUMANITY WIPED OUT BY…'*

greetings

According to Minnock, the crowd went silent as the visitor from the future started to speak. He told us: "He started to make an announcement in a loud, clear voice. He said something along the lines of 'People of 2019, I bring you greetings from the future. Do not be alarmed. I come with a great warning about the…'"

Business as usual: Mounted police help keep the crowd out of harm's way as the mammoth clean-up operation begins.

But the amazed onlookers never heard the rest of the warning, because according to Des, the time traveller then suddenly hunched over and pulled a face.

"He straightened up and tried to carry on, but when he repeated his line about 'I come with a great warning…', it happened again. He was bent double and even from where I was standing at my souvenir stall, I could hear this awful churning sound coming from his guts," said Mr Minnock.

credit

"It sounded like someone walking quickly through mince."

"The time traveller took a deep breath and carried on," said another witness, traffic warden Albert Crompton, who was patrolling Whitehall at the moment the mysterious visitor appeared. "He just said 'I come with a great warning; seventy years from now humanity will be wiped out by…'"

"The next thing, there was a noise like someone emptying a whoopee cushion full of porridge, then this horrible smell filled the air," Crompton continued.

"Folk were putting their sleeves over their noses and hiding their faces in handkerchiefs. It was bloody awful."

post

Footage shows that the miraculous visitor from the world of tomorrow kept talking, saying something about the only way for mankind to stop impending doom, but everyone was looking at the bottom of his futuristic silver trousers.

Millions around the world watched on the BBC live feed as caramel-coloured effluent streamed down the mysterious stranger's legs and began pooling around his feet.

"Maybe it was a side-effect of time travel, or perhaps he'd just had a dirty pint glass in the future pub the night before," said Dr Umberto Quang, a physicist who witnessed the event on his way to his lab at UCL. "Whatever it was, it was absolutely disgusting. And there was no end to it."

> **The next thing there was a noise like someone emptying a whoopee cushion full of porridge**

Cox: 'Fascinating'

Desperate to impart as much information as he could, the stranger continued to deliver his urgent portent. Deliveroo driver Dougie Mainsail told us: "I caught a couple of phrases: 'The only way to avert the disaster is…' and 'The one thing you need to know...' but to be frank, we were all just mesmerised by how much he was shitting."

"We were hoping to at least get a closer look at his newspaper to see what calamitous event the future had in store for us," said Mainsail. "But after a while he started using it to clean the shit off himself."

"I can see why, but it would've been great to get a look at it first," he added.

And a second disaster struck as the mysterious voyager from tomorrow started to hop up and down, trying to shake the shit out of his futuristic kecks.

"As he landed, an extra-large lump of foulage came down his trouser leg and he slipped on it," said van driver Hector Bandstand. "The poor sod went straight in front of a bus and was killed instantly."

keeper

Cern physicist and former D:Ream keyboardist Professor Brian Cox said that the incident was fascinating as it demonstrated that movement in any direction through spacetime is possible.

"We used to think that whilst movement through the three physical dimensions is multidirectional, the fourth dimension only allowed for unidirectional travel. We now have to think again," said Cox.

"We may also need to consider the possibility that time travel may lead to severe gastro-intestinal problems, or perhaps it might be something to do with realignment of the body's cells in the quantum nexus event horizon," mused Professor Cox, whose hit includes *Things Can Only Get Better.*

finder

And in an attempt to get hold of the knowledge the time-traveller attempted to impart before shitting himself and getting run over, boffins at the Geneva-based CERN particle accelerator are working on a device that could send a packet of Imodium forward in time.

"It is hoped that the Imodium will meet the mysterious stranger before he gets here, so that he can take a few before he lands," said project leader Dr Ulricht Vorst. "That way, hopefully he won't shit himself and get ran over by a bus."

"Although paradoxically, the very act of us having witnessed the event means it is now part of the timeline and may be remembered by our distant descendants as they prepare the brave adventurer for his future mission. In which case they'll probably send him off with a pack of squirts tablets in his time machine anyway," Dr Vorst added.

What's in a Name?
~Laura Kuenssberg

WE WELCOME BBC Political Correspondent **LAURA KUENSSBERG** into our homes every night on the news, as her insightful reports and interviews keep us all abreast of what's going on in UK politics. Whether she's on College Green making Nigel Farage look like a twat, or inside the Central Lobby of the House making Mark Francois look like a bellend, she is seldom off our screens. But how much do we really know about this Scotch lassie with her finger on the political pulse? Once more, the real Laura is revealed within the letters of her name...

L is for LACTOSE
MANY people these days are lactose intolerant, becoming flatulent if they consume dairy products. Fortunately, Laura is not one of them. The BBC political editor can happily tuck in to any amount of milkshakes, cream scones, Dairylea triangles and Cheese Strings without blowing off, a vital consideration for someone who spends so many hours in front of the live TV cameras.

A is for ANACONDA
AS A child, Laura had a pet anaconda which lived in a tank in her bedroom. One night whilst she was asleep, the 18-foot reptile escaped and ate her whole. Kuenssberg woke up in the morning and found herself inside the giant beast, being crushed by its powerful abdominal muscles and dissolved in its digestive juices. Thinking quickly, she took a penknife out of her pyjama pocket and cut a hole in the snake big enough to escape through. The traumatic experience put her off snakes for life, and she now has a gerbil and a terrapin.

U is for UNDERWEAR
IF THE man or woman in the street were knocked over wearing yesterday's underwear, then their embarrassment would be limited to the disdain of the ambulance staff and doctors and nurses at the hospital. However, Laura spends most of every day reporting on national TV, and if the same thing happened to her, the shame of unclean knickers would be seen live by millions of BBC News Channel viewers in the UK and around the world. For this reason, Kuenssberg puts on clean underwear every morning without fail.

R is for RASPUTIN
LAURA'S favourite song is Boney M's 1978 chart-topper *Ra Ra Rasputin*. "The character of the mad monk Grigori Yefimovich Rasputin has fascinated me since I was a child," she told *Desert Island Discs*'s Lauren Laverne. "They poisoned him, shot him twice, threw him in a river and flattened his knackers with a cricket bat, and he still kept getting up for more."

A is for ANGLESEY
ALTHOUGH Kuenssberg has visited most of the countries around the world during the course of her journalistic career, she has never been to the Welsh Island of Anglesey. "I've seen the Taj Mahal, the Victoria Falls, and Ayers Rock, but I've never seen that sign for the train station with the long name, and that's one of the biggest regrets of my life," she told Radio Northampton's Bernie Keith.

K is for KOALA
KUENSSBERG is one of the few BBC presenters to have been bitten on the arse by a marsupial. While she was on a school trip to Knowsley Safari Park in 1990, a koala bear got the scent of a packet of Mentholyptus cough sweets in her back pocket, leapt out of its enclosure and sank its front teeth into her backside. A quick-thinking keeper stunned the bear by hitting it on the head with a brush, and threw it safely back into its cage. Laura still bears two small scars on her buttocks and is well known for showing them off after a few drinks at BBC parties.

U is for UFO
KUENSSBERG was sceptical about the existence of flying saucers... until she was abducted by aliens herself in 1991 whilst working on a farm in Bolivia. She told *Fortean Times* magazine: "I was beamed aboard a Martian spaceship and subjected to a right old anal probing using a scientific instrument made from a metal unknown on earth. Next morning, I woke up in the middle of a field with no memory whatsoever of my harrowing experience."

E is for ELEPHANT
WHILST drunk one night, Kuenssberg bought an elephant on eBay, after placing a £45 bid for a laugh. However, once she sobered up, she realised the 5-ton beast wasn't quite the bargain it had seemed in her boozy fug of the previous night, as it was 'Collection Only' from Bangalore, India, and the cheapest quote from a courier she could find was a whopping £35,000. Fortunately, she was able to get the money back from PayPal, although the seller left her negative feedback, with the comment "Avoid this @!*kin timewaister!!!!"

N is for NUTS
MANY people are allergic to nuts, going into potentially life-threatening anaphylactic shock if they are exposed to even the tiniest amount of the wooden fruit. Fortunately, Laura is not one of them. The BBC political editor can happily tuck in to any amount of peanuts, cashews, walnuts and macadamias without her throat swelling up and having to stab herself with an epi-pen, which would distress viewers were it to happen live on air.

S is for SHOUTING
KUENSSBERG spends so much time shouting "Prime Minister! Are You going to resign?", and "Are you going to resign, Prime Minister?" at the resident of 10 Downing Street, that she has to suck her way through fifteen packets of Strepsils every day to stop herself going hoarse. Luckily for her, since these throat-soothing pastilles are essential for her to do her job, she is able to claim the cost back against tax when she completes her return each April.

S is for SANDCASTLE
In 1982, the 6-year-old Kuenssberg won a sandcastle competition while on a family holiday to whilst on holiday at Brean Sands Pontins near Weston-super-Mare. She was presented with her prize - a box of Maltesers and a bucket and spade - by the BBC's Chief Political

Correspondent Sir Robin Day, who had travelled from London to judge the competition. Kuenssberg was so impressed with Sir Robin's gravitas that she vowed there and then that when she grew up, she too would be the BBC's Chief Political Correspondent.

B is for BUNGLE

LAURA made one of her earliest TV appearances dressed as Bungle the bear on pre-schoolers' series *Rainbow* back in 1997. When the actor who usually played the happy-go-lucky character called in sick, Kuenssberg, who was working as a researcher in the Thames Television news department at the time, was called in at the last minute to don the famous bright orange furry costume. She later recalled: "Unfortunately, I couldn't remember the script, and just kept shouting 'Geoffrey! Are you going to resign? Are you going to resign, Geoffrey?' Luckily, no-one seemed to notice."

E is for ELECTRICITY

LAURA relies on the electricity board's cheap 'Economy 7' scheme to heat her home. Under the system, cheap excess power generated by the national grid during the hours of darkness, when demand is low, is used to warm up storage heaters filled with heavy clay bricks. Later, during daylight hours, these bricks give off heat via radiation and convection, thus warming Kuenssberg's house. The system is used in conjunction with a two-tariff electricity meter which separately records the electricity used during the off-peak period, which is then billed at a lower rate. "Economy 7 storage heaters are shit," says Laura. "The house is either stuffy and boiling hot, or cold as a witch's tit."

R is for RED ADAIR

WHEN they were small children, Kuenssberg and her sister Joanna (now the UK High Commissioner to Mozambique) were digging in their back garden in Glasgow when they struck oil. As thousands of gallons of crude oil shot fifty feet into the air, their father came out to investigate the commotion and a spark from his pipe lit the volatile geyser. There was little to do but summon legendary oilfield troubleshooter Red Adair, who flew from his Texas home to put out the blaze. Laura and Red hit it off immediately, and remained great friends until his death in 2004, when he got ate off a bear.

G is for GLUTEN

IT IS believed that up to 2% the population are gluten intolerant, suffering a range of unpleasant symptoms, including stomach cramps, bloating and chronic diarrhoea if they eat cereal-based proteins. Fortunately for her, Laura numbers herself amongst the 98% of the population who are unaffected.

This means she can enjoy her fill of cakes, bread, biscuits and pasties. And it's just as well, as the prospect of seeing the popular BBC Political Correspondent regularly farting and following through whilst questioning the likes of Jacob Rees-Mogg on College Green would have viewers turning over in their droves to watch Sky News's firm-stooled Adam Boulton.

Next Week: *It's All in the Name looks at 007 Gadgetmaster Q*

SPOT THE CLUE (IN) HORROR at the ORPHANAGE

with BBC ROYAL CORRESPONDENT NICHOLAS WITCHELL

SCOTLAND YARD: THE OFFICE OF DETECTIVE INSPECTOR NICK WITCHELL.

YOU'D BETTER GET OVER TO THE ORPHANAGE, INSPECTOR — A CRIME HAS BEEN COMMITTED!

SOON THE GINGER SLEUTH HAD ARRIVED AT SAINT BARNABY'S ORPHANAGE.

I'M D.I. WITCHELL — WHAT HAS HAPPENED HERE, CONSTABLE?

THE YOUNG CONSTABLE WAS ASHEN-FACED.

THE CRIME SCENE IS THROUGH HERE IN THE HALL, INSPECTOR.

IT... IT'S A PRETTY HARROWING SIGHT, SIR.

SOMEBODY HAS DEFACED THIS PORTRAIT OF OUR BELOVED QUEEN WITH A DRAWING OF A SPUNKING COCK!

GOOD LORD!

THEY'VE POSITIONED THE PENIS TO MAKE IT LOOK LIKE IT'S EJACULATING ONTO HER MAJESTY'S FACE!

YES, AND THEY'VE ADDED A SPEECH BUBBLE SAYING "YUM YUM"...

YUM YUM

...AS IF TO SUGGEST THAT HER MAJESTY IS RELISHING A FACE FULL OF CUM!

THIS IS NOTHING SHORT OF HIGH TREASON — A CRIME PUNISHABLE BY DEATH!

WELL, I HOPE YOU CAPTURE THE CULPRIT, INSPECTOR!

I AM SIR DIGBY EFFING-FARQUHAR, THE DIRECTOR OF SAINT BARNABY'S...

OF COURSE, THIS DREADFUL CRIME MEANS THAT THE ORPHANAGE WILL HAVE TO BE CLOSED DOWN...

WE CAN'T ALLOW THESE POOR CHILDREN TO BE EXPOSED TO IMAGES OF ROYAL BUKKAKE!

YUM YUM

I'LL JUST HAVE TO DEMOLISH THE ORPHANAGE AND SELL THIS VALUABLE PIECE OF LAND TO PROPERTY DEVELOPERS FOR A VAST PROFIT, INSTEAD.

PERHAPS YOU COULD TELL US WHAT HAPPENED, SIR DIGBY?

I WAS THROUGH HERE IN MY OFFICE, INSPECTOR...

"I WAS SITTING AT MY DESK, IDLY CALCULATING HOW MUCH PROFIT I WOULD GAIN IF I DEMOLISHED THE ORPHANAGE AND SOLD THE LAND TO PROPERTY DEVELOPERS..."

"SUDDENLY I HEARD A SOUND FROM THE HALL — LIKE THE SCRIBBLING OF A MARKER PEN!"

"WHEN I CAME OUT TO INVESTIGATE, I SAW A SPURTING NOB HAD BEEN DRAWN ON THE QUEEN'S PORTRAIT!"

"THERE WAS NOBODY ELSE IN THE HALL, AND THE FRONT DOOR STOOD OPEN!"

THE VILLAIN MUST HAVE MADE HIS ESCAPE AS SOON AS HIS EVIL WORK WAS DONE...

INSPECTOR WITCHELL! LOOK AT THIS...

IN SIR DIGBY'S WASTE PAPER BASKET — IT'S A USED MARKER PEN...

...ALONG WITH SEVERAL PRACTISE DRAWINGS OF A SPUNKING COCK — SIGNED BY SIR DIGBY HIMSELF!

IT LOOKS LIKE SIR DIGBY EFFING-FARQUHAR DEFACED THE PORTRAIT SO HE COULD DEMOLISH THE ORPHANAGE AND SELL THE LAND TO PROPERTY DEVELOPERS!

I THINK NOT, CONSTABLE!

CAN YOU SPOT THE CLUE?

THE CULPRIT IS NONE OTHER THAN...

...THE LOCH NESS MONSTER!

AS I ARGUE IN MY 1974 BOOK "THE LOCH NESS STORY", THERE IS COMPELLING EVIDENCE THAT THIS MYSTERIOUS AND ELUSIVE CREATURE EXISTS...

THE MONSTER COULD EASILY HAVE TIP-TOED IN THE FRONT DOOR AND DRAWN A PUD EJACULATING ONTO THE QUEEN'S FACE...

...BEFORE DISAPPEARING AS MYSTERIOUSLY AS IT CAME!

I'M AFRAID THERE'S LITTLE CHANCE OF US FINDING THE LOCH NESS MONSTER AND BRINGING IT TO JUSTICE...

OH WELL, NEVER MIND! I'LL GET ON WITH DEMOLISHING THE ORPHANAGE, THEN!

AMAZING, INSPECTOR! ALL THE EVIDENCE POINTED TO SIR DIGBY BEING GUILTY!

WHAT MADE YOU DECIDE THAT IT WAS THE LOCH NESS MONSTER?

DID YOU SPOT THE CLUE?

ON THE BOOKSHELF IN THE STUDY I SAW A COPY OF "WHO'S WHO" — WHICH REMINDED ME THAT SIR DIGBY IS A DISTANT COUSIN OF THE QUEEN!

IF I ARRESTED THE QUEEN'S COUSIN, THE ROYAL FAMILY MIGHT GET CROSS WITH ME AND REFER TO ME AS "THAT AWFUL MAN" AGAIN. AND SO I BLAMED THE LOCH NESS MONSTER INSTEAD!

SHERLOCK HOLES

TV sleuth plans dig to earth's core

TELLY favourite **BENEDICT CUMBERBATCH** yesterday announced that he would be taking a break from stage and screen work so that he can concentrate on a personal project he's started in his back garden… *Digging a hole to the centre of the Earth!*

The 43-year-old *Sherlock* actor revealed he has already started work on his back yard project and hopes it will be open to the public by the end of the year. Cumberbatch went on to explain that he intends to capitalise on the venture by opening up a small cafe next to the gaping void, which he plans to turn into a tourist attraction.

EXSLEUTHSIVE!

string

"My wife and myself have just returned back from a holiday in the USA, and they've got all sorts of interesting roadside attractions over there," Cumberbatch told reporters. "For example, whilst we were in Wisconsin, we saw the world's biggest ball of string."

"It was utter shite, but they were raking it in," he continued.

The 6-foot tall *Tipping the Velvet* actor said that his own hole will

pretty much back directly onto the A339 near Basingstoke, and provide anyone travelling between Guildford and Reading on the M3 a welcome break and something to visit.

Hole-y mole-y? Cumberbatch's hole 'loads wider' than Russian equivalents.

The current record for the deepest manmade hole belongs to the Kola Superdeep Borehole in north west Russia, which reaches a depth of 40,230ft (7.619 miles). However, Cumberbatch claims that his effort will blow that out of the water.

stab

"I can't say I'm particularly impressed by any of these Russian research boreholes," he said. "The deepest one doesn't even get halfway through the Earth's crust and it's only 9 inches in diameter."

"Mine's already loads wider than that and it's pretty deep as well. If you fell into it you could really do yourself a mischief and I've only been at it for a week."

And the 12st 4lb *Cambridge Spies* actor was unconcerned by claims from experts that the mud would start boiling with highly flammable hydrogen by the time he reaches a depth of 7 miles. "I've got a TradePoint card at B&Q and that means I can afford some pretty serious gear," he said. "The gloves and boots that I picked up look more than up to the job of protecting me from things like geothermal silicon dioxide."

Can he dig it? Cumberbatch.

But the 35" inside leg *Tinker, Tailor, Soldier, Spy* actor may have his work cut out for him when he breaks through the crust and hits the mantle, an 1800-mile-thick layer of 1000°plus molten rock that flows with the consistency of asphalt. "At that point I may have to put down my spade and pop to Lords Tool hire to get a digger for the day," he confessed.

bulletproof

"I just think it's bonkers that we can put a man on the moon but we don't even know what's in the centre of our own planet," he said. "All we need to do is roll up our sleeves and put in a bit of effort."

Asked what he'll do when it's finished, Cumberbatch joked: "My mum, Wanda Ventham is going to run the cafe, so I think my first job will be to nip in for a cup of tea and a few buns. I'll be spent."

NOBODY (with the exception of scientists) has a clue what's in the centre of the planet we all live on. Travelling to the Earth's core has long been the subject of science fiction stories, but just what would that be like if it was possible? Which it isn't. We asked some of Britain's favourite celebs…

What's In The Centre Of The Earth?

MONTY DON *(Gardener's World Presenter)* 66

"Well I spend a lot of time in my vegetable patch, fannying about with my trowel, and the main thing I seem to come across is worms. I've also noticed that the deeper I dig, the larger the worms seem to get, which makes me wonder whether there's one giant earthworm in the centre of the Earth's core. My wife thinks I'm mad, but I spend a lot of time fantasising about a vast sub-terrestrial leviathan writhing around at centre of our planet. I've even taken to worshipping the beast and performing sacrificial rituals in its honour. I don't know, maybe I'm being a bit daft."

TOMASZ SCHAFERNAKER *(TV weatherman)* 42

"As someone who occupies their time thinking about what's going on above us rather than below, I must confess I've never really given it much thought at all. But I think there's probably a race of anaemic, subterranean rat people who live in a network of underground caves and have no idea that we live out here on the surface. Given that the temperature inside the Earth is the same as that on the surface of the sun, these troglodytic humunculli won't have to worry about things like rain and drizzle. But when it comes to withstanding high pressure they'll have their work cut out for them, as it'll be somewhere in the region of 360 gigapascals, which makes the current pressure sweeping in on the Gulf Stream pale into insignificance."

NADIA HUSSEIN *(TV chef and Bake Off winner)* 35

"If I was making a planet, I'd probably pipe it full of something like tomato and passionfruit jam or chocolate stout jelly. I reckon it's nice and cool in the core of the Earth because it doesn't get any sunlight, so even if you used something like clotted cream, it would possibly stay fresh for absolutely ages. That's what I'd do if I was in charge, but if you're asking what I actually think is in centre of the Earth, then I reckon it's just full of rocks and mud and that."

JUSTIN WELBY
(Archbishop of Canterbury) 65

"Well, I've never really been that sure about the idea of the centre of the Earth being a place where demons live and prick at the damned with their pitchforks for eternity. For me that just seems a little far-fetched. But I sometimes think about all those billions of tons of molten magma down there and wonder whether it might be like God's oven. Maybe there's a massive baked potato or hotpot or something that the Lord is cooking and when it's ready he'll incite the Rapture and then dig it out to enjoy a well-deserved snack."

PROFESSOR RICHARD DAWKINS
(Atheist author) 80

"I've noticed that when you water the garden, the water just disappears and doesn't ever seem to come back out, which makes me wonder whether the Earth is just full of water and could burst at any point like a giant water balloon. This idea frightens the life out of me and makes me wish that I had some kind of faith in an afterlife. I also stay up all night worrying that the ground's probably full of skellington bones."

DAPPY *(Former N-Dubz rapper)* 34

"I've always been quite interested in the Hollow Earth theory. As a fan of the Jules Verne classic *Journey to the Centre of the Earth*, I do think it would be amazing if the Earth's core was a vast, volcanic, landscape inhabited by prehistoric beasts and giant insects. Even if that's just the stuff of fiction I still reckon it's likely that Earth is hollow, because that would sort of explain how it floats in space. If it was full up then I reckon it would just fall out of the sky and smash on the ground somewhere like a massive egg."

WHOOPS AISLE APOCALYPSE

Do we *need* two trolleys?

Yes.

I want that fridge behind a wall of wire.

Remember, get your handle *tight* into my left buttock, and pivot off –

Oh no.

They finally did it. The fools...

SLUMP

Did what?

ts low-fat spreads

DAMN YOU!

GOD DAMN YOU ALL TO HELL!

Please get up, you embarrassing twit.

I knew this day was coming.

There's been talk, ever since the boy with the price gun was –

I meant him no harm...

What have you done now?

We killed the fridge.

It's over. Gone. Bargains scattered to the wind.

Maybe they just moved it.

Will you *please* stop being so bloody naive?

Excuse me, have you moved the reduced fridge?

No, it's finished now.

Reduced stuff stays in its normal place on the shelf.

It was getting mental. One of our lads got badly bitten.

So instead you spoonfeed *savings* to idle browsers who've never *fought* for a bargain in their *lives*.

That is what I call *mental*.

t I'm going to look at the tights.

SSSH! Let me think.

Okay, here's the play.

First job, we need to get the discounts out of the reach of *shoppers*.

Trolley the lot, keep them *mobile*, even things we don't like or need.

The game now is catch as catch can!

Items we don't want can be bartered with the others.

eats low

There *will be* others.

Then, simply track the movements of the boy with the price gun –

– and get it *all* back on the shelf *just* in time for the final whoops!

You patrol greengrocery, deli and bakery, I'll cover the rest.

Liaise by the eggs every half-hour starting... now.

Soon

Enjoying the tights are you?

What kind of wife...

Until

Well, I hope you're quite satisfied.

172

Nösferatu the Driving Instrüctor

BRITAIN'S BEST-LOVED SINGLE-COTYLEDONED FLORA FORUM, HOSTED BY EX-BARGAIN HUNT MAN TIM WONNACOT

WONNACOT'S MONOCOTS

Hi readers, **TIM WONNACOT** here. You may know me best as a twat, but you might not realise that I'm also crackers about monocotyledons - *that's grasses and palms to you!* I just can't get enough of these flowering plants with embryos that contain a single seed leaf. And judging from the huge pile of correspondence on the Wonnacot's Monocots desk, I'm not on my own. But that's enough "grass"ing on. Let's see what "stalk"ing points *Viz* readers have raised this week.

Cheers, Tim x

EVERYONE knows that Pampas grass planted in the front garden of a house is a sure sign that the homeowners are swingers. So when me and my wife saw a clump of it growing in the garden of the couple who'd just moved in over the road, we decided to pop round for a bit of how's-your father. After we had introduced ourselves on the doorstep, I made a clumsy grab for the woman's breasts while my wife attempted to rub the husband's penis through his trousers. To our surprise, the couple failed to respond in kind, telling us to "eff off" in no uncertain terms. As we walked back down the path with fleas in our ears, we realised our mistake. It wasn't Pampas grass (*Cortaderia selloana*) after all, but the very similar-looking Mexican feather grass (*Stipea tenuissima*).

Albert & Dolly Uddersthwaite, Glossop

READERS' CHIVES

£25 paid for submissions

SENDER: Mr B, Surbiton

THE BLOKE next door recently treated himself to a brand new state-of-the-art Atco petrol lawnmower. It was a real beauty, much better than my rusty old Flymo, so when he was on holiday I borrowed it from his shed to cut my grass. Unfortunately, my lawn's not as well kept as his, and the blades kept hitting stones and half-bricks hidden in the grass. I also scraped it along the side of an old car engine that's half-buried in the front garden. I have to admit the damage to the mower was quite extensive, but it looked much worse than it really was; I'm sure it was all readily repairable. But when he got home from his holidays and found it in his shed, he went mad with me, calling me all sorts. Whatever happened to old-fashioned good neighbourliness?

Reg Feet, Tunbridge Wells

AS Emeritus Professor of Botany at Oxford University, I can state with scientific certainty that monocotyledons are the best sorts of plants, end of. And if there's any professors who think dicots are better than monocots, you can come outside with me in the quad at Wolfson College and we'll have a right old sort-out. And you can bring someone to help you, if you like, and you can bring your fucking dinner. Because you'll need it when I'm finished with you.

Professor John Sitton, Wolfson College, Oxford

YOU DON'T get so many cartoons with two hairy men in raggedy trousers sitting with their backs to a palm tree on a small desert island any more, do you? I dare say it's something to do with political correctness, so-called 'diversity' or health and safety. Not that I ever found them funny, but I did like the palm trees in them. They also used to do cartoons with two hairy men in raggedy trousers hanging from chains on a dungeon wall, but I didn't like them because they didn't have palm trees in them.

Terry Towelling, Hull

THE IDIOT next door has planted bamboo in the back garden after he saw that other idiot Monty Don doing it on *Gardeners' World*. It's only a small clump at the moment, but I am worried that it will quickly get out of hand and attract pandas. I know pandas look quite cute, but they apparently can be quite vicious. The last thing me and my wife want is hordes of these ravenous black and white bears roaming round next door and climbing over our fence. They might even come into the house looking for more bamboo, and the place is already overrun with rats and cockroaches. I don't want to have to start leaving bear-traps all over the place, as I've got eight children.

Ian Ossifrage, Burton Coggles

HAS Mr Ossifrage (*previous letter*) thought of controlling his pandas using natural methods? I successfully treated the greenfly on my roses by encouraging ladybirds to visit my flowerbeds. If he introduced whatever it is that eats pandas to his garden, I am sure the problem would solve itself.

Bob Honeydew, Yeovil

I'VE always prided myself on my ability to 'think outside the box', so when all my neighbours planted their lawns with grass seeds, I planted mine with onions instead. My onion lawn grew quickly and became quite a talking point in the village. Although I have to cut it twice a week in the summer, I never get it finished. That's because the smell of chopped onions once I start mowing is so overpowering that my eyes start stinging and I have to go back inside and wash them out with Optrex. I am now thinking of taking up the whole lawn and re-laying it with artificial "Astro-Onions", if such a thing exists.

Brian Lampstoft, Norfolk

INSTEAD of ripping up his lawn and replacing it with the plastic monstrosity that is Astro-Onions, has Mr Lampstoft (*above*) considered merely re-turfing it with a milder variety of onion, such as salad onions or Spring onions?

Bob Honeydew, Yeovil

WITH reference to Mr Lampstoft's letter (*above*), why don't farmers plant their cow fields with onions? That way, all the beefburgers would come out onion-flavoured, thus killing two birds with one stone.

Turpentine Dyall, Durham

IT'S ALL very well the onion-fed beef coming out ready onion-flavoured (*previous letter*), but I wouldn't want to put onion-flavoured milk in my tea or on my cornflakes. Actually, it just occurred to me that normal grass-fed cow's milk isn't grass-flavoured, so kindly disregard this letter.

Renee Traintimes, Giggleswick

AS A keen Brexiteer, I was appalled when my next door neighbour planted Calla Lilies in his flowerbeds. How dare he put foreign plants in his garden, against the clearly expressed will of 65 million British people? I thought we had voted to take back control of our borders.

Tommy Proud, Epping

PS. In reality, I don't believe this at all, I simply wrote this letter after thinking up a particularly weak pun on the word border. I actually voted Remain.

I LIKE monocots, but speaking as a nun, it's a good job that the Lord decided to create dicots too. That's because monocotyledonous leaves, such as lilies, bamboos and grasses, are all long and thin. Had these been the only leaves available for Adam to hide his shame in the Garden of Eden, he would have only been able to cover his cock, leaving his balls poking out the sides for all the world to

see. So I say hooray for the cock-and-balls shaped dicotyledonous fig leaf!

Sister Mary Assumpta, Norwich

WITH reference to the previous letter, I fear that Sister Mary may be somewhat underestimating the Lord's capacity for problem solving. If He had created only monocots in the Garden of Eden, I am sure that He would have had Adam's bollocks hanging in a straight line behind his charlie, so that a single thin leaf would have covered the lot from Eve's lustful gaze.

Rev. J Pendletuum, Harwich

I CAN'T imagine why florists are allowed to sell lilies, with their male parts poking out of the flower all proud and turgid. What's more, if you brush against them, they go off, leaving pollen stains all over your clothes, which is just the same as flower spunk. It's high time this sort of filth was banned, or at least kept in a plain brown wrapper behind the florist's counter where children can't see it. I'm not a prude, but if anyone wants lilies, they should have to ask for them discreetly, like farmyard pornography or scat.

Audrey Harbinger, Tiverton

MY HUSBAND uses the grass clippings off our lawn to brew up 'grass tea', which he glugs down by the mugful all day. He says he likes the flavour, but I think it tastes horrible, not least because he never cleans up after our eight dogs before he gets the mower out.

Mrs Poppins, Henge

Miriam

YOUR PALM TREE PROBLEMS SOLVED

Dear Miriam

THE man next door has a lovely 12-foot palm tree in his garden and it's his pride and joy. It really is a beautiful tree; it blooms every year without fail in a spectacular cascade of creamy white flowers. As you can imagine, it makes my garden, with its weeds, threadbare dog-shitty lawn and housebrick rockery, look quite ordinary in comparison.

I am 43 and my wife is 46. We have been together for 22 years, and we have enjoyed an active sex life throughout our marriage. Just lately, however, whilst making love to my wife I have found myself thinking about my neighbour's palm tree, and my feelings of annoyance and jealousy about it have caused me to lose my erection.

Now I am worried that my inability to satisfy my wife in bed may drive her into the arms of another man who isn't subject to the same bitterness and resentment that I am over my neighbour's lovely palm tree. Please help me, Miriam. I don't know which way to turn.

Frank L., Morecambe

Miriam says: *Don't worry about your inability to maintain an erection. There is nothing physically wrong with you, and it happens to every man in a long-term relationship at some* stage. Having said that, you will have to deal with the underlying situation that is leading to your problem.

You could of course plant your own palm tree. But they are very expensive and slow-growing, and it could easily be ten years before it rivals your neighbour's magnificent specimen. By that time, your wife will almost certainly have gone off with another man who is rock hard through not worrying about palm trees.

If you want to save your marriage, your best bet is to sneak into your neighbour's garden under cover of darkness with a ladder, climb up the tree and pour a can of paraffin or sump oil into the crown of his palm tree.

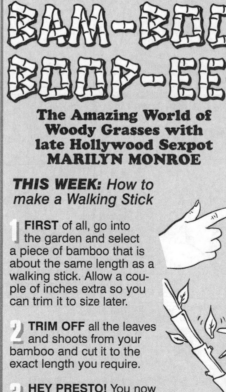

BAM-BOO BOOP-EE-DOO!

The Amazing World of Woody Grasses with late Hollywood Sexpot MARILYN MONROE

THIS WEEK: *How to make a Walking Stick*

1 FIRST of all, go into the garden and select a piece of bamboo that is about the same length as a walking stick. Allow a couple of inches extra so you can trim it to size later.

2 TRIM OFF all the leaves and shoots from your bamboo and cut it to the exact length you require.

3 HEY PRESTO! You now have a super walking stick that will be the envy of all your friends, such as JFK, Bobby Kennedy and Mafia boss Sam Giancana!

Bam-Boo Boop-ee-Doo!

snip!

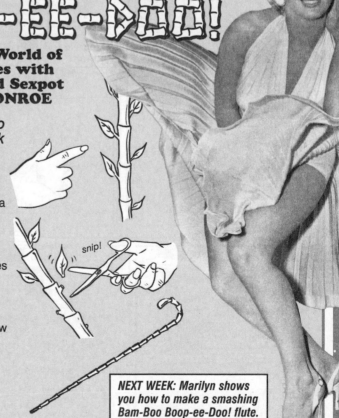

NEXT WEEK: Marilyn shows you how to make a smashing Bam-Boo Boop-ee-Doo! flute.

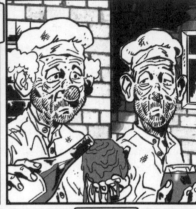

Mrs BRADY OLD Lady

OH, I DO LOVE CHRISTMAS, ME, YOU KNOW..! IT'S SO NICE TO SEE EVERYONE AND CATCH UP WITH ALL THEIR DOINGS...!

I WONDER WHERE DOLLY IS. IT'S NOT LIKE HER T'NOT BE 'ERE FOR ALL THE FESTIVITIES.

I DO HOPE NO MISFORTUNE'S BEFALLEN HER. IT'D BE A SHAME IF SHE'S PASSED ON OR BROKEN A HIP FOR CHRISTMAS.

'ELLO DOLLY... IT'S ME, ADA. I WERE JUST WONDERIN' WHERE YOU WERE, ONLY I'VE JUST TOOK TH' TURKEY OUT TH'OVEN.

'AVE YOU, ADA..? I WERE JUST GOIN' T'RING YOU, AS IT 'APPENS...

...ONLY I'VE JUST TOOK MINE OUT 'ERE. I THOUGHT YOU WAS COMIN' T' ME THIS YEAR...

OOH NO...

IT'S AN ODD YEAR, IN'T IT, 2019..? SO IT'S MY TURN T'DO CHRISTMAS DINNER. YOU DO TH'EVEN YEARS, DOLLY.

DO I..?

YES. I DO ODDS AND YOU DO EVENS, LOVE.

BUT YOU DID DINNER LAST YEAR, ADA.

DID I..?

YOU DID.

I REMEMBER IT WELL. YOUR OVEN TIMER WERE BROKEN AN' TH' TURKEY WEREN'T COOKED THROUGH PROPERLY...

OOH YES IT WERE PINK, WEREN'T IT.

WE WAS A BIT POORLY, WASN'T WE...

AYE...

CAMPYLOBACTER ENTERITIS, TH' DOCTOR SAID IT WERE.

I WERE SHITTIN' OVER NINE HEDGES TILL GONE TWELFTH NIGHT.

STILL, IT WERE NICE, WEREN'T IT, THAT TURKEY. VERY TASTY, I THOUGHT.

I SUPPOSE, CONSIDERING...

CONSIDERING!? AND WHAT DO YOU MEAN BY THAT, EXACTLY, DOLLY EARNSHAW..?

WELL, Y'KNOW, ADA... TH' FOOD POISONING...

...ALL THE VOMITING AN' HAEMORRHAGIC DIARRHOEA...

I'M NOT CRITICISIN' PARTICULARLY, I'M JUST SAYIN'... I LOST 4 STONE, Y'KNOW, MAINLY IN BLOODY FOULAGE...

WELL IT SOUNDS T' ME LIKE YOU'RE CRITICISIN'!

AN' IF THAT'S YOUR ATTITUDE, DOLLY, THEN Y'KNOW WHAT Y'CAN DO... BECAUSE I'LL TELL YOU THIS, YOU'RE NOT WELCOME IN THIS 'OUSE!

WELL, REALLY.

SHORTLY...

...MY HUSBAND END AT...

BLOOARGH!

BL-BL-BL- HUUUURGH!

SQUONK!

177

The SpringWatch Mysteries

with **Strachan & Packham**

Hello, and welcome to SpringWatch, live from the Kirkdouglas Estate here in the beautiful Scottish Highlands.

And let's go straight to our NestCam to check on our two osprey eggs.

There they are, Michaela.

Yes, no sign of mum and dad. They must be off catching some fish for dinner or something.

My God! Someone's stealing the eggs!

We've got to stop them! Ospreys are one of this country's most endangered birds!

Come on, Michaela. Into the SpringWatchmobile!...

...There isn't a moment to lose!

Shortly…

Here's the nesting tree, but there's no sign of the thief!

Let's check the Nest-Cam footage for clues.

Inside the SpringWatchmobile... *THERE!* Freeze it!

Play it back slowly...

Now zoom in.

Look! The thief's got Eton cufflinks... so we're looking for an old Etonian.

And if I'm not much mistaken, he's wearing a Reform Club signet ring.

That's no help. The Reform Club keeps its membership list a closely guarded secret.

Yes, but there's one thing all members of private clubs have in common... they're all twats for joining.

So we're looking for an Old Etonian who's also a twat.

Yes!

And look at those perfectly manicured nails. Those hands have never done a proper day's work in their fucking life.

An Old Etonian twat who's never done a proper day's fucking work in his life?...

Hmmm...

...That doesn't narrow it down very much, does it, Chris?

Perhaps not anywhere else in the world, Michaela...

...but we're in the Scottish highlands. There can't be many people answering that description around here.

You're right, Chris!...But look!

Hmmm!...

Kirkdouglas Catholic Church
Tonight
from LONDON
Mr JACOB REES-MOGG
will be holding a **Tridentine Mass** in **Ecclesiastical Latin**
FREE ENTRY NO FOREIGNERS

I think we may have identified our culprit!

But where is he? We've got to find him before them eggs go cold.

Michaela - What's the most expensive hotel in the area?

Erm... that'll be the Glenmiller Imperial in the next valley... The Penthouse Suite is £1500 a night.

Well, as a man who insists on the best of everything, that's where he'll be!...

...Let's go!

178

Minutes later...

Come on, Michaela!

I'm right behind you, Chris!

Och the noo! Staup!

On the top floor...

Quick!

I hope we're in time!

Stop right there, Rees-Mogg!

Goodness. What is the meaning of this?

I'll take those!

I say!...

Just in time, Chris. He was about to cook these osprey eggs into an omelette.

What!?

How did you know?

I read his entry in Who's Who on the way here. He lists his hobbies as Extreme Catholicism, Coitus Interruptus and eating omelettes made from the eggs of endangered birds.

The **bastard!**

Over the years, he's eaten a Golden Eagle omelette, a Condor omelette, and even a Kakapo omelette...

...The osprey was the only one he had yet to tick off his list.

Yes... *et successissem dum ne vos Ver-Contemplantes mihi immiscuissetis.*

Get that four-eyed weedy streak of piss out of my sight.

Chris! The eggs are getting cold.

Don't worry, Michaela... stuff them down the back of my trousers...

...they'll be safe and warm down there until we get them back to the nest.

Next day...

Hello and welcome to SpringWatch.

And we've got some very exciting news for anyone who is following our coverage of the osprey's nest.

You may remember that yesterday someone stole both of the eggs from the nest.

Well, we managed to track them down and got them back... and the good news is they hatched...

...*down the back of Chris's trousers!*

And here they are!

Aren't they cute!

They are indeed, Michaela...

...And my bottom was the first thing they saw when they come out the eggs, so they think it's their mum.

Cheep! Cheep!

Yes, so they'll have to stay in the crack of Chris's arse until they've fledged in about six weeks' time...

Okay! Now, it was all go in our badger sett last night, when a hungry fox came sniffing about!

More SpringWatch Mysteries next time!

IT SHOULDN'T HAPPEN

BACK in the 1970s, James Herriot's gently amusing memoirs of his years as a northern vet regularly topped the book charts. His heart-warming anecdotes about sheepdogs, carthorses and dairy cattle in the Yorkshire Dales kept millions of readers chuckling and were even made into feature films and a successful television series starring Christopher Timothy sticking his arm up cows' arses. Sadly, Herriot died in 1995, but now his mantle is being taken up by another retired veterinarian with a host of equally hilarious anecdotes about his own career.

- **FRANKIE ASSISI** spent years as Hollywood's most famous vet, and when theTinseltown stars' pedigree pets fell ill, he was the go-to guy to make them better. "They called me the Ray Donovan of the animal world," he says. "If an A-lister had an ailing Alsatian, a cat with a cough or a fish with a fungal infection, they had my Beverly Hills surgery on speed-dial. In fact, my star-studded clients file read like the guest list for the top table at the Oscars!"

Assisi's latest book *It Shouldn't Happen to a Hollywood Vet* is packed with star-studded, pet-related anecdotes set in glamorous Beverly HIlls, and will soon be hitting movie screens as a major big-budget blockbuster starring **CHRISTIAN BALE** as Frankie and **SCARLETT JOHANSSON** as his estranged wife Joan.

When my surgery door opened, you never knew who was going to walk in. But even I was surprised when porn star **STORMY DANIELS** sashayed into my consulting room, dragging a decidedly overweight bull mastiff on its lead. I immediately recognised her from her long-running legal feud with Donald Trump, as well as my large stash of tenth generation pirated porn videos.

EXCLUSIVE!

She explained that her dog had been dragging its arse around the carpet in her apartment, a behaviour we vets refer to as "yachting". The condition is generally caused by one of two things – worms or an infection, so I put the dog on my examination table and lifted up his tail to take a look at his business end. I immediately saw what the problem was when I clocked his anal glands – *they were swelled up like cherry tomatoes!*

> *No sooner had I slipped my finger up Fido's teatowel holder, than both of the swollen glands went off like a double barrelled shotgun.*

Any vet will tell you that a dog with infected glands is bread and butter stuff, and the remedy is simple. You simply stick your finger up its nipsy and give the glands a squeeze from the back. I asked Stormy to hold her dog's back legs in case the procedure made it jump – just like when someone sticks a finger up your arse, it can come as a bit of a surprise – and I did my stuff.

No sooner had I slipped my finger up Fido's teatowel holder, than both of the swollen glands went off like a double barrelled shotgun. Poor Miss Daniels was right in the firing line and got splattered with foul-smelling brown sludge for her trouble. Now I've seen a few of her videos over the years, and I know she's no stranger to a pop-shot facial, but believe you me there was nothing remotely erotic about the scene that had just unfolded in my surgery. I handed her a fistful of tissues and she wiped herself down as best she could, gagging all the while from the stench.

In this job, you get used to bad smells, but the stink from that dog's arse really was something else. In fact, it was so bad that I haven't been able to watch one of Stormy's videos since. When she comes on the screen, I simply have to stop, pick up the remote control, and fast forward till the next bird appears. **"**

hollywood

5'2" Frankie, 55, who never technically qualified as a vet, learnt his animal husbandry craft over nearly four decades working as a kennel hand at greyhound and whippet tracks in and around his native Penrith, Cumbria.

From an early age, I loved animals and I always knew that I wanted to work with them, so it was a dream come true when I was permanently excluded from school at fourteen and got a job working at the local dog track.

The men who worked there had a way with animals. They were hard but fair, and I learnt my trade as a vet through watching them. They taught me everything I know, from what to give a dog to make it shit before a race, to what to rub round its arsehole to make it run a bit faster and what to slip in its dinner to slow it down a bit so it loses. **"**

Poo's a pretty boy? Pampered pooch Fido's arse-based antics created havoc in Frank's surgery.

Frank confession: Vet Assisi spills the beans on his star-studded surgery in new book.

After forty years working with racing dogs, Frankie lost his job following a theft from the Tote office, which track owners suspected was an inside job. He told us: "I had nothing to do with that robbery, and I have no idea how my fingerprints ended up on the cashbox, or how that cashbox ended up under my bed." Unemployed and with his previously good name blackened, he made the decision to wipe the slate clean and start over in the USA.

He told us: "You can't practise as a vet in Britain without qualifications, so making a fresh start across the pond was my only option. It wasn't long before I was building up an impressive, star-studded clientele at my brand new practice in the heart of Hollywood."

daniels

One the first customers through the door of Assisi's swish Bel Air clinic was muscle-bound Rocky star **SYLVESTER STALLONE**, *who turned up with a sickly pet parrot perched on his shoulder.*

Sly explained that he'd won the bird in an arm-wrestling competition against **CARL WEATHERS** on the set of *Rocky II*, but that it recently had started pulling its feathers out. It was now completely

Shit storm: Daniels was in the firing line.

TO A HOLLYWOOD VET

bald, and he was very worried about it.

I'd seen similar behaviour in my days working at the dog track, with whippets chavelling at their own fur when they were at a loose end in the kennels. Sly had to go to pick up his dry cleaning, so I told him to leave the parrot with me for an hour or two. My plan was to get it playing with a bell or something to stop it getting bored and cheer it up a bit.

mcgee

Once he'd left, I thought I'd best give the parrot a quick examination, but as I reached out to grab it, it bit down hard on my thumb with its razor sharp beak. If it had been a dog biting me, I would have known exactly what to do; a finger slipped quickly up its arse makes any dog's jaws open as a reflex action. But parrots are nothing like dogs, in that their arses are much too small to get your finger up, so I started batting it gently against the top of my desk in an attempt to get it to loosen its vice-like grip.

Polly fill-in: Quick-thinking Frank made sly swap with Beyoncé's bird.

However, I can only assume I was a bit too forceful with the treatment, because after a couple of dozen blows, the parrot fell off my finger and flopped to the floor, stone dead. My heart sank. I certainly didn't relish phoning Sly to break the tragic news that his beloved pet had succumbed to its injuries. He doted on that bird, and I knew he wouldn't take too kindly to me having brayed it to death, albeit accidentally and in self defence. What's more, I'd seen his films and knew he had a pretty good left hook on him, so I had to think quickly.

I ran down the road to the Beverly Hills Pet Shop on Sunset Boulevard, and as luck would have it they had a parrot in stock that was just the

Beak careful! Sly's colourful pet bit off more than he could chew.

right size. The assistant explained that it had been bought by **BEYONCE** as an anniversary present for **JAY-Z**, only its droppings had given him bird fancier's lung, so she'd brought it back to the shop for a refund. It was completely the wrong colour, but that didn't matter because I was going to pluck the fucker anyway. I handed over my twenty bucks, picked up the replacement bird and hot-footed it back to my surgery.

I spent the next half hour pulling the new parrot's feathers out with pliers. When I'd finished, it was bald as a coot and looked exactly like Sly's bird. He was delighted when he came back from the launderette to pick it up. I explained that I had cured it of depression, told him not to worry if its feathers grew back a different colour, and handed him a bill for a thousand dollars. Job done, and another satisfied customer!

reynolds

Whilst Frankie's training was mainly done on racing dogs, he maintains that all four-legged animals are much the same. He told us: "When all's said and done, a giraffe is just a big, spotty whippet with a long neck. As long as you remember to multiply the drugs you give it by how many times higher a giraffe is than a whippet, you won't go far wrong."

So he wasn't worried at all when Peter Pan of Pop **MICHAEL JACKSON** phoned him up to ask if he could pop round to his Neverland Zoo to take a look at one of his exotic pets.

❝I couldn't believe it was really Jacko phoning my surgery. I thought it must be someone taking the piss, so I told him to fuck off and hung up the phone, but he rang straight back. I told him the only way to prove he really was who he said he was would be to sing *Billy Jean* down the phone. When he did, and I heard the telltale sounds of him grabbing his bollocks and moonwalking up and down his hallway, I realised he was telling the truth, and told him I'd be round straight away.

Half an hour later, I got off my bike outside the Neverland Ranch and knocked on the door. Jacko answered, and led me to the elephant house of his private zoo, where one of his elephants – a gift from **ELIZABETH TAYLOR** – was constipated.

Now, when a racing greyhound is eggbound, about half a spoonful of paraffin poured down their neck usually sees them shitting properly again in no time, so I did a quick mental calculation that a couple of buckets of the stuff would soon put two-ton Gypsy right. Three buckets full to be on the safe side. I told Jacko I'd need four dozen buns to soak the paraffin up, and he rang his personal chef to order them.

kwouk

When the buns arrived at the elephant house, I poured the paraffin onto them, and they soaked it up like sponges. The elephant eagerly scoffed them down as me and Jacko shovelled them into its hungry mouth. In retrospect, I think I must have got my maths wrong, because what happened next wasn't quite what I was expecting.

As the gallons of paraffin reacted with the elephant's guts, it let out a deafening trumpet of pain, started spraying liquid shite out of its arse, ran out of its enclosure and galloped off towards Jacko's private funfair, where a load of children were queuing up for a ride on a roundabout. To the day I die, I don't think I'll ever forget the screams of those poor kids as that big grey bastard sprayed them with its liquid paraffin shite, before running off to do the same to the kids on the dodgems.

I didn't hang round to see what carnage it would wreak on the kids queuing up at the helter skelter and the coconut shy. By that time, I had got back on my bike and was pedalling back towards my Beverly Hills surgery as fast as I could, with the horrified screams of those poor, shit-covered kids, echoing in my ears.❞

> ❝To the day I die, I don't think I'll ever forget the screams of those poor kids as that big grey bastard sprayed them with its liquid paraffin shite❞

Bumbo: Gypsy's dodgy tummy spelled big trouble for onlookers.

Tiring of his jetset lifestyle, Frankie eventually swapped his luxury $10million Bel Air condo for a two-room bedsit above a fish and chip shop back in his native Penrith, where he is currently looking for a publisher for his memoirs. He told us: "I know there's been a rumour that I've been in Wakefield Prison following that theft at the dog track, but that's not the case. I've been in Hollywood, and now I'm writing my sensational star-studded memoirs."

"I've only just finished the first chapter at the moment, because my typewriter ribbon dried up and the man in Smiths said they don't make them any more. I sprayed it with water, which worked, but it made some of the keys go rusty and jam up, so I'm going to get some WD40 to spray on them to loosen them up a bit."

"It's not actually WD40. It's this stuff they have in the pound shop in Penrith, but it's just the same and it's got one of them long red tubes on it so I can get right in where the keys have all rusted. Then, once I've done that, I'll be able to finish my book about how I was a vet in Hollywood and not in Wakefield Prison."

Smelly Jean: Parrafin-soaked buns caused jumbo trouble for Jackson's pet pachyderm at his Neverland ranch.

BIG NAN ON CAMPUS!
80ft grandmother terrorises university

STUDENTS at the University of Goole were left reeling in shock yesterday after an 80ft tall grandmother-of-six ran amok on their college campus.

The giant granny, who has been named as 79-year-old Edna Dunnock, is thought to have acquired her monstrous size after being bitten by a radioactive spider at her East Yorkshire care home.

fusion

"The care home is right next to the Goole nuclear power plant," said Humberside county councillor Nashville Fishwick. "We believe that a radioactive arachnid scuttled out of the fusion reactor and entered the Autumn Grove Nursing Facility next door. Once there, we presume it must of sank its tiny teeth into Mrs Dunnock's arm, causing her to shoot up to the size of a King Kong," he added.

The confused and frightened 80ft pensioner proceeded to break through the roof of the care home and stomp across four lanes of traffic to enter the nearby university campus.

EXCLUSIVE!

Second-year English Literature student Natasha Capsule told reporters: "It was terrifying. I was leaving a lecture when I came face to face with a wool-trimmed tartan slipper the size of a Smart car. I looked up and there was a little old lady as tall as a fully-grown oak tree roaring down at me about how small and fiddly the new five pence pieces are."

"Then she bellowed something about an Ormolu clock that her sister was supposed to leave her in her will and started having a go about immigrants, but I didn't catch the end of it as I was too busy running in terror," Miss Capsule said.

Mrs Dunnock's terrifying rampage across the 300-acre campus lasted nearly two hours. Luckily no-one was badly hurt, although two dormitories, a staff canteen and a lecture hall were partially destroyed and several students sustained mild concussion after being struck by falling Werther's Originals.

The octodecafoot septuagenarian was eventually shot with a tranquiliser dart the size of a rolled-up carpet by an armed police unit, after she climbed a block of flats near Humberside Airport.

magazine

Once she was anaesthetised, a team of doctors was quickly able to extract the radioactive venom from her blood, at which point she returned instantly to her regular height of 4'11", went back to her care home and had a cup of tea, a digestive biscuit and a nap.

There's no-one quite like Grandma: University buildings lie in ruins after octogenarian was bitten by radioactive spider (top right).

MAJOR MISUNDERSTANDING

MARCEL PROUST and his MAGICAL MEMORY CAKES

PETITES MADELAINES

D.J. '19

PARIS IN THE EARLY NINETEEN HUNDREDS

M. PROUST NOVELIST

YOUR MOTHER WILL BE COMING ROUND FOR AFTERNOON TEA ANY MINUTE, MONSIEUR PROUST...

I'VE ARRANGED EVERYTHING TICKETY-BOO, JUST AS YOU LIKE IT...

NOT QUITE, MADAME ALBARET— I CAN'T FIND MY SILVER CUFFLINKS ANYWHERE!

THOSE CUFFLINKS WERE A PRESENT FROM MOTHER!

SHE WILL EXPECT ME TO BE WEARING THEM WHEN SHE COMES TO TEA!

LET'S SEE... I HAD THEM THIS MORNING, AND I PUT THEM IN A SAFE PLACE...

IF ONLY I COULD REMEMBER WHERE!

BUT WAIT! I JUST NEED TO EAT ONE OF MY SPECIAL LITTLE CAKES!

THEY HAVE THE MIRACULOUS POWER OF CONJURING UP REMEMBRANCES OF TIMES PAST!

ONE LITTLE NIBBLE WILL SUMMON UP A VIVID MEMORY OF WHERE I PUT THOSE CUFFLINKS...

MUNCH!

OOH LOOK, MONSIEUR PROUST...

THAT'S YOU THIS MORNING, PUTTING THE CUFFLINKS ON THE MANTELPIECE!

EH BIEN! OF COURSE!

HERE THEY ARE, MONSIEUR P!

CHOMP!

MM! THESE CAKES ARE A BIT MORE-ISH! I'LL HAVE ANOTHER ONE...

ZUT ALORS!

THIS SECOND CAKE HAS EVOKED A BOYHOOD MEMORY OF PICKING MY NOSE AND WIPING THE BOGIES ON MOTHER'S CURTAINS!

COO-EE! MARCEL!

GASP! HERE COMES MOTHER!

IF SHE SPOTS MY BOGEY-PICKING RECOLLECTION SHE'LL SLAP MY LEGS!

AH MOTHER, COME AND LOOK AT THE DOOR HINGES INSIDE THIS WARDROBE...

HUSTLE

THEY REALLY ARE MOST INTERESTING!

???

MARCEL! WHAT'S GOING ON? LET ME OUT AT ONCE!

CLICK!

MON DIEU! I MUST DELETE THAT NOSE-PICKING MEMORY BEFORE MOTHER SEES IT!

A BLOW ON THE HEAD WILL CAUSE MEMORY LOSS - QUICKLY MADAME ALBARET, HIT ME OVER THE BONCE WITH THAT POKER!

RIGHT YOU ARE, MONSIEUR P!

LET ME OUT!

OOPS! I'VE HOOKED THE CAKE STAND BY MISTAKE!

GRACIOUS! MONSIEUR PROUST HAS SWALLOWED A WHOLE LOAD OF HIS MEMORY CAKES!

LE GLUMPH!

MARCEL! ARE YOU THERE?

uh! uh! uh!

SACRE BLEU!

NOW THE CAKES HAVE CONJURED UP A HIGH-DEFINITION MEMORY OF THAT TIME I HAD A WANK WHILE WEARING MOTHER'S BRA ON MY HEAD!

MARCEL! I AM COMING OUT OF THIS WARDROBE WHETHER YOU LIKE IT OR NOT!

FWAP! FWAP!

OH MON DIEU! NO MOTHER, YOU MUSTN'T...!

BANG! THUMP!

CRACK!

OOF!

AHA! THAT'S GOT THE DOOR OPEN!

UH-WHAT HAPPENED? WHERE AM I?

PHEW! AT LEAST THAT BANG ON THE HEAD HAS DELETED MONSIEUR PROUST'S EMBARRASSING RECOLLECTION!

THESE MAGICAL MEMORY CAKES ARE NOTHING BUT TROUBLE!

I'LL GIVE THEM TO THE DOG — HERE, FOO FOO!

OHO! LOOKS LIKE LITTLE FOO FOO IS RECALLING A MEMORY FROM EARLIER TODAY!

WHAT ARE YOU REMINISCING ABOUT, FOO FOO?

SPLUTTER!

LETTERBOCKS

The Comic, P.O. Box 841 Whitley Bay, NE26 9EQ | letters@viz.co.uk

LAST week, a wasp flew into my living room, so I sprayed it with wasp killer. However, some of the spray landed in my fish tank and killed all my goldfish. Why don't wasp spray manufacturers call it 'Wasp and Goldfish Killer'? I think the marketing boys missed a trick there.

Neil Johnson, Durham

TODAY, I cleaned out the fuel injectors in my Subaru Impreza. All my wife did was change our baby's nappy and then warm up a bottle of milk. Who says women are as good as men?

Rev. S Dolphin, Ipswich

MY cat was away at the vets for two days last week, but my three pet mice, if anything, were less playful than usual during that time. Who makes up these sayings?

Lee, Fleet

I JUST saw that Steph woman from the popular TV show *Shop Well for Less* in my local shop, and she was buying Nescafé branded coffee despite there being a jar of Happy Shopper coffee next to it. I feel betrayed. Betrayed and angry.

Cath Jones, email

REGARDING witches, Lancashire, Pendle Hill and all that stuff. Do you really think that if witches existed, they would hang about damp and grim Lancashire, being dunked and burned at the stake? No, they'd be off on their broomsticks to tropical climates like Bora Bora or Fiji.

Jimmy, Preston Lancs

WHENEVER we see a gazelle being torn asunder by a lion or a tiger on TV, the camera crew never interfere because they say they have to uphold the laws of nature. However, I'm betting they'd soon get their arses in gear if a lion started munching on Sir David Attenborough.

Edna Bloemfontaine, Ely

IF you shrank to the size of an ant, you wouldn't be able to piss because the surface tension in the piss would be so great that it wouldn't travel down your microscopically thin urethra. It would be a ruptured bladder and the subsequent infection that would be the most likely thing to kill you, not a spider or a kid with a magnifying glass.

Brampton Carlisle, Carlisle

FAT blokes' tits are often referred to as 'moobs' - a contraction of 'man boobs'. So I was wondering if overweight male cows had tits, they would have to be called 'bull boobs', because just contracts to 'boobs', which wouldn't differentiate them from cows' normal tits. Although cows' tits are called 'udders', so perhaps bulls' tits would be called 'budders.' Or am I over-thinking this?

Hector Yaffle, Penge

WHY does my dog insist on maintaining eye contact with me whenever he has a shit? Animal experts?

Dudley, Donnehugh

I LEARNED with some disgust recently that the Latin word for 'old woman' is "anus". Speaking as a lady of 91, I find this ageist slur utterly sickening, and it only serves to support my view that being sacked by marauding Visigoths in 410AD was nothing less than the Romans deserved. I, for one, am glad they're all dead.

Edna Sphincter, Fulham

COME on *Viz*, you're getting stale. Without fail I know within the second last caption of *Eight Ace* that 'Eight' is going to buy Ace again. Hardly Agatha Christie is it?

Gordon Bennett, Auckland

I WOKE up the other night to find a masked intruder holding a knife to my throat. Normally, that would be terrifying, but as I had been having a dream about being stuck in a lift with Piers Morgan, Katie Hopkins and Gemma Collins, it was actually quite a relief. The intruder took my wallet, my watch and my mobile phone, but it was worth it.

Frampton Golightly, Deal

IT'S great to see women's football growing and developing, with higher attendances and the Lionesses representing England so well at international tournaments. But until the female supporters get violently engaged with foreign police forces, throwing cafe furniture about amid a fog of teargas, the female game will never be taken as seriously as the men's.

Patrick D, Aghalee

WHY do we describe something small as 'fun-sized'? That's just silly. My wife has tiny tits, and they're no fun at all.

Martin, London

I DON'T really believe these experts when they say that dogs have a great sense of smell. If that were the case, why do they need to get their nose right up another dog's backside for a sniff? I can smell my dog's farts in the next room.

Richie B, Leicester

HOW about a picture of that bloke out of that picture of that bloke kissing that bird' arse, kissing the arse of that bloke in that statue of that bloke getting bit on the arse off of a lion?

Cheadle Hulme, Thornaby

✱ *No problem, Mr Hulme.*

YOU sometimes hear about men who piss sitting down, but you never hear about men who shit standing up. So much for equality.

Palmer Jorhend, Portstewart

THEY reckon that the mayfly only lives for one day, and that its only purpose is to mate. Well I'm no expert on insects, but I bet the male comes up with some pretty desperate and shite chat-up lines. I know I have in the past when I was out of a night and desperate for a shag.

Hampton Bootleby, London

I'VE had a dusty old rug on my washing line for 3 weeks. Can any of your readers beat that?

The Incredible Sulk, Greenland

DOES anyone know if you're able to nominate people for Sports Personality of the Year? My mate Baz who plays for Morley Town AFC played every game last year hungover to fuck and still managed to score ten goals and only be sent off six times. Absolute hero. What's Andy Murray ever actually done?

Tommy Marsh, Morley

YESTERDAY I was enjoying reading *Viz* on a sunny day in the garden. Last night it rained and my magazine is now sopping wet and completely unreadable. Perhaps you could consider printing a warning, advising people that your magazine is not waterproof.

Helen Shanahan, email

GIVEN that Jesus died for our sins, couldn't the church give him a better title than Lord? Even David Dickinson is nicknamed the Duke. Surely the son of God deserves an earldom at least?

Miss S E Hall, Jesmond

I'M sick of wearing light-coloured, loose-fitting trousers in the summer because any light splash shows up. Roll on the cold of winter so I can wear dark jeans and piss all over myself in peace.

Smithers, Durham

IT seems extremely cruel that scientists do their experiments on mice and rats which invariably lead to these animals' deaths. Why don't they simply use lemmings instead? After all, when the experiment was over, they'd all just jump off the laboratory roof and kill themselves anyway. So they wouldn't care if they'd been made to smoke fags or injected with chemicals earlier on.

Barry Carbondale, Tooting

I REALLY don't see the point of hares. We already have rabbits, and there's no way a magician could fit a hare into a top hat even if there were no rabbits available. We don't eat them, we don't write books or make films about them, so they are no use whatsoever, as far as I'm concerned.

Billy 'no hares' Crumpet, Leeds

ISN'T it strange that you can say "I had a shit" and "I had a wank", but whilst "I did a shit" is perfectly correct, "I did a wank" is grammatically incorrect? They say English is the hardest language to learn, and they might be right.

Frank Tarpaulin, Birmingham

I'D like to go up to that Ralph Fiennes bloke and call him by his name the way it is written - Ralph - instead of Raif like he says it. And if he complained, I'd tell him to stop being such a stupid, stuck-up, luvvie tosspot. He's a good actor and all that, but he needs to be put in his place.

Paul Foy, Aberdeen

THE other day I fancied a mega hot curry and remembered all those shameless plugs you used to do for the Rupali Restaurant and that Curry Hell they used to do. However, after a bit of research on Google, I was disappointed to find out that it shut down a number of years ago. Could you get a medium to contact the late owner Abdul Latif and ask him where I could get a good curry that would burn the inside of my arse out? Ideally round my neck of the woods, as I can't be arsed trekking up to Newcastle and the accent gets on my tits.

Joe Hartshorn, Chesterfield

HAVE any of your readers ever come across their mum in a video whilst casually browsing hardcore pornography on the internet? Because I have, and let me tell you, it's an absolute wank killer.

Anonymous, Bognor Regis

WATCHING *Rambo: First Blood* the other night got me thinking. Although it would have possibly diminished the overall appeal of the story, surely a visit to the local Citizens' Advice Bureau to report the sheriff's bullying would have sorted out the problem and could have prevented all that unnecessary bloodshed and violence.

Tommy Foghorn, Belper

PALM Oil plantations may be taking over Borneo, but I watched *Our Planet* the other night and they looked far tidier than the jungle, with their neat, straight runs of trees. If the Orangutans want to move out because they prefer to live in squalor like animals in their messy rainforests, then that's their lookout.

Sidney Sedgewick, Higham Ferrers

I WAS driving along today at 50mph into a 60mph wind, and yet still went forwards. Work that one out.

Sir Roland Butter, Leics

IF atheists want to be taken seriously, they should come up with new names for the planets, rather than continuing to pay respects to supposedly fake Roman gods like Mars and Neptune. Maybe a naming competition could be opened up to the public, in which case I'd like to suggest renaming the planet Mercury after Scotland and Leeds United frontman Arthur Graham.

Calvin Graham, Phili, USA

THEY say don't store raw meat next to cooked meat, but apparently it's okay to keep potatoes in the cupboard next to crisps. It's one rule for vegetarians and another for the rest of us normal people.

Brian Saxby, Chicago

SCIENTISTS say that sea levels could rise by 10 metres in the next 50 years. Well, I live about half a mile from the coast, and by my calculations this will make my house into a nice sea-front property. Bring it on, I say.

Tarquin Bookbinder, Looe

THE world has changed so much. I remember in the old days there used to be these highly specialised postmen who only delivered milk. Nowadays, postmen only deliver letters, and you have to travel to a shop to get milk, or send a drone or something. Although I guess a postman might still deliver milk if it's sent in a big envelope.

Liamo Cummins, Waterford

It's a Colourful, Colourful, Colourful, Colourful World

with colourful charity queen *Camila Batmanghelidjh*

THE FASHION industry has announced that the colour for 2019 will be blue. This takes over from last year's colour, which was green. The decision was announced in New York by *American Vogue* editor Coco Solidz at a Ritz Hotel press conference attended by clothing designers, haute couture magazine journalists and style critics from around the world.

The announcement came as a surprise, as red or yellow had been expected to be awarded the coveted title. A fashion business spokesman told us: *"We were all really surprised when we heard that blue was this year's colour. Those of us who have bought loads of red and yellow cloth will now have to throw it all away."* Clothes factories will now go into overdrive, producing blue hats, dresses, jackets, trousers and jumpers for the coming year, and the price of blue fabric is expected to rise along with increased demand.

The decision has not been without controversy, after it was revealed that Coco Solidz's husband, textile billionaire Hymen Prepuce III recently opened the world's largest blue cloth factory in Mumbai.

ANYONE sporting a Trump-style tangerine tan may well be shortly receiving one of the ex-American President's trademark legal writs. That's because the former POTUS has copyrighted his lurid skin colour. Officials at the US Patent Office say that the Donald has registered his skin colour - Pantone 021 - as a legally protected trademark.

The former President's mental attorney Rudy Giuliani advised anyone with the same colour face to act quickly before court proceedings were instigated. He told Fox News's Sean Hannity: *"If we catch you with a tangerine face you've got two weeks to let it fade before Mr Trump comes down on you like a ton of bricks."*

"Our message to the American people is simple. Mess with us and we will pursue you to the highest court in the land and destroy you," Mr Giuliani added, tipping his head back and looking like a silent movie villain.

Ex-White House Press Secretary Sarah Huckabee Saunders later tweeted: *"Mr Trump is not being unreasonable. The copyright on the color of his bright orange face doesn't extend to the stupid white bits round his eyes, or his pale forehead that you can see when a breeze gets under his barnet when he's going up the steps of Air Force One."*

A PERUVIAN farmer who was beamed up by aliens says that when he was on their flying saucer he saw a colour that is unknown on earth. Boco Perez, 58, was strapped to a table in a laboratory aboard the UFO and had his anus probed with some sort of metallic instrument.

"I caught a glimpse of it before they forced it up my bottom," Perez told his local paper the *Lima Telegraph e Argus*. *"The colour of it was like nothing I've ever seen. I can't describe it as a greeny-blue or a reddy-orange or a purple, because it wasn't like any of those colours or any colour I can imagine."*

The farmer, who has been beamed up off his tractor and anally probed by space aliens over 250 times in the last 30 years, told reporters: *"It was absolute agony. If you can imagine getting a filling off the dentist with no anaesthetic, but up your arse, that was what it was like."*

"But it was worth it, because I've seen a colour that no other human being has ever seen or could imagine," Mr Perez added.

ASK ANY CHEMIST what their favourite sort of table is and they won't say a coffee table, a snooker table or a dining table. They will almost certainly tell you that the best table in their opinion is *The Periodic Table* - a systematic tabular representation of all the atomic elements that make up the universe, grouped according to their atomic weights, chemical properties and behaviours. Hydrogen, Helium, Lithium, Beryllium… every schoolchild has it beaten into them until they can recite it parrot fashion, and we can all list its 118 elements in order off the top of our heads. But how much do we really know about it? How old is it? Who invented it? What's the best sort of atoms in it? The answers are elementary, because here are…

25 THINGS YOU NEVER KNEW ABOUT THE PERIODIC TABLE OF ELEMENTS

1 THE Periodic Table was invented in 1869 by Russian chemist **Dmitri Mendeleev.** Whilst visiting his local Spar supermarket in Tobolsk, Siberia, he noticed that the various tinned fruits were stacked together on their own shelves, as were the tins containing vegetables, fish and soups. Struck by the notion that chemical elements could be arranged in a similar manner, Mendeleev immediately went home and drew up his first, rough version of a Periodic Table. Ironically, he forgot to include one element… *tin!*

2 MENDELEEV gave the Periodic Table to the world, but he very nearly didn't become a scientist at all. As a young man, he was a keen amateur stage magician, and toured theatres throughout Eastern Europe performing with his glamorous assistant as The Amazing Mendeleev and Janet. However, during a summer season in St Petersburg, Janet was lured away to join a rival magic act - *Michael Faraday, Man of a Thousand Doves.* His heart broken, Mendeleev gave up conjuring and instead threw himself into chemistry.

3 AFTER working day and night on his first Periodic Table for several years, Mendeleev was all set to finally unveil it before an audience of his peers at the 1865 conclave of the Russian Academy of Sciences. However, the night before his keynote presentation, his dog ate the only copy and he had to start again from scratch. "I definitely did do it, but the dog grabbed it off the table when I wasn't looking and ate it," he told the Academy's President, Professor Oleg Mikhaylovich.

4 ON HER 17th birthday, Australian pop star **Olivia Newton-John** had the Periodic Table tattooed across her buttocks in honour of her late grandfather, eminent Nobel Prize-winning scientist **Max Born.** The cheeky tattooist used Newton-John's ringpiece as the "O" of Osmium, which conveniently features in the dead centre of the table.

5 THE smallest element in the Periodic Table was named after its discoverer, the world's smallest man **Calvin Phillips.** Working in a laboratory no bigger than a shoebox, he synthesised the minuscule element Calvinphillipsium - which has an atomic weight less than a hundredth that of Hydrogen - in a test tube no bigger than a pine needle held over a bunsen burner the size of an upturned drawing pin.

6 FOR his discovery, Phillips was awarded the world's smallest ever Nobel Prize for Chemistry, a gold medal the size of a pinhead.

7 DESPITE its almost universal acceptance, a small but vocal clique of scientists continues to cast doubt on the accuracy of the Periodic Table. These 'Periodic Table Deniers' controversially maintain that there is a conspiracy of silence to conceal the truth, that Mendeleev's arrangement of the elements simply doesn't make sense. *"The Periodic Table simply isn't true,"* said Dr Adam Rutherford of Radio 4's *Inside Science* programme, one of the maverick boffins. *"The atoms are supposed to get heavier as you go from left to right, yet Iron is on the left of Oxygen. Any scientist who reckons a bag of oxygen weighs more than a bag of nails is talking out their arse."*

8 IT IS possible to make several obscene swear words using only the abbreviated symbols for elements that are in the Periodic Table. For example Sulphur, Hydrogen, Iodine and Tellurium spells out "SHITe", Argon and Selenium makes "ArSe", whilst Cobalt, Carbon and Potassium spells out "CoCK".

9 IN 2011, the name of element number 117 was changed from Ununseptium, with the symbol Un, to Tennessine, with the symbol Ts, meaning that it was now possible to make both "TiTs" and "CuNTs".

10 THE letter J doesn't appear anywhere in the Periodic Table. *"It's not a big problem in the great scheme of things, but it does mean that we can't spell out the word "JISm", which we otherwise be able to do by using Iodine and Samarium,"* says TV egghead Dr Jim Al-Khalili.

11 YOU can make "FUCK" using Fluorine, Uranium, Carbon and Potassium.

12 THROUGHOUT the ever-popular Radio 4 show's 76-year history, only one of the guests on *Desert Island Discs* has ever chosen the Periodic Table as their luxury item. And contrary to what to you might think, it wasn't an eminent chemist, it was actually King of the Jungle **Joe Swash.** However, moments after the ex-*EastEnders* star arrived on his island and pinned the poster to a palm tree, a parrot shat on it and then a gust of wind ripped it off and blew it in the sea.

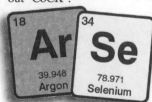

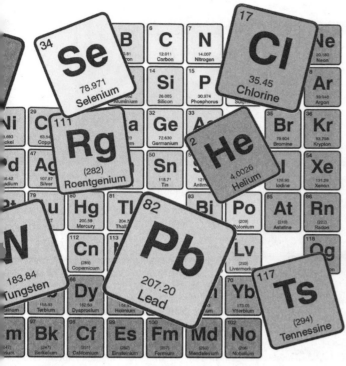

MANY symbols in the Periodic Table are obviously derived from their respective chemical names, such as C for Carbon, H for Hydrogen and O for Oxygen. However, many others bear no no relation to the chemicals to which they refer. *"Why Tungsten is W, Gold is Au and Tin is Sn is any fucker's guess,"* says TV scientist Dr Dallas Campbell. *"Honestly, it does my fucking nut in. This shit's already hard enough without fucking about with all the letters."*

19 **THE** Royal Institute of Chemistry recently voted to change the symbol of element number 45, Rhodium, from Rh after members complained that it was the same initials as disgraced Australian entertainer Rolf Harris.

13 **IN 1867**, Mendeleev made a second attempt to unveil his Periodic Table before a peer review panel at St Petersburg University. However, when he stood up to address his 24 eminent colleagues, he suddenly realised he had mislaid the bag containing his only copy. "I definitely did it," he announced. "But I think I must of left it on the bus."

14 **MERCURY** is the only element in the Periodic Table that is a liquid at room temperature, except Bromine.

15 **EVEN** though the Periodic Table claims to include all the 118 chemical elements that make up the fabric of the Universe, there are several notable omissions, including water, air, sand, clouds, monosodium glutamate and fire.

16 **WHEN** producing his now famous table, Mendeleev decided to arrange the elements in order of their atomic mass, and so set about weighing each of them in turn. However, he immediately hit a snag when trying to weigh element number one in his table - Hydrogen - as the balloon it was in kept floating off his scales and up to the ceiling of his laboratory.

17 **AND YOU** can make "PISS" out of Phosphorus, Iodine and two Sulphurs. And "KNaCKErS" from Potassium, Sodium, Carbon, Potassium, Erbium and Sulphur. And "KNoCKErS" can be synthesised from the same coumpound if the Sodium atom is removed and replaced with an atom of Nobellum.

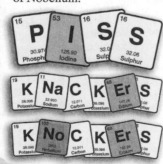

18 **MANY** symbols in

20 **MIX ANY** two elements from the Periodic Table together and they will change colour and acrid white smoke will billow out the top of the test tube. If this doesn't happen immediately, heat them over a bunsen burner to get the reaction going.

21 **IN 1868**, a third attempt to present his work at the Biennial International Inorganic Chemistry Symposium in Utrecht foundered when Mendeleev realised he had inadvertently brought a bag containing potatoes to the meeting instead of the one that he had put his finished Periodic Table in. "Oh no! I've picked up my mam's shopping bag by mistake. I definitely did do it though," he announced to the delegates.

22 **ONLY** six of the 118 symbols in the Periodic Table are complete words in their own right; Helium, Nobelium, Beryllium, Indium, Astatine and Molybdenum.

Amazingly, put together in a sentence, they make up what a Scottish Highlands farmer's wife might say if you knocked on the door of his croft while he was out tending his sheep: "He No Be In At Mo."

23 **IF YOU** hear chemists discussing "moles", they're not talking about velvety burrowing mammals or brown spots on their faces. That's because in the world of science, a mole is a standardised quantity of an element, equivalent to 6.0221×10^{23} atoms of it.

24 **UNLESS** they're on a tea break and one of them's lawn is fucked or the other is worried about a spot on his arm that's started getting bigger.

25 **THE** last ten elements in the Periodic Table are all man-made, and don't exist in nature. The final three or four are so difficult to synthesise and so unstable that they only exist as an individual atom for fractions of a second in a particle accelerator before decaying. Scientists have decided they are only going to do another two elements to take the Table up to a nice, round 120, and then call it a day.

A PROFESSIONAL illusionist, who broke a centuries-old pact of silence by revealing the secrets of his craft, says that the Magic Circle is out to kill him. IAN COPPERBOLT, 63, who works under the professional name of The Amazing Copperboltio, self-published a book setting out how many of the most mystifying magic tricks and stage illusions are performed, and is now living in fear of his life as a result.

The Bolton-based bachelor told us: "The kids' party work, which had been my bread and butter for many years, had dried up a bit following a court case. I thought writing a book about magic would be a good way to make a bit of cash to tide me over until the tag came off and I was allowed to travel more than six hundred yards from my house again."

"I realised that I would probably be drummed out of the Magic Circle as a result, but that didn't bother me because I wasn't even in the Magic Circle," he said.

"It never crossed my mind that they'd try to bump me off for revealing the centuries-old closely guarded secrets of my trade."

cake

The first attempt on Ian's life came very shortly after his book – *And Thats' Not Magic!* (Copperbolt Publishing, £5 cash) went on sale. "I'd printed up ten copies on my computer for the launch party at my local pub, and the first one had sold like a hot cake," he told us. "I could smell success as I staggered home at closing time. This book may

EXCLUSIVE!

have been just six sheets of A4 folded and stapled down the middle, but those 24 pages were going to turn the world of professional magic upside down."

"Little did I know that unwittingly, I was already on the Magic Circle's radar, and they were out to silence me … for good. They wanted to do a disappearing man illusion on me, only this time it wasn't a trick."

"I got home and started climbing the stairs up to my bedsit above the wet fish shop, and immediately sensed that something was wrong. The room seemed to be spinning, as if someone had slipped a Mickey Finn into some of my pints, using sleight of hand."

"When I got to the top step, an empty tonic wine bottle appeared from nowhere. It was clearly the work of a very skilled professional illusionist, because one second the step was empty, and the next there was this bottle straight in front of

Out of thin st-air: Copperbolt was on way home when tonic wine bottle appeared from nowhere.

me. It was too late for me to avoid it, and I stepped on it."

"I went down the stairs, arse over tit. Luckily, I'd taken similar tumbles several times in the past, and I knew the old window cleaners' trick of relaxing into the fall. If you tense up and try to land on your feet, your leg bones smash through the top of your hips. It was only this knowledge, and the fact that I was already quite relaxed anyway, that saved me from certain death when I reached the bottom step."

bob

The Magic Circle may have failed to silence Ian that time, but it wasn't long before they made a second attempt on his life.

"I was on my way back from the Duke of Wellington. I'd had a good night, selling three of my books, and I'd invested the proceeds – and quite a bit more – into the till behind the bar. On

my way home, I suddenly found myself bursting for a tom tit."

"I could only imagine that the barmaid had been some sort of close-up magician, and she must have drawn my attention with her big tits and low-cut top while she slipped a powerful laxative into some of my pints from up her sleeve. It's an old conjuror's technique that we call 'Distract and Drop', and after all my years on the stage, I could have kicked myself for falling for it."

"Over the years, I'd been fined a number of times for indecent exposure, so I decided to pop down onto the canal towpath to drop my shopping. I'd occasionally curled one out there before on the way back from the Welly, and I'd always found it nice and quiet."

"But just as I pulled down my trackie bottoms, edged my buttocks out over the edge of the towpath and started relaxing, the assassins struck again. Suddenly, two youths in hoodies appeared from nowhere; they couldn't have been more than thirteen or fourteen. I immediately spotted the technique they had used to manifest themselves. It's called Pepper's Ghost, and it involves a complex system of angled mirrors and plate glass to create the compelling illusion that someone has appeared as if by magic. The Magic Circle had clearly decided to use members of their junior branch – The Young Magicians Club – to do their dirty work for them."

"The youths kicked me backwards

TRICKS OF THE TRADE

Here are some extracts from Ian's book that pulls back the curtain on the closely guarded secrets of the Magic Circle…

…The secrets that could cost Copperbolt his LIFE!

The levitating lady

The ilusion
A bird in a bikini lies on a table and the table is removed and she floats. a hoop is past over her to show their is no wire holding her up.

How its' done
The bird is suspended from a realy thin wire that is tied to a belt the same coluor as her skin. The hoop has a slit in the hoop that the magican has to make sure gos over were the wire is.

And thats' not Magic!

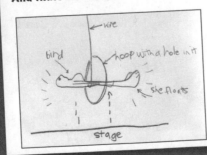

The rabbit in the hat

The ilusion
The magican shows the audiense an emptpy top hat and he puts it on the table and puts his hand in and pulls a rabbit out of it.

How its' done
The rabbit that has been made drowsy with some terps so it dosent' strugle you put it in the hat.Then you stick a cirlcel of black tisue paper over the rabbit end of the hat so when you show it to the audiense it look's like their isn't a rabbit in. When you reech in and pull out the rabbit you push your hand throuogh he black paper and pull it out.

And thats' not Magic!

Catching a bullet in yuor teeth

The ilusion
The magican is blindfloded and the magicans' asitant shoot's a gun at his face. Then the magican catchs the bullet in his teeth and spits it into a metal dish and i forgot a member of the audiense has singed the bullet and his singiture is still on the bullet.

How its' done
It is a trick blindfold made ot of black mesh and you can see thruough it. The bullet flys at the speed of suond so the trick is you have to bite the bullet when you see the flash from the gun not when you here the bang or you will be shot.

And thats' not Magic!

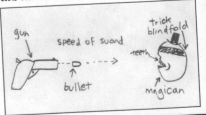

into the water and ran off, laughing. Tangled up in my half-dropped trackies, I found myself being dragged further and further down into the murky black depths of the canal. Handily, I had made a study of Houdini's famous Underwater Strait Jacket escape – indeed, it was one of the chapters in my book – so I knew exactly what to do to break free from my predicament."

"As it happens, I didn't have to call upon my specialist knowledge, as the canal was only waist deep. Once I had found my footing, I was able to wade to the edge and climb out. Nevertheless, my trolleys were full of stinking canal-bottom sludge, and it was an uncomfortable waddle back to my bedsit."

bath

So far, the Magic Circle had relied on small-scale tricks in their attempts on Copperbolt's life. But their next hit was on a much bigger scale, involving a Las Vegas-style super-illusion.

"I went to the White Hart one morning, because someone said there was a bloke there who might have been interested in buying a copy of my book. Unfortunately, he never turned up, and at closing time that night I set off home. I had to cross Shakespeare Street, which is usually very quiet after midnight. Nevertheless, I still remembered my Green Cross Code."

"I looked right, I looked left, I looked right again. There was nothing coming,

so I stepped off the kerb. Suddenly a horn blared and the next thing I knew, I was rolling across the bonnet and along the side of a taxi."

"It was clearly another assassination attempt by the Magic Circle, and I have to admit it was one of the most impressive illusions I had ever seen. That car literally appeared out of thin air. One moment the road was clear, and the next it was there, running into me at thirty mph. If I'd have seen it done on the telly, I'd have assumed it was a camera trick."

Puff of smoke: Ian had lucky escape when kitchenette caught fire.

"My near namesake David Copperfield has made a career out of making planes, trains and automobiles vanish – indeed, he once made the Statue of Liberty disappear. I have to admit, I don't know how he does it, but to make a taxi appear from nowhere like that would simply be a case of doing the same trick David Copperfield does, only backwards."

"However it had been done, it had failed. I was still alive, so the driver tried to make it look like an ordinary jaywalking accident. He got out to examine the damage to his vehicle, and the sick across his bonnet, all the while calling me all the names under the sun. Then he drove off, probably to tell his paymasters that he had failed."

table

The ability to conjure fire from the most unlikely places – such as a top hat, a bunch of flowers or a handkerchief – has always been a staple of many magicians' stage acts. Little did Ian suspect that the same techniques he had used to riotous audience applause throughout his career would be pressed into service in an attempt to kill him while he slept.

"I'd had a slow day selling books, so I decided to cheer myself up with a few swift pints at the Robin Hood. At closing time, the landlord announced that they were having a lock-in, and I was asked to leave. My journey home was uneventful,

and when I got back to my flat I fell fast asleep on the sofa."

"I don't know how long I'd been in the land of nod when I was suddenly awoken from my slumbers by the sound of my portable black and white telly exploding. As I opened my bleary eyes, I realised with horror that my bedsit was on fire. The whole place was in flames, and the room was rapidly filling up with thick, black, acrid smoke."

"It was immediately obvious to me what had happened. While I had been asleep, a Magic Circle hit-man and his glamorous assistant had crept in. The conjuror had produced a dove from a pair of white gloves, and handed it to his assistant, who had placed it inside a lidded metal pot."

"The magician must then have tapped the pot three times with his wand and removed the lid, revealing a blinding flash of flames, that he had used to set fire to the kitchenette curtains behind the hob."

"Thinking quickly, I switched off the chip pan that I had put on when I got in, because I didn't want that bursting into flames and adding to the problem. Then I called 999, gathered together a few precious valuables – such as some cigarettes and a half bottle of whisky that had particular sentimental value – and made my escape down the stairs."

"As I stood on the street, watching my bedsit – and eventually the wet fish shop underneath it – going up in flames, I had a chance to reflect."

"My decision to go public and reveal the secrets of my profession had now robbed me of my home and everything I owned. What's more, the Magic Circle were clearly were not going to rest until they had hunted me down and killed me. But if I had my time over, would I do the same thing again?"

"My answer was clear. Yes, before you could say Abracadabra."

Just like that! Magician Ian fears for his life after revealing Magic Circle's best-kept secrets.

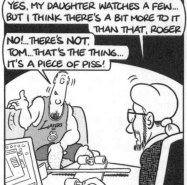

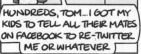

Twinkle, Twinkle, Hollywood Stars

EVERYONE loves a traditional nativity play. Except the kids who only get to be sheep in them, and their parents. These simplistic dramatisations of the events in Bethlehem two millennia ago are highlights of everyone's festive season. But for all their charm, these productions are far from perfect: the scenery is very crude, the costumes – generally home-made from tea-towels and bed sheets – lack authenticity, and the acting is very wooden, with the toddler cast either parroting their lines with little feeling and dramatic passion, or forgetting them completely.

Invariably, the result is a stilted, amateurish production that would stand little chance of winning any awards for theatrical excellence. *How much better would these hammy shows be if the toddlers simply got off the stage and allowed the professionals to perform in their place?* Our favourite Hollywood stars as Mary and Joseph, the Angel Gabriel and the Three Wise Men would all deliver 5-star, Oscar-worthy performances that would earn repeated standing ovations from even the most jaded school hall full of parents who have either phoned into work sick or are having to take the afternoon off without pay.

Just for fun, we've asked veteran theatrical agent **ALEC SEEDY**, better known in his native Nottingham as "Mr Fifteen Percent", to cast an imaginary star-studded school nativity play using nothing but top-drawer Tinseltown A-listers. He told us: *"Believe me, if this production hit the stage of your local primary school, it would be the hottest ticket in town!"*

Joseph

THIS is arguably the biggest part in the show, so it needs a big name, not just some 10-year-old nobody with a cotton wool beard and a teatowel on his head. Joseph's a carpenter, and as luck would have it, that was **HARRISON FORD**'s job before he hit paydirt in *Star Wars*. He already knows his way around a toolbag, so he would bring a real sense of believability to the role of the a chippie who has got God's sloppy seconds.

Having said that, Ford's getting a bit long in the tooth these days, and it might make sense to cast someone a bit younger in such a physically demanding role. I'm thinking of someone like **COLIN FIRTH**, who wowed as Mr Darcey in *Pride and Prejudice*, and would get all the Primary School mums frothing on their little chairs the moment he stepped onto the stage.

Of course, nothing gets bums on seats like a famous face, and if the primary school wants to push the boat out and wallop some serious dosh on the production, you couldn't book a bigger name than **GEORGE CLOONEY** to be Jesus's dad. With the Californian Nescafe Gold Blend heart-throb up on stage giving it the "We have travelled long and far" bollocks, they'd have to mop the fucking floor under the front ten rows after the final curtain. Believe me, that show would run and run.

Mary

ASK any West End theatrical agent, and they will tell you that Mary is always a difficult part to cast. But in my opinion, someone like **SHARON STONE** would be a red hot choice to play the Saviour's famously chaste mum. Oozing raunchy sex appeal, the men in the audience would be gripped, waiting for her to recreate her notorious *Basic Instinct* beaver shot every time she climbed on or off her donkey.

But Sharon's one of the busiest actors in Hollywood, and may well be unavailable during the traditional primary school nativity play season, so it's always worth keeping your options open. As a back-up choice, pop singer **BRITNEY SPEARS** ticks all the Mary boxes, and is generally available in early December. The problem is, she's got a reputation in the business for being a bit flaky, and there's every chance that at the last minute, she'd be nowhere to be seen backstage and you'd find yourself saying:

"Whoops! She's done it again". Where's the fucking stand-in?"

Supermodel **NAOMI CAMPBELL** is my back-up choice to play the Virgin Mary if the other two stars fall through. She's expensive – famously not getting out of bed for less than fifteen grand – but she's undoubtedly got star quality and she's a hard worker and reliable.

The only drawback is that Naomi never goes anywhere without her entourage of fifteen hangers-on, make-up artists, hairdressers and nail technicians, and once these have commandeered all the best seats in the school hall, there'll be nowhere to sit for the mums, dads and grandparents. Also, there's also a risk that Naomi might throw one of her famous hissy fits halfway through the play and, in the absence of a diamond-studded mobile phone, might throw the Christ child at someone who has inadvertently annoyed her in some way.

The 3 Wise Men

THE Three Wise Men were kings who traversed afar to see the Christ child in his lowly stable, and it would only be right to cast Hollywood royalty in these parts. And Tinseltown stars don't come any more blue-blooded than the **SHEENS** – Dad **MARTIN** and his A-list sons **CHARLIE SHEEN** and **EMILIO ESTEVEZ**. They've undoubtedly got the acting chops to put in a great performance, hilariously ad-libbing and riffing off each other in true *Three and a Half Men* style. The problem is, co-ordinating their busy working diaries would be harder than a priest's cock in a nunnery.

The Shepherds

IN a familiar school nativity play, the shepherds who are summoned to the stable to kneel at the feet of the newly born baby Jesus are not given any lines. For this reason, notorious Tinseltown bad boys with a tendency to shoot their mouths off would be well cast in these parts. My first choice would be Aussie *Mad Max* actor **MEL GIBSON**. He's well known in Hollywood as a religious nut-job, but he'd probably keep his foul-mouth shut for the duration of the nativity play out of respect for his favourite fictional character.

Another Hollywood bad boy on anyone's shepherd shortlist is *American Psycho* actor **CHRISTIAN BALE**. However, there's a clip doing the rounds on the internet of him blowing his bollocks off at a lighting technician on a film set. If there was a similar mishap during the nativity play – such as a toddler forgetting his lines or the teacher missing her cue to start the introduction to *O Little Town of Bethlehem* – he could really lose his shit, leaving all the mums and dads in the school hall not knowing where to look.

If these two aren't available, **MELVYN HAYES** off *It Ain't Half Hot Mum* could step in and do the job, and I know he's available early December, because he was going to be an Ugly Sister in *Cinderella* at the Glossop Hippodrome, only it got cancelled due to a combination of poor ticket sales and an outbreak of suspected Legionnaires. If Mel and Christian aren't available, Melvyn could do the job, and I know for a fact he'd be glad of the cash. I've not seen him in anything since he was in *Benidorm* and he must be on the bones of his arse. He's on his third wife, and I bet the poor sod hasn't got a pot to piss in.

The Innkeeper

THE innkeeper only appears in one scene, but it's a pivotal scene in the play. In my opinion, you couldn't do better than casting spaghetti Western star **CLINT EASTWOOD** in this part. Just imagine him narrowing his eyes and huskily telling Joseph: *"There's no room at the inn, punk,"* before explaining that him and his pregnant wife could kip down in the stable *"for a fistful of dollars."* It would be a great little Christmas 'Easter egg' that would go right over the kids' heads, but definitely give their mums and dads a bit of a giggle.

Of course, it's 2019 and in these days of equality there's no reason why the innkeeper can't be played by a bird, and veteran *Dynasty* star **JOAN COLLINS** would bring a bit of posh, top drawer, glamour to this traditionally gruff, male-dominated role. Of course, at the age of 87, Dame Joan doesn't get her kit off at the drop of a hat like she used to any more, but it's a primary school nativity we're talking about her, so getting her wizened old knockers out would be completely inappropriate anyway.

If Clint and Joan are doing something else, or perhaps dead, another good choice to play the innkeeper would be *Lord of the Rings* wizard **SIR IAN McKELLEN**. At a normal primary school nativity, you're always having to lean forwards to hear what the little bastards are saying, but McKellen's a proper old-school luvvie who belts out his lines like a foghorn. Trouble is, you'll probably find yourself sitting through half an hour's worth of arse-numbing theatrical anecdotes about Maggie Smith and dear Ralphie-Walphie Richardson before he finally gets round to telling poor old Joseph that there's no room at the fucking inn.

As a slightly more left-field choice, another time-served three-piece act that would do well as the Three Kings would be The **BROTHER LEES**. These lads used to knock the crowd dead back in the seventies on *The Generation Game*, and they'd undoubtedly do the same if they rocked up to Mary and Joseph's cardboard box stable on the school hall stage with their gifts of gold, Frankincense and Myrrh. Trouble is, back in the seventies, the lads used to do an impression of the Three Degrees that you just couldn't do these days, and the more politically correct parents might stage a walk-out or even decide to boycott the show.

Talking of the seventies, back then the **BEE GEES** would have been shoo-ins to bring a bit of high-pitched *Saturday Night Fever*-style disco pizzazz to proceedings. Unfortunately, the Gibb brothers started dropping like flies a few years back, and these days I think there's only one of the bastards left.

The Arch Angel Gabriel

THIS is the plum part in the production, so I'm looking for an A-list actress who's as big as they come, and they don't come any bigger than **SCARLETT JOHANSSON**. Amazingly, she's the third highest-grossing box office star in movie history, so she'd no doubt pack them in in any school hall. And although she's got a big reputation, she's famously petite in stature. So if the caretaker wanted to rig up some kind of pulley with which to lower her from the heavens in her tinsel halo, it wouldn't be too hard a job.

Alternatively, the headmistress could plump for **WHOOPI GOLDBERG** to play God's heavenly messenger with a leftfield dose of sass and attitude. Mind you, Ms Goldberg has packed on a bit of beef since her *Color Purple* heyday, so lowering her from the ceiling might be a non-starter.

★ STARS OF BETHLEHEM! ★

WHETHER we played the Infant Christ or a lowly sheep, we all have fond memories of our school Nativity play. And our fave celebs are no different. That's why, for a bit of festive fun, we rounded up four of the planet's top A-Listers and asked them one simple question: What part did YOU play in YOUR primary school Nativity?

Bono, *pop bell-end*

I PLAYED one of the Wise Men, but unfortunately my entrance onto the stage was delayed by several hours as it turned out I had accidentally left my papier-mâché crown in Australia. By the time I'd had it flown it back to the primary school on a private jet, half the audience had got bored and fucked off home. On the plus side, though, a quarter of the ticket sales was going to a local charity, so I was able to write the whole thing off against tax a few years later.

Daniel Day-Lewis, *famous actor*

I WAS cast as 'Third Donkey' in my school Nativity, and I immersed myself so fully in the role that it soon became impossible to tell where I ended and Third Donkey began. Every morning, my mother would drive me to an ass sanctuary where I would spend hours walking on all fours among the humble domesticated creatures, living as one of them and learning their ways. In the afternoons, I would head down the beach and charge toddlers 50p to ride around on my back. When the night of the performance arrived, I spent the entire hour braying wildly and defecating on the stage. My teachers and the other children weren't best pleased, but the stunned look on the audience's faces told me that my methodical realism had paid off.

Kim Jong-un, *North Korean supreme leader*

FOR MY school Nativity, I played Norm from *Cheers*. Obviously, Norm from *Cheers* is not traditionally part of the Nativity story, but he's my favourite fictional character, and my father - the late Kim Jong-il - had warned the teachers that if I wasn't allowed to play him, the retribution would be swift and brutal. It all worked out very well, though: just after Christ had been born, I entered the stable with a hangdog expression and said, *"Evening, everybody"*, and all the shepherds and Wise Men cheered *"Norm!"* in unison. Then Joseph asked: *"What's shaking, Norm?"* and I replied, *"All four cheeks and a couple of chins, Joe."* Everyone fell about, and the audience gave me a 4-hour standing ovation at gunpoint.

EXCUSE ME, THERE'S A QUEUE

CRACK!

GNNN!

CRACK!

GNNN!

REET, SON... SIT DOON!

THANK YOU... WE'LL BE IN TOUCH

RIGHT... WHO'S NEXT?

THAT'S US, TIMOTH...

CRACK!

GNNN!

COME ON, SON

CRACK!

OOOF!

RIGHT... AND WHO IS THIS YOUNG MAN?

THIS IS BIFFA... AN YUZ CAN SEND AALL THEM FUCKAZ OOT THERE HURM

...COZ THIS UNS YUZ NEXT MILKY BAR KID

ERM... OKAY... WELL, CAN YOU STAND IN FRONT OF THE CAMERA AND READ THE WORDS ON THE CARD, BIFFA

REET!

198

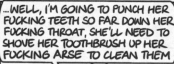

THE REAL ALE TWATS

DJ '19. TA TO ST.

AT 8PM
RIGHT, I THINK EVERYONE'S HERE...

WELCOME TO OUR TOUR OF FULCHESTER'S MOST MYSTERIOUS HISTORIC PUBS...

OUR FIRST STOP WILL BE THE CROWN AND GIBBET ON FULCH STREET...

THIS IS A SPLENDID VARIATION OF OUR USUAL THURSDAY NIGHT DRINKING SESSION, CASKETEERS...

I HAVE ALWAYS BEEN FASCINATED BY LOCAL HISTORY AND FOLKLORE...

THE STORIES FROM OUR PAST GIVE US A MORE PROFOUND PERSPECTIVE ON WHO WE ARE AND WHERE WE COME FROM...

NOW, THE CROWN AND GIBBET WAS BUILT IN THE SIXTEENTH...

EVEN AS A LAD MY INTEREST IN HISTORY WAS INSATIABLE. A TEACHER AT MY SCHOOL — "OLD WHISKERS" WE CALLED HIM — COMMENDED ME ON MY OMNIVOROUS APPETITE FOR BOOKS OF A HISTORICAL PERSUASION...

IT WAS BUILT IN THE SIXTEENTH...

WE CALLED HIM "OLD WHISKERS" ON ACCOUNT OF HIS LUXURIANT HANDLEBAR MOUSTACHE. I RECALL A TERRIBLY AMUSING PRANK WE BOYS ONCE PLAYED UPON THE UNFORTUNATE GENTLEMAN...

EXCUSE ME!

SOME OF US ARE TRYING TO LISTEN TO THIS YOUNG LADY SPEAK!

AHEM. THE PUB WAS BUILT IN THE SIXTEENTH CENTURY AND HAS MANY SPOOKY LEGENDS ASSOCIATED WITH IT.

LET'S TAKE A LOOK INSIDE...

IT IS SAID THAT THE GHOST OF AN ELIZABETHAN POTMAN CAN SOMETIMES BE SEEN FLOATING THROUGH THE BAR...

HO HO! NOT THE KIND OF SPIRIT WHICH ONE USUALLY GETS IN A DRINKING ESTABLISHMENT!

ANOTHER LEGEND RELATES TO THIS OAK CHAIR, KNOWN AS "THE DEVIL'S SEAT"...

HO HO! 'SPIRIT', DO YOU SEE? AS IN DISTILLED ALCOHOLIC LIQUOR...SPIRIT!

IT IS CLAIMED THAT IF ANYONE SITS IN THE DEVIL'S SEAT, SATAN WILL APPEAR AND CAST THEM INTO HELL...

HO HO! THE KIND OF SPIRIT WHICH ONE USUALLY FINDS IN A PUB WOULD BE WHISKY OR VODKA, RATHER THAN A GHOST!

MIND YOU, I CAN'T SAY I APPROVE OF THIS CURRENT FAD FOR VODKA WHICH APPEARS TO BE SWEEPING THE NATION...

EVERYWHERE YOU LOOK PROPER ALEHOUSES ARE CLOSING DOWN AND THESE WRETCHED "VODKA BARS" ARE SPROUTING UP...

FOR CHRIST'S SAKE, WILL YOU JUST SHUT UP!

WELL REALLY!

AHEM! THE NEXT PUB ON OUR TOUR WILL BE THE PIG AND WHISTLE IN TANNERS LANE...

IT APPEARS THAT GENIAL BANTER IS NOT PERMITTED ON THE HAUNTED PUB CRAWL!

LET US LEAVE THEM TO THEIR SILLY TOUR, CASKETEERS, AND REMAIN HERE FOR A PINT OR TWO OF CHEERING ALE, INSTEAD!

HONESTLY!

SIT!

THE FULCHESTER FOLKLORE SOCIETY TAKES ITSELF SO SERIOUSLY!

PUNY MORTALS! I COME TO CAST YOU INTO THE NETHERMOST PIT OF HELL!

GULP!

AND SO

LOUD MUSIC

SKY SPORTS

NO CASH — CARD ONLY

STRICTLY NO WITTY REPARTEE

NOISY CHILDREN WELCOME

TEENAGERS TEXTING AREA

STRAWBERRY VODKA SHOTS

SORRY MATE, WE DON'T SELL CASK ALE. WE GOT FOSTERS.

NOTRE DAME FIRE

LeTTERbOcks

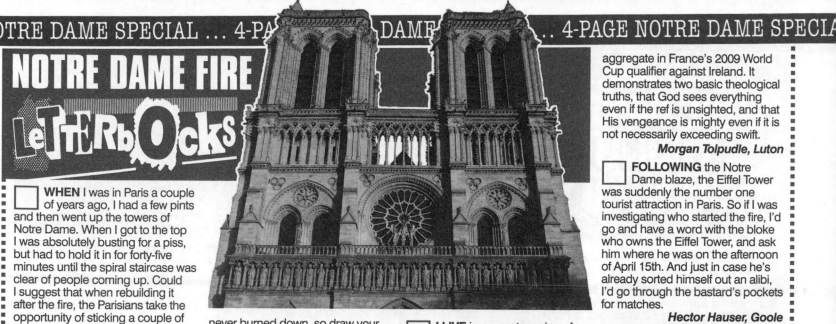

WHEN I was in Paris a couple of years ago, I had a few pints and then went up the towers of Notre Dame. When I got to the top I was absolutely busting for a piss, but had to hold it in for forty-five minutes until the spiral staircase was clear of people coming up. Could I suggest that when rebuilding it after the fire, the Parisians take the opportunity of sticking a couple of bogs on the top?

Brandon Crumbs, Tooting

IT wouldn't surprise me if the April fire was God's judgement on us for something. I'm not sure what He'd be judging us for, probably same-sex marriage or gays in the priesthood. It'll definitely be something to do with homosexuals, anyway, as they seem to really boil His piss.

Egbert Juicer, Crowden

LIKE your previous correspondent, I think that the fire was God's judgement. But it don't believe it was anything to do with the gays; I think He was angry at the prices they were charging to get into Notre Dame. It was twenty Euros the last time I was there. The Louvre was free to get in, and that's never burned down, so draw your own conclusions.

Crawford Spume, Hull

I THINK the Notre Dame fire is a blessing in disguise. The cathedral was originally built in the thirteenth century, and in the twenty-first century, it looked really dated and old-fashioned. In the wake of the fire, they should take the opportunity to bulldoze the rest of it and put up something modern, using today's building materials, such as mirror glass and stainless steel. A bang-up-to-date cathedral that looked like the Shard or the Gherkin would provide a real tourist boost for Paris, in my opinion.

Stan Oregano, Leeds

I LIVE in a remote region of Malawi and we have been saving money for years to buy a pump to provide our village with clean water. We finally raised the 26,000 Kwacha necessary, and we were all set to order the pump when we heard about the terrible fire in Paris. We held a village meeting and unanimously decided to send the money to the Catholic church instead, in the hope that in some small way it might help to restore Notre Dame cathedral to its former opulence.

Pipi Okwekwe, Malawi

I THINK the fire was God's judgement on Thierry Henry controlling the ball twice with his hand before Gallas made it 2-1 on aggregate in France's 2009 World Cup qualifier against Ireland. It demonstrates two basic theological truths, that God sees everything even if the ref is unsighted, and that His vengeance is mighty even if it is not necessarily exceeding swift.

Morgan Tolpudle, Luton

FOLLOWING the Notre Dame blaze, the Eiffel Tower was suddenly the number one tourist attraction in Paris. So if I was investigating who started the fire, I'd go and have a word with the bloke who owns the Eiffel Tower, and ask him where he was on the afternoon of April 15th. And just in case he's already sorted himself out an alibi, I'd go through the bastard's pockets for matches.

Hector Hauser, Goole

I HAVE been buying Cathedral City Smoked Cheddar for twenty years or more. But following the Notre Dame fire, even as the ashes of the building were still smouldering I was disgusted to see the company selling this same cheese in my local supermarket. It was sick. Have these people no shame?

Audrey Spite, Redditch

HATIE COCKPINS — *Viz*'s Most Vitriolic Columnist

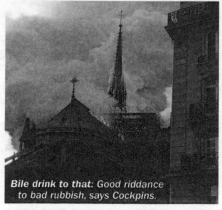

WHEN Notre Dame Cathedral caught fire last month, there was an immediate international outpouring of grief. Well newsflash ... *Not in the Cockpins household there wasn't*. And if that shocks you, *tough titty*. Get over yourself.

Because get this, *I hated the place*.

So what if it was big in the thirteenth century? *So was the Black Death, and I don't see anyone raising money to bring that back*.

Having said that, I'd happily put my hand in my pocket if I thought it would bring the Black Death back.

A dose of Bubonic Plague might do this country some good. If it saw off a few social security scroungers, asylum seekers and returning Isis brides, *I for one would be delighted*.

And if that offends your precious liberal sensibilities, *then good*. Because *I don't give a monkeys* that some overgrown Froggie church has gone up in smoke. *I've*

Notre Dame Destroyed? Tres Bien! says Hatie

never been to it, and I've never wanted to go. And if they do rebuild it and it burns down again, *I'll still shed no tears*.

I was sickened by the sight of the so-called French President and his garlic-chomping chums jibbering away in foreign about what a tragedy it was. Well I've got one message for Macron: *Spare me your crocodile tears, monsieur*.

And it's not just French politicians and French buildings I hate. The French fire service are on the Cockpins radar too. Dipping their croissants in their coffee, supporting French football teams, and talking in the same unintelligible jibber-jabber language as their politicians. *What utter pigs*.

The morning after the fire, these puffed-up pompiers were all over the news, congratulating themselves that they had managed to save the cathedral's medieval rose windows. *Big deal*.

Give me five minutes with a dumpy bag of half-bricks and I'll soon wipe the grins off their filthy foreign faces.

Hatie Cockpins spews confected bile for cash in Viz every week

Bile drink to that: Good riddance to bad rubbish, says Cockpins.

I'M A NOTRE DAME FIRE SPECULATING CELEBRITY

Get My Theory Voted Into Viz!

AS SOON as the flames had been extinguished, fire investigators moved into the smouldering ruins of Notre Dame Cathedral to begin sifting through the ashes for clues as to the cause of the devastating conflagration. It could be months or even years before the results of their painstaking forensic enquiry are made known. But time is a luxury we don't have, as countless other tinder-dry cathedrals are just sitting there waiting to go up in smoke. So we decided to ask the former *I'm a Celebrity* Kings and Queens of the Jungle to speculate about how *they* think the Paris fire started.

When you have read and considered all the suggestions, pick the one that you consider the most likely and return the polling form to the usual address. We will add up the votes and submit the *Viz* readers' findings to the French investigating authorities.

Tony Blackburn – Radio 1 DJ and 2002 KOTJ

WHEN I was young, like all schoolboys I used to burn ants with a magnifying glass as a hobby. It was the Easter holidays in France, and perhaps there was a French schoolboy – perhaps the Archbishop's grandson – up on the cathedral roof merrily incinerating these comical insects alive, and he accidentally focussed the sun's rays on a particularly dry bit of timber, which caught fire with disastrous consequences.

Phil Tufnell – England cricketer and 2003 KOTJ

AS ANYONE who has ever tried to light a woodburning stove will tell you, oak is a very dense hardwood that is actually quite difficult to set on fire. In my opinion, it's possible that a medieval stonemason, back in the thirteenth century, may have discarded a cigarette end on a beam in the roofspace, and it smouldered away for eight-and-a-half centuries before suddenly bursting into flames in April 2019.

Joe Pasquale – High-pitched funnyman and 2004 KOTJ

MAYBE THERE was some sort of short circuit inside the Notre Dame organ, that only gave off sparks when a particular note was played. Perhaps only one hymn has that note in it, and that very hymn was played for the first time ever at the afternoon service on April 15th. It chills me to the bone to think that the moment the organist pressed that key, the fate of the cathedral was sealed.

Carol Thatcher – Late PM's daughter and 2005 QOTJ

I THINK it is possible that a cleaner was up on the cathedral roof, scrubbing bird shit off the gargoyles with a Brillo pad, which was then discarded in the roof space. In an ironic twist of fate, a 9V battery could have fallen out of a smoke alarm and landed on the volatile wire wool. You only have to look on Youtube to see that when them two things come into contact, they don't half go up like a rocket.

Christopher Biggins – Actor and 2007 KOTJ

I WAS a Boy Scout, and we were taught how to light a fire by rubbing two sticks together. I've given this a lot of thought and I believe a bird could have been building a nest in the Notre Dame bell tower. If it was weaving the twigs together fast enough, sufficient heat could have been generated to set the tinder dry nest alight, leading to the dreadful sights we all saw on the news.

Joe Swash – Person and 2008 KOTJ

I GOT this weed burner thing off the internet to get the weeds off the drive, and honestly it's *fucking lethal*, this thing. It runs off pressurised paraffin, and if the caretaker was using one of them to burn some moss off his gargoyles, I'm frankly not surprised the cathedral burnt down. I used mine once and gave myself such a fright I put it back on eBay.

Gino di Campo – TV Chef and 2009 KOTJ

EVERYONE LOVES to get out in the garden for a bit of a barbecue on a sunny day, and I should imagine that the Archbishop of Paris is no different, although not having a garden as such, he probably just lights one of those disposable ones up on the roof of Notre Dame. However, they are notoriously flimsy, and a sudden gust of wind could have upended it while he was getting his sausages out the packet, spreading burning charcoal far and wide across the roof timbers.

Charlie Brooks – EastEnders Star, 2012 QOTJ

IN ALBERT SQUARE, people are always burning things down for the insurance. Pubs, car lots, cafes... you name it, someone's set it on fire and put a big claim in. Perhaps the Archbishop had hefty gambling debts, maybe he owed money to a Paris loan shark, or was being blackmailed by a stripper in the Moulin Rouge. Though it broke his heart, the only way he could see to get the money he needed was to torch the cathedral he loved.

Carl Fogarty – Motorcycle Racer and 2014 KOTJ

I RECENTLY watched a documentary on Quest about spontaneous human combustion. It's always happening, apparently, and no-one knows what causes it. People just burst into flames for no reason while they're just minding their own business. Perhaps a nun went up into the roofspace for a look around and ... *BOOF!* up she went like a rocket. I bet you anything when they're going through the ashes they'll find a nun's leg still with a shoe on.

Vicky Pattison – Reality Show Geordie, 2015 QOTJ

WHAT NOBODY else seems to have noticed is that the cathedral went ahad just three days before the end of Lent. I wonder whether the vicar had given up smoking for Lent, but with just three days to go, he was absolutely choking for a tab and went up in the belfry where no-one would see him. Then, in his eagerness to enjoy his first puff in nearly forty days, he dropped his still-burning match into centuries of dust and wood-shavings – the perfect conditions to start a major conflagration.

Scarlett Moffat – Reality Show Geordie, 2016 QOTJ

I HAD a look on Google and apparently they have these things called fireflies in France, whose arses are all lit up with fire. If one of them farted while it was in Notre Dame, a flame would have shot out its ringpiece. It would only have been a little flame, because fireflies are only small, but if it was sat on a bit of dry wood when it dropped its guts, that could have been the cause, in my opinion.

Harry Redknapp – Football Manager and 2018 KOTJ

ALTHOUGH there isn't a lot of pure hydrogen in the atmosphere, it is nevertheless the lightest element and as such always floats upwards. Over 850 years, small amounts of hydrogen floating upwards will have completely filled the cathedral's roofspace with this potentially explosive gas. All it took was an overweight building worker to walk along the scaffolding wearing nylon trousers. As his thighs rubbed together, a static charge built up that then discharged as a spark. *Ka-Boom!* It must have been like the Hindenburg all over again.

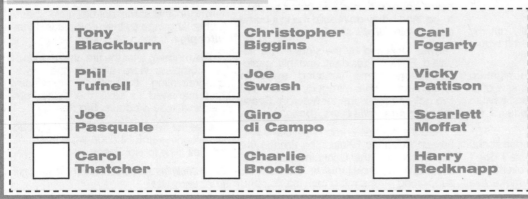

☐ Tony Blackburn	☐ Christopher Biggins	☐ Carl Fogarty
☐ Phil Tufnell	☐ Joe Swash	☐ Vicky Pattison
☐ Joe Pasquale	☐ Gino di Campo	☐ Scarlett Moffat
☐ Carol Thatcher	☐ Charlie Brooks	☐ Harry Redknapp

Put a cross next to the name of the King (or Queen) of the Jungle who you believe has come up with the correct theory on how the Notre Dame fire started. You may vote for only one theory. Multiple votes will be deemed spoiled papers and will not be counted.

Send your completed form to: *Notre Dame Kings of the Jungle Fire Theory, Viz Comic, PO Box 841, Whitley Bay, NE26 9EQ*

TONY  PARSEHOLE

Why I Weep for the Cathedral of Hearts

LAST MONTH, when the news broke that Notre Dame Cathedral was on fire, I am not ashamed to admit that I cried.

As I sat in disbelief, watching the live pictures of that iconic edifice being consumed by flames, the tears sprang unbidden from my eyes. And as the flames leapt higher, my tears wept higher.

For millennia (subs pls check that means thousands not millions), this iconic edifice had stood sentinel over the French capital, a testicle to what man can achieve when moved by the power of the Lord.

But what had taken countless centuries past to build was laid waste in mere minutes on a single night in April in Paris in France by the the fickle finger of fire.

And that is the true tragedy of Notre Dame, and that is why I cried as I sat in disbelief watching the live pictures of that iconic edifice being consumed by flames. Especially that bit where the pointy tower fell over.

For at that moment, as the pointy tower fell over, the realisation that we would never see its like again pierced my heart like a sword of grief.

Like a scimitar of sadness.

Like a cutlass of dejection.

A carelessly discarded match. A carelessly discarded cigarette. A carelessly discarded lighter that you can buy for three for a pound on the Chomps Elisays (susbs check sp), on the banks of the Sane or on the Rue Morgue. A carelessly discarded cigar or pipe.

That is all it took to reduce this priceless architectural jewel in the crown of Paris to a worthless heap of ashes.

But let us not weep for that iconic edifice. For in the midst of our despair, there is hope.

In the heart of our disconsolateness, there is optimism. In the kernel of our disheartenment (661 n.), there is (subs another wd for hope here).

For be in no doubt the iconic edifice of Notre Dame Cathedral will rise once again from the ashes of the iconic edifice of Notre Dame Cathedral.

It will rise again from the flames, like the Phoenix in Harry Potter. It will rise again from the dead, like Icarus in the Bible. It will rise again from the grave, like them zombies in The Walking Dead.

And just like Steve Austin, the Six Million Dollar Man out of the 1970s television series of the same name – The Six Million Dollar Man, starring Lee Majors as Steve Austin the Six Million Dollar Man, we can and will rebuild it.

Better than before. Stronger than before. Faster than before.

It may take years. It may take decades. It may take centuries. It may take millenniums. It may take there thats 500 wds inv enc.

LEAVE IT TO TOMMY
DIY star set to rebuild cathedral

TV HANDYMAN "BIG" TOMMY WALSH yesterday announced that he had set himself his biggest DIY challenge yet … to rebuild Notre Dame Cathedral. And despite expert predictions that it could take twenty years or more to restore the fire-ravaged 13th century gothic masterpiece to its former glory, Tommy reckons he will get the job finished *in just THREE DAYS!*

"This is going to be the biggest task me and the *Challenge Tommy Walsh* team have ever taken on," the 62-year-old builder told reporters. "We've given ourselves from Friday to Sunday to crack on and completely rebuild the gaff."

"And to add to the complication, we're going to do it as a surprise for the Archbishop of Paris," he continued. *"He's going to get the surprise of his life."*

Walsh explained that the rector and dean of the Cathedral intend to take Archbishop Michel Aupetit to Center Parcs in Rheims for what he thinks is a long weekend of prayer and reflection.

truck

"The moment his taxi leaves, me and my team will be waiting round the corner in the *Challenge Tommy Walsh* truck, loaded up with eighteen thousand oak beams, a million-and-a-half roofing slates and a lorryload of medieval stained glass windows and carved stone tracery," said Tommy. "From that moment on, the clock will be ticking."

"We'll be working to a very tight schedule, because this is by far the biggest three-day build we've ever taken on," said Walsh, still 62. "But I dare say there'll still be a bit of light-hearted horseplay on the site. Regular viewers know the sort of mallarkey we get up to, filling each other's pockets with sand and standing on hosepipes."

my luck

"Putting the roof back on will be a doddle. It's a bread-and-butter job for any time-served brickie worth his salt," said Tommy. But he admitted the team's biggest headache would be constructing a 300-foot spire to replace the one that was destroyed in the fire.

"The 19th century original was three-hundred feet tall, and made of seasoned Versailles oak covered in lead," said Tommy. "But our plan is to knock another one up using breezeblocks and MDF, and hopefully you'd be hard pushed to tell the difference from the ground."

a duck

Walsh continued: "On the show, we always try to get local firms to donate building materials. I'm sure the French equivalent of B&Q or Wickes will be happy to chip in and provide a few dumpy bags of sharp sand and loose aggregate, especially as it's such a good cause."

"It's going to be three days of proper graft," said Tommy. "But I'm not scared of hard work, and it'll all be worth it when the Archbishop rocks up on the Sunday teatime. When his taxi comes round the corner and he sees what we've been up to, his boat race is going to be a proper picture!"

Asked what the first job would be once the team get on the site, Walsh joked: "Once we've got the vans parked up and the old cement mixer going, we'll knock off and have a nice cup of tea."

"Milk and three sugars in mine," he added.

High a-spire-ations: Walsh hopes to rebuild the historic 19th century spire (far right) in record time.

ALL THE CELEBRITY NEWS AND GOSSIP

PIERCE DORGAN

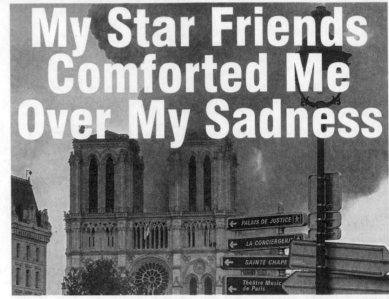

My Star Friends Comforted Me Over My Sadness

ASK any of my very best friends, including *Leonardo di Caprio*, *Goldie Hawn*, *Kiera Knightley*, *Tiny Tempah*, *Princess Michael of Kent* or *George Lucas*, to name the most famous building in Paris, and they will tell you without hesitation: *The Eiffel Tower*.

Ask them to name the second most famous building in Paris and some of them would say the Pompidou Centre, while others would say the Arc de Triomphe. However, all of the rest of them, including *Barbra Streisand*, *Gloria Hunniford*, *Matthew Kelly*, *Russell Crowe*, *Rizzle Kicks*, *Sir Elton John* and *Ben Fogle*, would name Notre Dame Cathedral.

When the news came through that this mighty building, dating back 850 years, was being consumed by fire, I was in exclusive London eaterie The Ivy, having dinner with a few very close friends, including *Tyson Fury*, *Diana Ross and the Supremes*, *Dallas Campbell*, *Sir Steven Redgrave*, *Bjork* and *Sade*.

The terrible news upset me so much that I was unable to finish my starter, which was Seared Foie Gras with Muscatel Grapes and Chickweed, the most expensive thing I could find on the menu.

I'm usually the life and soul of any party, and everyone always hangs on my every word. But not that night. My very close friend *Ellen de Generes*, who is a lesbian whose house I have been to and she has been to my house as well, noticed I was unhappy, and put her hand on mine.

"What's the matter, Piers? You're clearly not your usual self, and I should know being one of your very closest best friends who has been out with you many times," she said.

"I'm just so sad about Notre Dame Cathedral burning down," I told her. Later on, my despondent mood didn't improve as I picked listlessly at my main course, which was the Grilled Veal Cutlet with Morels, Artichokes & Hedgerow Garlic, again the most expensive thing I could find on the menu.

"Still sad about the fire in Paris, Piers?" asked a concerned *Dwayne "The Rock" Johnson*, who was sitting between my good friends *Roger Whitaker* and *Lara Latex*. "I've never seen you so down, and I've seen you loads of times because we are very close friends and you've been on my yacht and are also the godfather to my children, if I have any." I had to admit that I was.

Later still, as my dinner companions – including *Barry Manilow*, *Sinitta*, *Chevy Chase*, *Boutros Boutros Ghali*, *Sir Bradley Wiggins*, *Dame Tiri Ti Kanawa*, *Darcey Bussell*, *Harry Redknapp*, *Angus Young*, *Placido Domingo* and *Herb Alpert* – hungrily tucked into their desserts, I merely toyed distractedly with my Burnt Banana & Butterscotch Tatin with Rum & Raisin Ice Cream and Crushed Pecans, unable to get the image of the burning Parisian landmark out of my mind.

"It's no good. I can't eat this, even though it's the most expensive item on the desserts menu," I told my Oscar-winning very close friend *Clint Eastwood*. "Seeing 850 years of ecclesiastical history going up in smoke has robbed me of my appetite. Everybody at the table, including *Sir Tim Berners-*

Lee, *Kerry Katona*, *Cliff Thorburn*, *Sean Connery*, *Tom Cruise*, *Lewis Hamilton* and *Kim Kardashian*, suddenly became silent as the gravity of my words sank in.

Suddenly, *David Copperfield* spoke. "Why don't you use your celebrity status to raise money to rebuild the cathedral, Piers?" he said. There was a chorus of agreement from everyone sat at the table, including *Tom Jones*, *Woody Allen*, *Dolly Parton*, *Taylor Swift*, *George Foreman*, *Ringo Starr*, *Kirk Douglas*, *Dame Vivienne Westwood*, *Madhur Jaffrey*, *Monty Don*, *Rod Stewart* and *Bob Carolgees*, all of whom's personal phone numbers I have, and when I ring them up I just say 'Hi, it's Piers,' and I don't even have to say my second name and they know it's me.

So that is what I am going to do. Here and now I am launching the Piers Morgan Notre Dame Cathedral Restoration Fund. I understand that,

unlike me, many ordinary members of the public – the sort of people who I have no interest in befriending – have very limited disposable incomes. But just imagine how rich you would feel in your heart if you donated everything you can afford to this very great cause.

All of your money that I collect will be donated in my name to pay for the rebuilding this magnificent structure that has been so tragically burnt down. And rest assured that once Notre Dame has been restored to its former glory, me and my very closest friends – including *George Ezra*, *Warwick Davis*, *Nigella Lawson*, *George RR Martin*, *Clive Webb*, *Woody Harrelson*, *The Edge*, *Kevin Costner*, *Michael McIntyre*, *Keith Urban*, *Seth Meyers*, *Mads Mikkelson*, *Gary Oldman*, *David Dickinson* and *Jennifer Aniston* – will be there with me to see it reopened once more.

© Pierce Dorgan 2018

HOLY SMOKE!
Atheist Dawkins sees the light

PROFESSOR Richard Dawkins yesterday announced that he has started believing in God after witnessing what he described as "a miracle". The previously hardline atheist academic, 78, said he was converted after seeing news footage of fire crews entering the smoking ruins of Notre Dame Cathedral, where the gold cross atop the altar had remained undamaged in the midst of the fire that destroyed the rest of the medieval interior.

Dawkins: Converted.

He told the *Church Times*'s Fergus Butler-Galilee: "The pews, the roof and the reredos had all been reduced to ashes, and yet this shining symbol of the Lord God's love for His only son remained intact."

"As a scientist, I understand that gold melts at 1064°C, and that wood burns at around 600°C," he said. "But it could have been the other way round, with the melting point of gold being lower than the burning temperature of wood."

"However it is not, and it is not because it was designed that way when the world began."

"And from that fact it follows that you have to ask yourself, why is that so? Whose ineffable decision was it to create the laws of physics in such a way that a wood fire can never melt a gold cross?"

"To design the world in that particular way, there must have been an omnipotent deity with the power of all creation in His hands," said the professor. "And when

you print this, can you put a capital 'H' on that 'His', please? If you don't, God will cast me for all eternity into a lake of sulphur, and that fucker boils at 444.6°C."

Dawkins said he had now bought a new suit for going to church on Sundays. And he vowed that from now on he would be praying three times a day, every day, and obeying all the various commandments contained in the Old and New Testaments.

He told Butler-Galilee: "I intend to stone my children to death if they cheek me, not eat anything that dwelleth in the sea that hath not fins nor scales, and from now on I'll not be gathering any more sticks on the Sabbath, for that would be an abomination in His eyes."

"What's more, I shan't be making any baldness between my eyes for the dead, whatever that means," Professor Dawkins added.

THE BROON WINDSORS

207

LETTERBOCKS

Viz Comic P.O. Box 841 Whitley Bay NE26 9EQ · letters@viz.co.uk

ST★R LETTER

IF lionesses are such great, caring mothers like all the wildlife experts like to tell us, how come their kids always fuck off and leave home when they're about four? At least I hung on until I was sixteen.

Barry Trumptons, Hull

I'VE just noticed that if you take the first three letters of the word 'banana' and add them to the last five letters of 'toffee', you get the word 'Banoffee'. Astonishingly, banana and toffee are the two main ingredients in Banoffee Pie! Do I get a *Viz* pen for pointing out this incredible coincidence?

Brian Oliver, email

PEOPLE always criticise the so-called "white van man," but today I saw one of them kindly leaving an old sofa on a countryside footpath. As a keen hiker, I know how nice it is to have somewhere to put your feet up when you're tired. So credit where it's due.

Hector Bolweavil, Derby

I'VE been trying to shag the barmaid in my local for ages with no success. I've tried praying, but I've realised that with seven billion people on earth praying for world peace, an end to hunger and all that shit, my prayer was hardly going to go to the top of His inbox. I was just wondering if everybody could just stop praying between 7 and 8 next Tuesday, which is darts night in my local, and it might give my prayer a fighting chance.

Jimmy Murphy, Clonmel

WITH reference to your article on the Periodic Table *(page 190)*. Tungsten has the chemical symbol W because it used to be called Wulfram. And Gold has the symbol Au because the Greek or Roman word for gold started with Au. As for why Tin is Sn though, sorry, haven't got a scooby doo.

Stuart Jenkins, email

I AM meeting a friend for coffee today at 4.30pm, but unfortunately my watch battery ran out yesterday. Luckily, the watch stopped at 4.25pm and it's a five minute walk to the cafe, so I should arrive bang on time.

Gareth Price, Portland

I REALLY think the only way to get back at the vegans is to make meat look like vegetables; black pudding could be fashioned to look like aubergines, for example, or chicken legs could be dyed to resemble butternut squashes. I've written to you on this subject several times and repeatedly not printing my letters is no way for a responsible publication to tackle the issue.

W Beef-Sandwich, Helston

THEY say no man is an island. But what about that John Ireland who played the gladiator Crixus opposite Kirk Douglas in *Spartacus*? I wonder how the "so-called" experts will try to wriggle out of that one.

Barrington Normal, London

I WAS wondering whose job it is to decide when light engineering becomes heavy engineering. I'm not an engineer, but I would imagine if one engineer can pick up the things he needs to engineer, it's light engineering, but if he needs another engineer to help him pick them up, then it's heavy engineering. That sounds logical to me, but as I say, I'm not an engineer.

Terry Farricker, Blackpool

MANY American states use Lethal Injection as the preferred method for executing murderers, but as many people are not keen on needles this does seem rather cruel. Perhaps it would be more humane to borrow from smoking cessation technology, and use a "lethal injection patch" to gently deliver a dose of deadly poisons into the condemned person's bloodstream over several months. Of course, this would also require a certain amount of willpower. It would be no good if the inmates were to give up being executed and rip the patch off after only a few weeks.

David Plums, Berkshire

IT really makes me laugh whenever I see a love scene on TV or in films, as the women always overact big time. All that moaning and groaning is right over the top in my book and just shows their inadequacy as actresses. My wife doesn't make a single sound, and she's never been to drama school.

Stan Duckbutter, Glossop

THE candidates on *The Apprentice* have it far too easy in my opinion. When my mate Deggy became an apprentice, him and four other 16-year-olds were wrapped up in cling film, chucked in a two-ton skip and had a shit load of fireworks chucked at them on their first day. And he didn't get £250,000 at the end of it either, let me tell you.

W Cowell, Wrexham

I'VE never seen a squirrel take a shit, but I've seen one take a piss.

Gerry Paton, London

* How very interesting, Gerry. Perhaps one of our readers has seen a squirrel have a shit, meaning that between you, you have experienced the full gamut of these fascinating animals' toilet habits. Write in and tell us if you have seen a squirrel have a shit. And don't forget to tell us if it was red or grey. The squirrel, that is, not its foulage.

TOP

CONVINCE people taking the escalator up from the subway that it is raining outside by pouring a bucket of water over your head before you go down the escalator. The look on their faces as they exit onto the street and see that it isn't raining.

David Scroggs, S Korea

DRIVERS. In foggy weather, save wear and tear on your fog lamp bulb by simply driving with your left foot resting gently on the brake pedal.

David Craik, Hull

NOVICE spear-fishers. Become accustomed to the refraction of light in water by stabbing baked potatoes with knitting needles in a deep bath.

Ronny Gill, Manchestoh

IS it just me or are those Dyson Airblades a big con? Rather than drying, I find they simply blow and spray my piss absolutely everywhere. Personally, I don't know what was wrong with the old-fashioned trough urinal. This is one invention, Sir James, that we just didn't need.

Mark Beavan, Bristol

I'VE never seen any character in *EastEnders* stub a toe on a chair, then scream at the chair, calling it a cunt. But then again I don't watch *EastEnders*.

Ian Webb, Bury St Edmunds

WHEN I told a woman at work that she didn't have great tits, they hauled me into the office. The next day I apologised and told her she had smashing tits, and again I got a bollocking. Come on you women's libbers out there, make your minds up.

Hector Ballsack, Devizes

JOE PESCI THE CAT

Panel 1: JOE! APPARENTLY YOU'VE IMPREGNATED EVERY CAT IN THE NEIGHBOURHOOD! AND NOW I HAVE TO PAY TO REHOME ALL THE KITTENS! — BILL — WHAT CAN I SAY? — I GOT A LOTTA FUCKIN' LOVE TO GIVE!

Panel 2: WELL NO MORE! CHRISTMAS OR NOT— YOU'RE GOING IN THIS CARRIER AND WE'RE GETTING YOU SPAYED! — NOW GET IN THERE! — YEAH, THAT AIN'T GONNA FUCKIN' HAPPEN.

Panel 3: C'MERE!

Panel 4: A+E RECEPTION — UMM... IS IT POSSIBLE TO REATTACH THESE? — :SIGH: — For Stacey♥

ELDERLY and infirm people. Move to Lincoln, as the copious quantity of chewing gum on the streets will give you sure footing all the way.

Moira East, Lincoln

PERVERTS. Tie a piece of string to any foreign object you insert into your arse, so if it gets pushed in a little too far you can pull it out yourself and save that embarrassing trip to A&E.

Steve Crouch, P'borough

NEED packing crates when moving house? Simply order a thimble every day from Amazon and within 3 weeks you'll have enough giant boxes to load the contents of a stately home.

Craig Bradshaw, Girvan

TIP's

toptips@viz.co.uk

IMAGINE if, instead of carving pumpkins at Halloween, we had to stick them up our bums. I don't like the sound of that at all. Let's keep carving them, I say.

Du Singe, Lincoln

IT'S always depressing when there are roadworks, and you see a sign that says "Stop when lights on red." Surely it would be more positive and uplifting if the sign read "Don't stop when lights on green." Come on you local councils, let's have a bit more of the 'glass half full' attitude.

Bartram Golightly, Cardiff

YESTERDAY I was the victim of a baffling misfortune. Whilst doing the washing up, I accidentally got my shirt sleeve wet. Initially I shrugged it off as just one of those things. However, my blood ran cold when my wife reminded me of the date - Friday the 13th. Coincidence? I think not.

Phil Kitching, Isle of Jura

AFTER eating Penguin biscuits for some 35 years, it suddenly dawned on me today that they are just big Bourbon creams covered in chocolate. Fuck me! Talk about slow.

Graham Flintoft, Gatesheed

I HAVE just learned that the Dutch word for baseball is "honkbal." Can anyone else come up with a more useless - and yet strangely compelling - fact?

NY London-Paris, Munich

IF I was going to make the sequel to the *Scooby Doo Movie*, I'd call it *Scooby Movie Doo*, or perhaps *Scooby Movie Two*. Although in all probability I won't.

Tomo, Shrewsbury

WE were all taught in school about how gravity pulls everything to the centre of the planet. Well, I just farted in the bath and the bubbles went upwards! I'd be interested to hear how these boffins explain that one.

Johnny T, Kirkcaldy

SINCE being made unemployed from the local dogfood factory, I've become a freelance leek slasher. I'd like to remind readers that this is a busy time of year for leek slashing and that they should book early. I can also slash your rivals' giant onions and beetroots, but Nitromors on carrots is extra.

Neil Johnson, Durham

STATISTICS show that the team winning the coin toss in test cricket only lose the match 31% of the time. Given the foregone conclusion in the other 69% of matches, why do they bother playing them at all? I'm sure the players would prefer to stay at home and watch telly instead of standing around in a field doing nothing for five days.

John Kilo, Bellingen

I HAVE a spoon that I bought in 1974, and it still works. I use it to eat my porridge every morning. They don't make things to last like they used to.

Terry Farricker, Blackpool

I CAN'T help but think that eco-warrior Greta Thunberg would get more of a reaction from world leaders if she keyed their cars or put some dog shit through their letterboxes like a normal teenager. No one likes a goody-two-shoes.

Dudley Hill-Carpets, Bradford

IT'S all very well saying "feed a cold and starve a fever," but what if my cold gives me a fever? Do I eat half portions, or do I leave the crusts, or what? These old wives need to be a bit more specific with their respiratory-tract viral infection treatment plans.

Mark Glover, Coventry

AT athletics meetings, why don't they put the competitors for the 100 metres race in traps like they do at the horses and the dogs? It would prevent false starts and it would be very exciting watching them all getting loaded into their boxes before the doors swing open and they leg it. It's certainly food for thought for the IAAC.

Dan Charlton, Macclesfield

DOES pissing on the plants in the garden at night do them harm or good? I'd really appreciate some help on this, as we're having quite a barney about it at home at the moment.

Puggy, Redditch

★ Well, that's a tricky one, Puggy. Whilst piss contains a lot of nitrogen, essential for healthy plant growth, it is very alkaline and may raise the pH of the soil to unhealthy levels. Are any Viz readers plant scientists who could give us their opinion? Or perhaps we have some readers who are keen horticulturalists who do or do not piss on their plants at night. Write in and let us know.

WHEN British Poet Laureate Sir John Betjeman was asked if he had any regrets in life, he said that he wished that he had had more sex. When British grumble supremo Ben Dover approaches his end, I wonder if he will regret not having written enough poems about dropping bombs on Slough. I doubt it, but you never know.

J Creasy, Beckenham

TO aid understanding when describing a land area, news reporters regularly state the number of football pitches it is equivalent to. However, when my partner recently asked me if her bottom looked big, her response to my answer - "it is less than the size of one football pitch" - suggests that this device has limited use in other scenarios.

Simon Hoffmann, Chichester

WITH reference to the toilet photo from Mel Horton in issue 289, but which you edited out of this annual. I think my toilet is equally happy, perhaps even more so.

Sid Sidney, Sydney

PISS was invented way before Sugar Puffs, so it's actually Sugar Puffs that stink of piss.

Gav H, Hebden Bridge

IN 1960, Blues singer Ella Fitzgerald asked "How High the Moon?" About 384,400 km. Next.

D Cooper, Malta

YOU see dog shit all over the place, but I've never once seen a spider's foulage after it's cut its cable. You'd think that after eating a big fly for its Sunday dinner there might be a few honking spider steamers in the garden, but after multiple searches I haven't found any.

Russell Hoare, email

IN The Police's hit single *De Do Do Do, De Da Da Da*, Sting sings "De do do do, de da da da, is all I want to say to you." Why on earth would he want to say that to somebody? If he said that to me, I'd think he was insane, or on drugs, I really would!

David Wood, Gateshead

THE UNFAITHFUL MRS BARRINGTON AND HER BEAR LOVING HUSBAND NORMAN

YOUR TEA, MY DEAR

I HOPE IT'S GOT ONE AND A HALF SUGARS

YES DEAR, ONE AND A HALF AS ALWAYS

AREN'T YOU GETTING THE CAR SERVICED TODAY?

TODAY, DEAR, YES, DEAR

MAKE SURE YOU TAKE IT TO A GARAGE WITH A GOOD REPUTATION

AA ACCREDITTED IDEALLY...

...AND RUN BY HUMAN BEINGS...

AND NOT, FOR EXAMPLE BY BEARS

HUMAN BEINGS, YES

DEFINITELY HUMAN BEINGS

AND NOT BEARS

DEFINITELY NOT!!

BEARS! HONESTLY!!

AS IF!!

HANK'S GARAGE
NON-URSINE MECHANICS GUARANTEED

BUT...
HANK'S GARAGE
NON-URSINE MECHANICS GUARANTEED

READER'S VOICE

UH OH!!!

SHORTLY...

BINGO!

ROLLO'S GARAGE
WANT BEAR MECHANICS? WE GOT 'EM!

FORTY FIVE POUNDS. IT WOULD OF COST ME A FORTUNE IF I'D GONE TO HANK'S

WONDER WHAT BERYL'S UP TO?

I HOPE SHE HASN'T BEEN UNFAITHFUL AGAIN

IF I CATCH HER IN BED WITH THAT MR. RUMBELOW IT'LL BE DIVORCE

THIS TIME I MEAN IT!

PIPE TOBACCO SMOKE??!?

RUMBELOW!!!!!

ALRIGHT BERYL, I'VE CAUGHT YOU RED-HANDED THIS TIME

I'M GOING TO INITIATE DIVORCE PROCEEDINGS IMMEDIATELY

FAIR DOS

THERE IS ONE THING HOWEVER

DID YOU KNOW MR RUMBELOW IS A KEEN AMATEUR CINE-PHOTOGRAPHER?

NO, NO...I DIDN'T KNOW THAT...BUT I HARDLY SEE HOW...

PERHAPS YOU COULD SHOW HIM BERNARD?

CERTAINLY

I'LL JUST GO AND GET MY STUFF

SO...

THIS IS MRS. RUMBELOW AND MYSELF LAST YEAR ON OUR TRIP TO MAJORCA

WELL, THAT'S FASCINATING BUT I DON'T SEE WHAT THAT HAS TO...

PATIENCE NORMAN. YOU SEE, EARLIER TODAY MR RUMBELOW WAS FILMING AT ROLLO'S GARAGE

SHOW NORMAN THE FOOTAGE, BERNARD

CERTAINLY

DO YOU RECOGNISE THE CAR? THE ONE THAT'S BEING SERVICED BY BEARS?

NO...

ARE YOU ABSOLUTELY SURE? BECAUSE IT LOOKS TO ME A LOT LIKE OUR CAR...?

WELL, A BIT... I MEAN, ALL CARS LOOK A BIT ALIKE...

BERNARD, PERHAPS YOU COULD CLOSE UP ON THE NUMBER PLATE

MY PLEASURE

KVL 741 Y

RECOGNISE IT NOW?

(SIGH) YES...

I DON'T THINK YOU'LL BE PETITIONING FOR THAT DIVORCE QUITE YET

I SUPPOSE NOT

NOW THEN, IF YOU'LL EXCUSE US, I THINK MR. RUMBELOW HAS SOME 'SERVICING' TO DO

PAH! I'M GOING TO THE ZOO

UGH! OOH! AAHH! OH MR. RUMBELOW, YOU'RE SO MUCH BETTER THAN MY BEAR-LOVING BUFFOON OF A HUSBAND

ALTHOUGH I WONDER IF WE MIGHT TRY IT WITHOUT YOU SMOKING THAT PIPE...?

PHUT

BUGGER!!

210

THIS leading rider wakes up in his hotel and makes his way to the ensuite bathroom to curl one out. It's probably the only time in the day when he'll have a chance of a relaxing toilet visit. He may take the opportunity to flick through a magazine, look at a map of the forthcoming stage, or check the weather forecast on his phone while moving his bowels. Whatever he does, it will be in five star comfort, with a fully flushing lavatory, a fresh roll of triple-ply bathroom tissue with the end folded into a triangle nearby, and a complimentary pump bottle of scented, high quality handwash for when he has finished wiping. Following a high-carb breakfast and a pint of sweet, black coffee, it's back to his room for a second sitting.

SAUVER LA PLANÉTE
S'il vous plaît laissez vos serviettes dans le bain.

THE TOUR DE FRANCE is one of the greatest sporting spectacles on earth. Over the course of three gruelling weeks, the world's best cyclists race the length and breadth of France, pedalling 2,200 miles up mountains, across plains and through villages and towns, climaxing with a thrilling sprint for the tape along the Champs Elysées in Paris. But the 176 elite sportsmen in the peloton are just the

The Toile
Tour de

ANOTHER rider, this one from a minor team, is staying in a motorhome where the toilet facilities are slightly less spacious. His morning stool is slightly less relaxed, as just a thin folding door separates him from the team nutritionist, who is preparing his breakfast just a few inches away. To save embarrassment, he has placed a raft of folded bog paper on the water surface to prevent splashing noises, and is pulling his buttocks apart to keep any accompanying flatulence to a minimum. In addition, because the motorhome is equipped with a chemical toilet, he must wipe his dirty bottom with special dissolvable toilet tissue, which tends to be a bit less effective in use, spreading it around rather than cleaning it up, as often as not leaving him with a ringpiece like Robert Smith's gob.

LOOK & LEARN & READ & WONDER & LEARN & LOOK

THE Grand Départ is the cyclists' final chance to crimp a last one off before the starter's gun sounds, and there is great demand for the portable toilets. These are premium quality facilities of the sort used at high-end corporate hospitality events, housed in luxury portable buildings with full hot and cold water hand-washing facilities. Each trailer is equipped with three flushing stalls, a basin and an electric hand-dryer, and there may be as many as ten trailers erected in the paddock for the use of all the competitors, support staff and Tour de France officials. As soon as the cyclists set off on the gruelling stage, the trailers, each one with anything up to 500 gallons of human effluent sloshing around in its underfloor septic tanks, is driven to the end of the stage for the use of the finish line officials and any riders who have been baking a loaf for the past 200km. When everyone has dispersed, the tanks are taken to a sewage facility to be emptied, before being driven overnight to the start of the next stage.

THE KENSINGTON EXECUTIVE

visible tip of a huge organisational iceberg. Each of the 22 racing teams includes a 60-strong back-up crew of drivers, expert mechanics, physiotherapists and dieticians. And with every person needing to go to the toilet at least twice a day, providing lavatory facilities for the Tour de France circus is a miracle of logistics that must run like clockwork to keep the race on the road. It's time to lift the lid and take a close look at...

ets of the France

THE race passes through some of the most spectacular countryside that France has to offer, but on many long and remote stretches there are no public toilet facilities for kilometres in any direction - a pressing problem for any roadside official who gets the turtle's head halfway through his shift. For just such eventualities, tour race organisers provide building site style 'portaloo' comfort stations at regular intervals. If the leading pack are well ahead of the peloton, the marshal knows he has a couple of minutes to nip into the nearest blue plastic turdis for a quick 'numéro deux'.

OVER the course of its 2,000-mile run through the country lanes of rural France, there are many places where it would be impossible to park and set up a bulky portable toilet. On these stretches, any rider or official who has 'une taupe' at the counter may have no option but to perform his ablutions *au naturel*. If so, he must make sure that he's well out of sight of the motorcycle TV cameraman, as his sponsors would probably not like their product linked with someone having a shit behind a bush. Alternatively, if he is passing through a village, he may opt to knock on a door and ask the occupier if they would mind him popping in and parking his breakfast in their toilet.

ON the notorious mountain stages, organisers face a tricky problem. Any rider who is caught short and attempts to sit on a portable toilet placed at the side of a fearsome 11% gradient would have to brace himself against the door so he doesn't slip off the seat mid-stool. To prevent such a mishap, house bricks, stones, and car jacks are pressed into service to keep the cubicles more or less horizontal.

THE last day of the Tour de France is the most exciting of all, as the riders sweep into Paris for the climactic sprint to the finish along the iconic Champs Elysées. Any competitor needing to strain his greens can make use one of the French capital's numerous 'pissoirs', which are like public toilets only more embarrassing and less civilised; with no doors to negotiate or hands to wash afterwards, they are ideal for anyone wanting a hurried 'splash and dash' before pedalling up to the Arc de Triomphe. If a rider wants to drop a length of dirty spine, he's in trouble. Paris is notoriously short of proper public lavatories, and even if he can find one he'll need a Euro to get in and there'll inevitably be a lengthy queue outside, meaning he'll be rejoining the Peloton right at the back after his shite.

NEXT WEEK: *The Home Diarrhoea and Constipation Remedies of the Miss World Beauty Pageant Contestants*

I DIY-ED IT MY WAY!

A **WEST** Yorkshire handyman says that a series of bizarre, billion-to-one coincidences have ruined his successful business, leaving him bankrupt, homeless, and facing a possible prison sentence. For six weeks, entrepreneur Ackworth Coxwold, 61, enjoyed a thriving career doing minor domestic repairs in and around the Castleford area, until a succession of remarkable twists of fate combined to leave his life in tatters.

Odd-job man Ackworth looks back on rollercoaster career

Ack-ed off: Unlucky Ackworth's handyman career was blighted by a series of bizarre coincidences.

He told us: "I'd always been a Jack-of-all-trades and good with my hands, so when I lost my job at the local recycling plant for reasons I won't go into, I decided it was time to strike out on my own and become my own boss. I put a card advertising my services as a handyman in the post office window. I felt I had a number of USPs that were bound to guarantee success: No job was too big or small, I offered competitive rates, and what's more I would happily give free estimates to prospective customers. I went home and waited for the work to start rolling in."

"Business was slow at first. I got a few jobs in the first week, boarding up a broken window, changing a fuse, and sawing a couple of inches off the bottom off a jammed door, and word started to spread about my friendly, low-cost, cash-only business. Pretty soon I found myself rushed off my feet. Sometimes there were two, three or four calls coming in every week. In the end, my wife Maureen even gave up her job in the launderette to become my full-time PA."

"I thought I was set up for life, with a booming DIY business that would continue to grow and grow. But then, just as everything seemed to be going swimmingly for me, the fickle finger of fate intervened. Bizarre coincidence followed bizarre coincidence, and before I knew what was happening, I was going under."

Ack Stumped Over the Candlesticks

❝ The first disaster that befell me occurred during my

EXCLUSIVE!

second week as CEO of Coxwold's Home Repairs. I had been called out to Featherstone to fix a leaky trap on a kitchen sink. As luck would have it, it was Maureen's birthday, and on my way to the job I spotted a couple of silver candlesticks in the window of a local antiques shop. I knew they were just the sort of thing my wife would love as a present, so I popped into the shop, bought them for a fiver, and popped them in my toolbag.

lady

I didn't give my purchases a second thought when I arrived at the job. The lady of the house showed me the problem and I immediately set about riving off the plastic U-bend with my biggest pair of molegrips. After a couple of minutes, she said she was just popping to the corner shop to get some milk. Moments later I heard the front door shut behind her as she left.

Candle in the bend: A simple plumbing job turned sour for Coxwold when he was accused of stealing pair of valuable silver candlesticks (below).

About ten minutes later she was back with the milk, and it was then that all hell broke loose. She spotted that two silver candlesticks were missing from the table in the hallway. I could only imagine that she must have left the door on the sneck when she went out to the shop, and an opportunist thief had sneaked in and made off with them while I had my head in the cupboard under the sink.

She didn't believe me, and demanded to have a look in my bag. Of course, I showed her because I had nothing to hide. She rooted through my tools and immediately produced the silver candlesticks that I had bought for Maureen's birthday present that very morning. *My blood ran cold: by a billion-to-one chance, they were identical to the ones I had eyed up on the hall table when I came in just a quarter of an hour previously.*

radio

I tried to explain that it was nothing more than a bizarre coincidence, but the householder was already on the phone to the local police. I'd had a run-in with the local rozzers just before I lost my job at the recycling plant, and I knew them to be unreasonable people who refuse to accept truthful excuses if they consider them far-fetched.

To save any grief, I gave the woman my candlesticks and quickly left, leaving myself £5 out of pocket. To make matters worse, she refused to pay me for the repair I'd done on her sink, claiming I'd bodged the job. But that wasn't my fault. Whichever cowboy had fitted the sink in the first place must have crossed the thread, because when I put the U-bend back in it was leaking worse than before. ❞

Hooky Knicker Tale Didn't Wash

❝ A week later, I got a call from a housewife in Allerton Bywater. She told me her washing machine was playing up. It wasn't draining properly, and she couldn't get the door open. She left me in the laundry room to work my DIY magic while she went off to make me a cup of tea. As a time-served handyman, I knew exactly how to fix the problem. A quick rive backwards and forwards in the side of the door with my biggest flat-headed screwdriver, and I soon had the troublesome catch forced.

As the door swung open, a little bit of plastic and a couple of circlips flew out. I picked them up to re-fit them, but I couldn't work out where they had come from. I assumed they weren't important, but I thought I had better test the washing machine before I left to make sure my repair had been successful.

There was a laundry basket in the corner of the room, so I took a load of clothes out and pushed them in the drum. Unfortunately, the door wouldn't stay shut, so when the lady of the house came back in with my cuppa, I explained that it was probably a manufacturing defect and she needed to get a qualified specialist out.

rosa

As I was talking to her, she looked down and her expression suddenly changed. For some reason I couldn't fathom, her eyes were fixed on the pocket of my overalls, and she looked absolutely furious. I couldn't imagine what it was that had caused the sudden change in the previously cordial atmosphere. I looked down and there, hanging out of my pocket, was the lacy hem of a pair of her knickers.

> *I looked down and there, hanging out of my pocket, was the lacy hem of a pair of her knickers*

Come out in the wash: A washing machine repair led to Coxwold being hung out to dry after lacy underwear was discovered in his pocket.

For a moment I was dumbstruck. I couldn't imagine where they had come from and how they had got there. Obviously, I was entirely innocent of any wrongdoing, but a bizarre million-to-one set of circumstances had conspired to make it seem like I was somehow at fault. And once again, my blustered protestations of innocence fell on deaf ears.

Thinking about it, it was clear to me what had happened. *As I was loading the washing into the machine for its test run, a pair of the woman's scanties must have hooked round one of my cuff buttons, later becoming detached as I reached in there for my vape.* But my livid customer had put two and two together to make five, and she was refusing to listen to reason. As she kicked me out of the house, she was calling me all the names under the sun.

Bad Luck On the Cards

> Matters eventually came to a head just before Christmas. I was in Knottingley, where an old lady wanted her chimney swept. I haven't got any proper professional sweep's brushes, but I managed to rig myself up a perfectly serviceable set using garden canes, a roll of duct tape and a lavatory brush.

About halfway through the job, I decided to take a short tea break. There was horse running at Chepstow that afternoon that I liked the look of, so I phoned my bookies to have a flutter on it. As I reached into my wallet to get one of my credit cards, they all fell out onto the floor by the side of the chair. Tutting at my clumsiness, I scooped them up and stuffed them into my pocket.

After having my flutter on Lucky Boy in the 3.30, I got back to work, although I didn't actually manage to finish the job in the end, because the bogbrush came adrift halfway up and got lodged in the chimney flue.

ernst

A couple of days later, however, I realised that I had once again been the victim of yet another freak, billion-to-one occurrence. To my horror, I discovered that I had somehow got the old lady's bank card in my wallet. It must have fallen out of her purse behind the clock on the mantelpiece, and I had clearly picked it up by mistake with my own cards when I dropped them.

What's more, I had unknowingly used it to make a whole series of contactless payments. But it was only when it was refused when I tried to use it to buy a big telly in Currys that I realised my mistake. I immediately decided to take the card back to its rightful owner, and set off to run the 8 miles to the old lady's house.

Unfortunately, I couldn't quite remember where her house was, and she'd blocked the card anyway, so I just chucked it in a bush.

Coxwold Battered Over Hooky Haul

> The straw that finally broke the camel's back and catapulted my thriving business into receivership happened one Friday in early January. I was in Townville, smashing up the asbestos roof on an old prefab garage. You've got to take the proper precautions when you deal with asbestos, as it's dangerous stuff, so I had a scarf tied round my mouth and nose and I turned my face away while I crammed the bits into the wheelie bin.

I knocked off at noon, and went to the local fish & chip shop for my usual lunch – haddock and scraps. However, this one was far from usual. As I chomped through the delicious crispy batter, I saw something glinting in the haddock. It was a pair of pearl earrings, with a matching bracelet and necklace. I decided to pop into my local pawnbrokers on the way home to see what he'd give me for them.

> *As I chomped through the delicious crispy batter, I saw something glinting in the haddock. It was a pair of pearl earrings, with a matching bracelet and necklace*

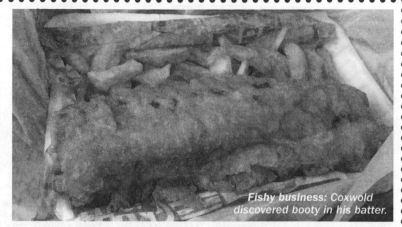

Fishy business: Coxwold discovered booty in his batter.

I was intending to give the money to a kiddies' charity, but I never got the chance, because it turned out the stuff had been hallmarked and the numbers showed up on the West Yorkshire CrimeStoppers database. Thinking about it, it was clear what had happened. The thief must have panicked after committing his crime, and thrown his booty in the sea. The fish had obviously eaten them before getting caught, ending up battered and wrapped in newspaper on my lap.

jaffa

But the amazing coincidences didn't stop there. By a billion-to-one chance, the jewellery had been stolen from a house not half a mile from my home. Even more bizarrely, it was a house where I had been working not a week previously, repairing a broken pane of glass in a bedroom window. Almost unbelievably, I had touched the very dressing table from where they had been stolen, probably from the middle drawer on the left, leaving my fingerprints on it.

The next morning I was up before the local magistrates, who met my protestations of innocence with outright derision. And I can see their point. The chances of such a bizarre chain of events occurring must have literally been trillions-to-one. I don't doubt if I'd been in their shoes, I might well have found my unlikely tale of woe a little bit implausible too.

Following the court case, during which he pleaded guilty to 18 charges of theft, credit card fraud and indecent exposure, Coxwold says his reputation as a trustworthy household handyman has been left in tatters. With his business destroyed, he has no way to raise the £1500 he needs to pay his fines, and now fears he may end up in prison.

NEXT WEEK: *While Ackworth is bleeding the radiators in a Cutsyke house, Police are called to a report of a naked man coincidentally fitting his description – and amazingly bearing an exact DNA match – who has been seen masturbating in the upstairs bedroom window.*

Don't bet on it: Chepstow flutter turned sour for Ackworth who keeps the slip as a reminder of his bad luck and on the offchance the case gets overturned on appeal.

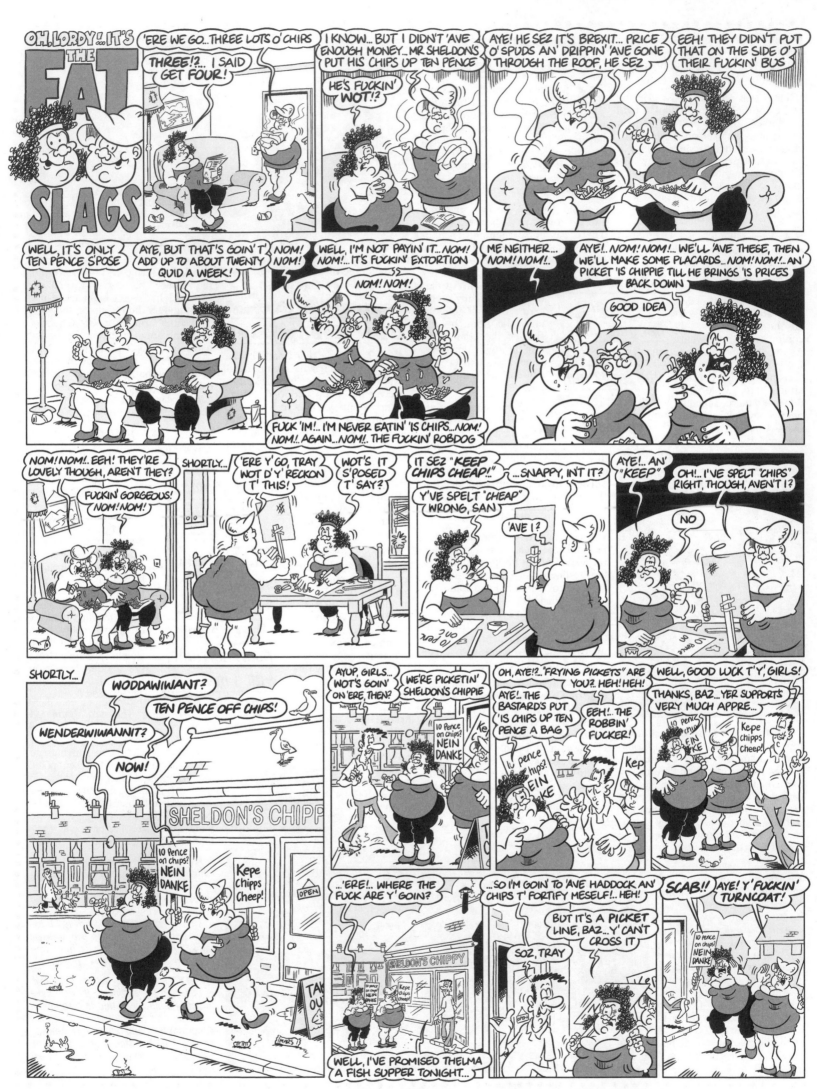

In their customised V8 race car - The Thunder Vixen - Roxy and Sugar have fought their way to the final of the San Antonio Illegal Topless Road Race Championships. Now they must battle with their arch rivals for the grand title over a supercharged, high-octane ten-mile course through the busy downtown streets of the metropolis, dodging pedestrians, jumping red lights… and avoiding the cops…

The race starts in ten minutes, ladies.

Let's get our knockers out, Roxy.

Not just yet, Sugar. The Thunder Vixen is running on fumes. We'd best fill her up at the gas station.

We haven't got much time. Let's go.

Minutes later…

Quick!… that pump's free.

The filler cap's on the wrong side, though.

It's alright. It'll reach.

Okay.

USE EITHER SIDE EXTRA LONG HOSES

But…

Goddammit! It says they're extra-long hoses, but they never are.

Turn the car round and reverse in.

So…

VROOOM!

VROOOM!

BOGGLA-BOGGLA-BOGGLA!

Did you see that?

The cheeky get! He could see what we were doing.

The fucking bastard!

Ooh, look! He's going! Quick!

VROOOM!

SCREECH!

Ah, bollocks. There's only that 98 RON super-unleaded on this pump. It costs a fortune.

Yeah, but you do get more to the gallon.

Do you shite. And anyway, even if you did, it still costs you more. It's just a rip-off, this bloody stuff.

Let's just fill up the Thunder Vixen, Roxy. We've only got six minutes to get back to the starting line and get our hooters out.

It's fucking annoying though, this.

Don't go over forty dollars. I've only got forty dollars on me.

CLICK!

$040:01

012:11

03:14

Ahhh…Fuck it. I hate these fucking things. They always do that.

Roxy, have you get a cent? The bastard on the till won't let me off.

I've nothing on me. There might be some coins in the car…

He said if he let me off, he'd have to let everybody off.

Stingy twat. It's just a cent.

Got one!

Great. I'll go and tell him to shove it up his arse.

Hurry, Sugar! The race starts in five minutes, and we've still got to get back to the start line and take our tops off.

Here you go, tight-arse.

Much obliged, ma'am. Have a nice day.

Right! Let's go and race topless!

SLAM!

CLICK!

V-ROOOM!

N₂O

WHOOSH!

Oh, for fuck's sake!

Jesus Christ!

Three minutes, Roxy.

BEEP!

BEEP!

BEEP!

The selfish old bitch. She could have let us out.

Back out, Roxy.

I can't, Sugar. There's a queue behind. We're blocked in!

Jesus… look, she won't be long, I'm sure.

Two minutes later…

Aw, for fuck's sake, how much is she putting in?

Christ knows!

I don't fucking believe it. She's going to do her fucking shopping now.

The fucking selfish old cow.

Next week: The old lady eventually comes out and gets back in her car, but then spends ages farting about with her seatbelt and adjusting the mirrors, before suddenly remembering that she came out for cat food, and going back in the shop.

HIGH COURT OF

WE were all **SHOCKED** by the recent round of drug confessions from a shameful roll-call of Prime Ministerial candidates. But whilst ordinary members of the public routinely find themselves heavily fined or even thrown behind bars for similar offences, a disgraceful gaggle of Number 10 hopefuls seemed to get off scot-free after their past narcotic secrets were exposed.

Well enough is enough. What's sauce for the goose should be sauce for the gander. It's time to finally put these shameful offences up before the beak so that justice can not only be done, but can be seen to be done.

We've asked impartial man-of-the-people **RICHARD LITTLEJOHN** to pick up his gavel and don his judge's robe and wig to belatedly re-try these sordid cases, before doling out imaginary punishments to a shamefaced parade of shameless junkie politicians of shame who have admitted their guilt to a shocking roll call of shameful drug offences.

EXCLUSIVE!

with Celebrity Judge His Honour Mr Justice Richard Littlejohn

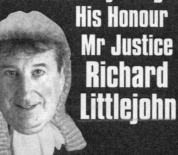

Defendant: Boris Johnson
Party: Conservatives
Admitted Offence: Snorting cocaine whilst a student at Oxford University

JUDGE LITTLEJOHN's SUMMING UP

"**THE IMAGE** of a bow-tied Old Etonian toff embarking on a Bullingdon Club rampage of vandalism through the dreaming-spired quads of Oxford University whilst ripped to the man-tits on California Cornflakes is not one that necessarily sits well with Britain's hard-working lower classes. Indeed, some might even maintain that your admitted history of Class-A drug abuse should even preclude you from ever holding any position of power or responsibility. However, your refreshingly candid admission to Piers Morgan that snorting marching powder did nothing for you, is one that almost certainly will have put many less expensively-educated people off trying the drug themselves. You tried it so they didn't have to, and that is greatly to your credit."

JUDGE LITTLEJOHN's SENTENCE

"**MR JOHNSON,** were it within my powers to award you a medal for your part in the war against drugs, I would do so. Sadly, however, that is not within my gift, but you nevertheless leave my court with the cheers of a grateful nation ringing in your ears."

Defendant: Michael Gove
Party: Conservatives
Admitted Offence: Repeated cocaine abuse whilst working as a journalist twenty years ago.

JUDGE LITTLEJOHN's SUMMING UP

"**MR GOVE**, many people would say that as a Home Secretary who called for the immediate sacking of teachers found guilty of even minor drug offences, your own history of repeated cocaine abuse is evidence of – at the very least – disgustingly rank hypocrisy. However, in my opinion, a few lapses in your youth and early middle age should not damn you forever. I believe that your unfortunate history as an innocent victim of your own cocaine addiction has given you a rare and valuable insight into the difficult problem of narcotics abuse, allowing you to draw up a raft of draconian measures to prevent others from following you down the same path of suffering. Your decision to speak out when threatened with a tawdry tabloid newspaper expose of your chequered, drug-addled past shows an impressive strength of character that is far too lacking in many of today's 'squeaky clean' politicians."

JUDGE LITTLEJOHN's SENTENCE

"**MR GOVE,** you may leave the dock with your head held high."

Defendant: Rory Stewart
Party: Conservatives
Admitted Offence: Smoked opium whilst on a walking tour of Iran fifteen years ago.

JUDGE LITTLEJOHN's SUMMING UP

"**MR STEWART,** ordinarily, I would take a very dim view of a sordid offence such as the one you have admitted. However, on this occasion, I think you should be applauded for your refreshing candour in owning up to this minor, one-time offence committed in a country with a much more relaxed drugs policy than our own, in a less policed, poorer, rural area. In many ways, your 'When in Rome' attitude displays a refreshing and admirable willingness to experience other cultures that should be applauded."

JUDGE LITTLEJOHN's SENTENCE

"**MR STEWART,** you leave my court without a stain on your character."

JUSTICE!

Defendant: Chuka Umunna
Party*: Liberal Democrats
Admitted Offence: Smoking marijuana

*at time of going to press

JUDGE LITTLEJOHN's SUMMING UP

"**MR UMUNNA,** I have to tell you that your admission – tantamount to a boast about how 'cool' you are – that you occasionally smoked marijuana during your youth has sickened me to my stomach. Your self-serving and mealy-mouthed claims that you now 'regret' what you did as a teenage club DJ are worthless. Is it the offence for which you are sorry, or the fact that you have been found out? I think we all know the answer to that question. Thousands of innocent people are slain each year by the drug cartels of South America and YOU, Mr Umunna, must shoulder a hefty proportion of the blame for each and every one of those countless tragic deaths. I realise that you may not now be the man you were as a youth, but were I to show leniency to you in my court, I would be setting a terrible example to the young people who may – like you – think it is somehow 'cool' to get themselves mixed up in this despicable and murderous trade."

JUDGE LITTLEJOHN's SENTENCE

"UMUNNA, you will go to prison for two years, and you may consider yourself fortunate that your sentence is not much longer. Take him down."

Defendant: Andrea Leadsom
Party: Conservatives
Admitted Offence: Smoking marijuana

JUDGE LITTLEJOHN's SUMMING UP

"**MISS LEADSOM,** last month you candidly admitted that you smoked marijuana whilst you were a student at Warwick University in the 1980s. As someone who has a lot to lose by coming clean about such an issue, your bravery in standing up and acknowledging this difficult episode from your past life does you great credit. Whilst I do not in any way condone what you did, your honesty in coming clean about this short-lived, insignificant episode during the course of your otherwise exemplary career, does you great credit. In your statement, you also made clear that you never took cocaine or other Class-A drugs, and as a 'glass half full' man, I would rather praise a person for the positive aspects of their character than condemn them for insignificant, youthful indiscretions carried out under no doubt intolerable peer pressure from ruthless junkies like Chuka Umunna."

JUDGE LITTLEJOHN's SENTENCE

"MISS LEADSOM, you have suffered enough. Put this episode behind you and move forward with your glittering career."

INNOCENT UNTIL PROVEN GUILTY?

Theoretical shame of MPs under drug rumour cloud

FOR every politician who admits a shame-filled history with drugs, there are many more who are keeping their narcotic-fuelled histories under wraps. Or have never done drugs. So, just for fun, it's time to speculate on just what these squeaky clean MPs may be keeping hidden from the Great British electorate.

Once again, Judge Littlejohn will pass sentence for a shameful catalogue of shocking – yet entirely hypothetical – drugs crimes committed by our above-the-law politicians.

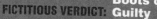

DEFENDANT: Keir Starmer / **PARTY:** Labour
FICTITIOUS OFFENCE: Possession of 3 packs of Boots own-brand paracetemol
FICTITIOUS VERDICT: Guilty

JUDGE LITTLEJOHN'S SUMMING UP: "Mr Starmer, you stand in the dock of my court and maintain that you do not believe that the possession of 3 packets of proprietary headache tablets is a criminal offence. Yet, as the former Attorney General, I am in no doubt that you know for a fact that it is against the law to purchase more than two packets of these powerful and dangerous drugs at any one time. Your defence is nothing more than a craven tissue of lies that demonstrates your ruthless arrogance and contempt for the rule of law. I have no hesitation in making an example of you, to deter others who think they can get away with buying more than two packets of headache tablets at once."

JUDGE LITTLEJOHN'S SENTENCE: "Mr Starmer, you will go to prison for life, with the recommendation that you serve at least thirty-five years before being considered for parole."

DEFENDANT: Jo Swinson / **PARTY:** Lib Dems
FICTITIOUS OFFENCE: Possession of opioids
FICTITIOUS VERDICT: Guilty

JUDGE LITTLEJOHN'S SUMMING UP: "Miss Swinson, you and your expert witnesses claim that the opioid residues found on the top of your desk in the House of Commons were from a Marks & Spencers poppy seed bun that you had eaten for your lunch. It is an excuse that, if it didn't demonstrate your arrant contempt for the process of law, would be frankly laughable. The fact that you smuggled Class A drugs into the hallowed halls of the Mother of Parliaments shows that you are not fit to hold public office."

JUDGE LITTLEJOHN'S SENTENCE: "Miss Swinson, as you are a new mother and this is your first offence, I am going to show leniency. You are fined fifteen thousand pounds and will serve a three-year suspended sentence, during which you will wear an ankle tag and be forbidden from venturing within 250 yards of the Houses of Parliament."

DEFENDANT: Jeremy Corbyn / **PARTY:** Labour
FICTITIOUS OFFENCE: Operating a marijuana Farm
FICTITIOUS VERDICT: Guilty

JUDGE LITTLEJOHN'S SUMMING UP: "Mr Corbyn, you stand before this court convicted of running a marijuana farm in the polytunnel greenhouse on your Islington allotment, passing the offending plants off to anyone who spotted them as innocent tomatoes. Indeed, so well-orchestrated was your audacious scheme that you even disguised the offending plants in your grow-bags to not only look and smell like innocent tomato plants, but also to bear the same juicy red fruits."

JUDGE LITTLEJOHN'S SENTENCE: "Mr Corbyn, you are an old man, and according to recent newspaper reports not in the best of health. You will go to prison for eight years, although it is my belief that it is highly likely that you may never taste freedom again."

DEFENDANT: Sajid Javid / **PARTY:** Conservative
FICTITIOUS OFFENCE: Possession of drugs with intent to supply, plus firearms offences
FICTITIOUS VERDICT: Guilty

JUDGE LITTLEJOHN'S SUMMING UP: "Mr Javid, this court has heard how more than 200kg of uncut heroin, along with 100 tubs of Vim, eight sub-machine guns and a machete, were found in your parliamentary office in the Department of Housing, Communities and Local Government. Whilst in general I take a dim view of this kind of activity, it is clear that your intent was to 'cut' the heroin in order to make it less potent. Were it not for this mitigating factor, and your clear concern for the wellbeing of your junkie customers, you can rest assured that you would find yourself in much deeper trouble than that in which you already find yourself. As for the firearms found in your desk, the narcotics trade is a notoriously violent one, and I am satisfied that this impressive arsenal was only maintained in the interests of your own defence."

JUDGE LITTLEJOHN'S SENTENCE: "As this is only your third or fourth offence, I am prepared to discharge you on condition that you visit a duly appointed probation officer every second Wednesday, Prime Minister's Question Time permitting, for the next three months."